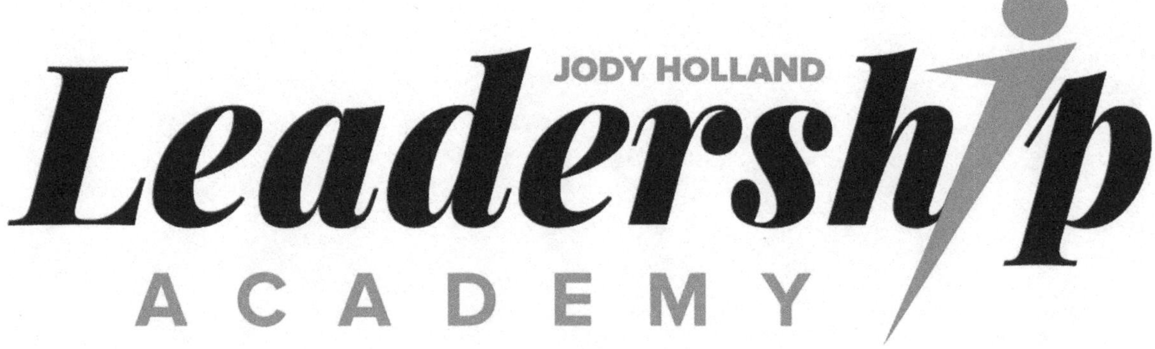

Learn-2-Lead Workbook

Jody N Holland

ISBN: 1-63390-067-7
ISBN-13: 978-1-63390-067-7

DEDICATION

This book is dedicated to you, the participant, the leader, the person on the front lines of creating a better culture for your teams. I applaud you for taking the next step in your leadership journey! You are now on the path to becoming all that you are capable of and all that you were meant to be. I look forward to the journey with you!
Jody Holland

Acknowledgements

I would like to thank all of the authors who have put themselves and their ideas out into the world. You create an energy of growth that makes the world a much better place. You gather, distill, and present information in a way that allows people to learn from the experiences of others. I would like to acknowledge those who are my support in life, in work, and in the journey to bring great leadership to the masses. I would like to thank the hundreds of companies who have allowed me to connect with your people, invest in their potential, and solidify my model of leading teams to success!

CONTENTS

Learn2Lead
Supervise * Influence * Motivate

Learn2Lead
Supervise * Influence * Motivate

1 MANAGEMENT VS LEADERSHIP

Management is the process of making the greatest use of human potential in the workplace. It is both an understanding of and a utilization of the resources that are available to you, including people, money, capital, and culture. It is the ability to shift your thinking from that of a worker to that of a motivator and manager of accomplishment. Your job is now more about getting work done through other people than it is getting work done on your own. One of the key errors that managers seem to struggle with is going from top performing individual to top performing manager. The two are not necessarily connected. In fact, the two are necessarily disconnected. By the same token, one of the greatest struggles that companies seem to have and a mistake that they make regularly is that they promote top performers "out of" their area of performance. Consider the following example:

Jason was an incredible car salesperson for Davidson Ford. He sold an average of 7 more cars per month than any other salesperson that they had at the time. He had a natural connection with people and his customers loved him. His steady stream of referrals kept him incredibly busy and kept the profits good for Davidson as well. After watching Jason for a year, Mr. Davidson decided that he really wanted to reward Jason for his great work. So, he promoted him to Sales Manager. Davidson's sales manager had just left, and the spot was available. Jason seemed like the logical choice. After all, a great salesperson should obviously know how to teach other people to be great at sales as well. The challenge they faced was that he was an incredible salesperson, but not an incredible manager. He wasn't prepared to manage. He didn't have the skills of a manager. Instead, he had the skills of a top performing salesperson. The even bigger challenge, once Jason and Mr. Davidson both realized that his fit was a bad fit, was that it was very difficult for Jason to swallow his pride and move "back down" to a sales position. In the end, Jason left the organization and went to work for a competitor as a salesperson, where he became their top performer. That was more than the loss of a salesperson to Davidson. That was the loss of 20 car sales per month, the loss of a friend, and the loss of a valuable team member. All of this could have been avoided, had Jason gone through a program ahead of time to determine if he was a good fit for being a manager.

This happens fairly regularly in organizations. Organizations will continue to promote people to positions that they simply aren't ready to handle. People will continue looking at their boss and believing that they could do a better job. Supervisors will continue feeling as if they have to know all the answers and will therefore tell people what to do instead of inspiring them to action. All of this continues to happen because people are missing key ingredients to creating success in their own lives. They are missing the tools that will ensure their success!

"If you only have a hammer, you tend to

see every problem as a nail."

Abraham Maslow

Throughout this book, you will learn the basic principles of managing people and accomplishing work through other people. I will prepare you to be in charge. You should have the right tools (leadership skills) in your toolbox to succeed at the end of this book. You will need to continue working on them and honing their implementation, but the tools will be there.

Wrong Tool, Right Car

My next door neighbor was a Mustang enthusiast. He had a Mustang 5.0, a Mustang GT, and one day he even drove home in a Mustang Cobra. I tried not to drool visibly as the new Cobra pulled into the driveway, which I was not very successful at. I walked across the lawn to his driveway and simply said, "WOW!" We stood there admiring the car and talked about the various differences between this car and the last one he had owned. We spent a good hour just looking at the car and talking. This was ample time for the car to cool off. Finally, he asked me if I wanted to assist him in changing the oil. He wanted to get to know the engine and learn what was different in this car versus his last one. I was very enthusiastic about the opportunity. We used some special ramps that would allow a low-profile car to pull up onto the ramps and we were ready to get to work.

I crawled under the car and snaked my hand up through the engine to find the oil filter and then pulled my hand back down. I just needed a bearing on where it was. Next, I removed the plug so that the oil could drain into the pan by my shoulder. The oil drained out and into the pan. Now that I knew where the filter was, I grabbed the filter wrench that he had provided me and I slipped it over the oil filter. It went over the filter very easily, a little too easily. I tried to clamp down on the filter to loosen it, but the filter wrench was too big. I tried it a couple of times, just to be sure. Finally, I decided I needed to get creative. So, I took a rubber hose that I could flatten from my garage and made my own makeshift filter wrench. I slipped it over the filter and tried, and tried, and tried to loosen the filter. It wasn't working. I tried a half dozen variations of made up tools, but nothing worked! So, I finally told my neighbor to hop in my truck and we went to the auto parts store. We bought the right sized filter wrench and then returned to the driveway, where the Mustang was still perched and ready for some attention. I crawled back under the car and worked my hand and the new wrench up to the filter, and voila, it worked. With one twist, the filter was loose and I was able to remove it without any real struggle. We put the new filter on, filled the engine with the proper amount of oil, and fired it up. It was incredible! It is extremely frustrating when you don't have the right tools. I have made it a point to always try to have the right tools in my toolbox since that day.

Management and Leadership are a lot like that experience with the Mustang. As we strive to accomplish great things in our organizations, having the right tools in place is crucial. You are embarking on a journey to become a people specialist. Training, learning, and practice will help you become a great leader. Despite what you might have heard, people are not born leaders. Some people seem to be naturally good at it because they were exposed to situations that taught them the lessons of leadership that they needed to know. Often times, their personality positioned them to be the "go-to" person in a group. They are confident, well-spoken, and conditioned to step up and take control of a situation. You can learn any of those things yourself. You don't have to accept the idea that you either are, or are not, a leader and that there is nothing you can do about it. You can absolutely take control of your destiny. The contents of this book will prepare you for being a great manager of people and an inspirational leader as well. I am excited that you are on this journey with me and look forward to helping you achieve all that you can through other people.

A manager's skills differ from an employee's skills and even from a leader's skills. Each of the skills that you will learn in this book are designed to make you a great supervisor/manager of people. In subsequent books, you will learn to be a great leader. For now, remember that your job is to accomplish great things through other people, utilizing their skills and motivation while leveraging their abilities. You can't do it yourself! You have to take the teams that you have and build them up, inspire them, and build their potential. You have to build a great culture from where you are and focus on making the environment easy for employees to choose motivation and performance. After all, each person has the choice of performing or not performing. It is up to them. Our job is to create the kind of workplace where people naturally move towards a desire to perform and create profits, fulfill missions, and build up their coworkers.

My desire is for you take each of these skills very seriously, that you discuss what you are learning with your coworkers, your boss, and your employees. My desire is that you create accountability for yourself and to keep yourself on track for success as a manager. Just like your employees, the level at which you perform will ultimately be your decision. You will choose whether to advance your skills or get upset with employees when they don't respond to you. The greater your level of skills, the more likely your employees are to perform at their best. But again, that will be your choice. Some will look at the skills and decide that people need to just "adjust to them." Others will look at them and embrace the challenge and the opportunity. I hope you are the latter. I hope that you embrace your full potential.

The next thing to keep in mind is that your mindset will massively influence the way that others look at you, and the world that exists around you. You have at the base of your brain what is known as the Reticular Activating System. This filter essentially determines what is accepted and processed by the conscious mind and what makes it to the subconscious mind. Your subconscious mind has the ability to process information at the rate of 400 Billion bits per second. Your conscious can only process at a measly 2 Thousand bits per second. If each bit were a drop of water, that is the difference in filling a glass in 60 seconds versus filling an Olympic sized swimming pool in 60 seconds. This means that what you set your conscious intention to see will ultimately show up for you. If you are determined to see good in your people, they will begin to demonstrate more and more good. If you are determined to see bad in your people, they will begin to demonstrate more and more bad behaviors. Pam Grout, in her book E-Cubed, demonstrated through several experiments that you literally create the world that exists for you by putting your focus on specific things. This principle, also discussed by Napoleon Hill in his book Think and Grow Rich, essentially can be summed up with the following statement…

What you focus on, expands.

You may have to do a little work on your mind to focus on the idea that employees desire to perform. Employees desire to make you and the company money. Employees want the best for you and for each other. Employees are a tremendous asset and are the lifeblood of the business. Take a minute and write down 3 things that you currently think about employees that could be holding you back from seeing their potential.

My limiting beliefs about employees…

1. ____

2. ____

3. ____

Now, what are three beliefs you could choose about employees that would make you look forward to seeing them every day and would make you value them immensely?

1. ____

2. ____

3. ____

Once you take control of your thoughts and beliefs about others, you will begin to see what you desire. The scary part is even if you have not been thinking about taking control of your thoughts, you are creating in others what you are looking for. Yes, you did read that correctly. This is often the most difficult thing for people to digest. We are creating specific response patterns in others because we are looking for those response patterns. We are, therefore, either our own best friend or our own worst enemy. It is up to us. It is up to you. What will you choose to believe about your people? What will you choose to look for in your people?

2 VALUES-BASED DIVERSITY

It is not just what you do that matters. It is who you are while you are doing it.

We are ultimately the sum total of the values that guide us in life. We treat people a certain way because of our values. We listen to the music that we do because it reflects our values. We associate with certain people because they complement our values, or they represent the values that we "think" we would like to express.

The debate has been around for quite some time as to whether we are born with our values or they develop over time. Do our values come from some genetic encoding or are they blended from genetics and from environment. Or, are we simply a "product of our raising?" The question for each of us is…

Why am I who I am?

Dr. Morris Massey, sociologist and great thinker of developmental thoughts, outlined the process of you becoming you into three distinct stages. The age bracket for these stages can vary, based on the development of the individual as well as the times in which they grew up. However, there are three specific stages that seem to guide us into becoming the people we are today. These stages are…

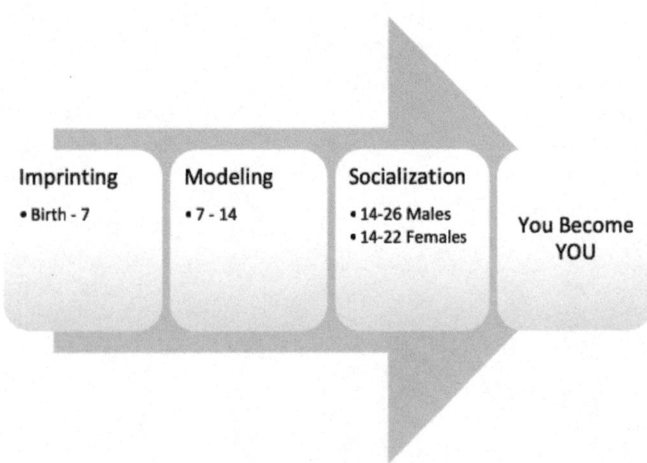

Imprinting

During this stage, we simply soak things up like a sponge. We are constantly observing what is going on around us, what our parents or guardians are teaching us, how they are behaving, and what right and wrong are. Most of us heard the word "NO" as much as we heard any other word during this stage. Because we generally soak things up and accept them as truth, we can often create false beliefs in our own minds. We are looking to our parents, primarily, as the bearers and creators of truth. If they have a false truth as their belief, we are likely to adopt the same belief. Right and wrong, good and bad, according to Massey, are human constructs. We often assume that they would exist even without us, but they are a definition that we have established in our minds.

Think about the idea of exposing two children to completely different environments. One is brought up with kindness and sharing and compassion. The other is brought up with anger and hatred. These two environments will be what the child knows as the truth of their lives. It is during the second stage of development that a child will begin to find someone else to model outside of their parents or guardians. This first stage is critical for establishing the underlying characteristics of their personality makeup.

According to Christopher Nave, from the University of California at Riverside, our personality is almost completely set by the end of first grade. His study observed children at the age of 7 and tracked their behaviors into early adulthood. Personality and behavioral indicators that were present in first grade remained present in the subjects' adult lives. During the first stage of development, as defined by Massey, we are developing strong behavioral and personality pathways. These will very likely stick with us for the rest of our lives.

It is important to create the best environment possible for young people, which includes chores and responsibilities. As a young person, when you learn at this early stage to be responsible for your actions and to be responsible for accomplishing work, you are likely to carry that behavior pattern with you as an adult.

My theory is that many young people today rely on their parents for financial support because they were not conditioned to be responsible at this early stage. Had parents and societal influences created a model for self-sufficiency and responsibility, for being responsible for chores, for their own homework, for sticking with tasks even when they are tough, etc., the work ethic and reliability of that child as an adult would very likely be strong. This leads us to modeling.

Modeling

If you want to know how a person sees the world, discover their heroes. When you can identify the people whom they look up to, you will see what the value and belief systems of the person are. You will see what they desire to model as the right path for themselves. This modeling takes place as children between the ages of 7 and 13 look around their world and choose who they want to emulate. They may choose teachers, religious leaders, sports figures, family, or even comic book heroes. Whoever they decide to look up to will have a strong impact on what they decide is the right path for their life.

Think back to when you were in 4th or 5th grade. Who was it that you looked up to? Was it your parents, your friends, the cool kid at school, or someone else? Take just a minute and write down who your hero was at that age and what it was about them that made you want to be like them.

My hero was: ____

This was my hero because: ____

____

The age of 10 is the most critical age in a young person's life in regards to the development of values, according to Massey. This is generally about 4th or 5th grade. What a child experiences at this age goes deep into their subconscious belief systems. They will develop their value models for integrity, relationships, work ethic, reliability, and a host of other value-based thought patterns during this time. Think about the difference in experiences that each of the generations had. Think about what your grandparents' lives were like versus your parents' lives, versus your own. How old were you when you began working? How old were you when you became responsible for taking care of yourself? How old were you when you began to truly be held accountable for your choices?

When I was 23 years old, I was attending a professional development course in the Dallas-Ft. Worth area. The speaker at this program looked out at the group of Generation Xers, me included, and said…

What really scares me is that I am looking at a group of people who never had heroes. You never had anyone that you looked up to.

I have never really been the type of person to hold my tongue, so I raised my hand to respond to what he had said. He pointed to me and I said the following…

That's not true. I had plenty of heroes when I was growing up. I looked up to Batman and Robin, Superman, Spiderman, The Green Lantern, Captain America, and even the Wonder-Twins.

He shook his head side to side and let out an audible sigh. *Those are not real people!*

I let a half grin go across my face and said, *Oh, well what about the Incredible Hulk? I met him when I was 12. That dude is huge!*

Side note: It turns out that was just Lou Ferigno painted green, but it was still very impressive to me.

He went on to chastise us for not looking up to political heroes and war heroes. The reality was that politics had been exposed as corrupt to us. We had seen so much of the darkness that existed in that realm that had not been brought to light for his generation. The difference in the heroes made a difference in what I valued and found important in my own life. Think about the hero that you described (your hero) earlier in this chapter and what the characteristics, values, and behaviors of that hero were, or are. How many of those do you strive to emulate? We created our ideal version of ourselves as young people and often strive to live into that self as we get older.

Socialization

The socialization period is from the ages of 14 to roughly 22 years old. A number of research projects have demonstrated that it can take up to 4 years longer for males to reach full maturity than females. This is a time of questioning what we have been taught is right and what is wrong. It is a time of challenging the construct of reality and values that our parents or guardians gave us. It is a time that people often experiment with which belief system will define them for the rest of their lives.

During this time, we are largely influenced by our peers. We are watching what they do, how they think, what they believe, and how they behave. We are often seeking to get our cues about what we should be doing from them. Thinking back on my own life, I know that it was very important which people I chose to associate with. There were times when I was friends with the "wrong people" and I ended up in trouble and heading down a path that could lead to problems later in life. There were also times when I was connected with people who brought out the best in me, challenged me, and pushed me to be more, do more, and have more than I would have otherwise had.

We are also influenced by the multimedia inputs we absorb. We are watching for what people should be like in the shows, movies, and even in the games that we play. Young people will often attempt to take on the persona of the characters they look up to. If our teenagers are being continuously exposed to deviant characters, it changes their perspective on what the right behavior set is or should be for them. From my own experience, when I watched shows with violence in them as a teenager, I became more comfortable with the idea of violence. When I was watching fighting programs regularly, I began fighting more myself. This is not to say that if a person watches James Bond they will become a spy for Her Majesty's Secret Service. It is meant to simply point out that we are continuously persuaded and influenced by the things that we expose ourselves to. Within the lives of my kids, when they watch shows where children are disrespectful to their parents, I see a marked difference in the way that they communicate with my wife and me.

When I was a teenager, the show "Beverly Hills 90210" was very popular. In this show, the kids were basically on their own to do whatever they wanted to do. The parents were there, but they barely registered as influencers in their lives. They were rich, had great cars, and could party whenever they wanted to. Those values were like the holy grail of teenage-dom. They resonated with the generation of young people as the ideal setup and therefore people were attracted to the show. Think about the shows that you were attracted to as a young person. What were the values of the characters and the overall theme of the show? Did those values represent the "ideal" setup for you?

Many of our mothers warned us, "Be careful who you hang out with. You will end up just like them." This was the harsh truth that is still relevant today. Even beyond this developmental stage, it is our associations that help to create us. Massey simply understood that this was a sociological principle of development.

The Generations At Work

There are four distinctive generations at work today, with a 5th one on the way. Each of the generations has a unique perspective on reality, as defined through their experiences. The three stages of psychological development that you just reviewed each held a different set of experiences for the generations. Think about what you experienced, for example, in 5th grade. What was school like? What did you do during your summer break from school? Now, think about what a 5th grader today would experience. Some of the differences between today's 5th grader and what you were like as a 5th grader actually hold the key to why people work differently from one another.

Let's travel back in time to 1932, to the Traditionalist generation. This generation was born from 1922-1945. Imagine that you are in 5th grade, assuming you are in school at all. Summer break comes around, and it is time to be off from school for the next 90 or so days. Just like last year, you go to work for your family. You just don't work for money from your parents. Instead, working for your parents is simply an expectation of being a part of the family. You get up at 5AM every day in order to take care of the animals. At 5:15, you head out the door with a biscuit that your mom made that morning from scratch. She was up at 4:15 to get breakfast ready for the family. You work until 11:30 that morning and then stop work in the field. You head toward the one existing shade tree at the edge of the field. In a few minutes, your mom shows up with lunch for everyone. You drink some lemonade and eat your sandwich as you rest a little from the hard work. At around 12:15 PM, you go back to work and you work until 6PM that evening. Your family, like many families during that time of depression, works hard for everything they have. You don't waste anything. You don't walk away from your food because it isn't the brand name microwave meal that you really wanted. You eat what you have, and it is often what you grew or raised, not what you bought. You see only your family during the week. Church was often the only time that you saw anyone besides family or a close neighbor during the summertime. You didn't have a TV to watch, and you only listened to the radio on Saturday night for the weekly show. You entertained yourself when you weren't working, which wasn't often. You didn't have extra money. Not many people had extra money during that time.

During this time in the United States, only 9% of women worked outside of the home. Unemployment hit as high as 35%. This meant that 35% of able-bodied people who wanted to find a job, couldn't find one. If you compound that with the gender roles, it means that more than 50% of our country was out of work. 61% of men were active duty military at one point or another during their lives. This one fact alone helps to explain the methodology of management that exists and existed as they entered into leadership roles. They believed in hierarchical structure, which meant that communication and leadership all flowed from one level to another, and that sticking around meant the opportunity for a promotion. Tenure meant success! Respect of authority was tantamount to having your next opportunity. Work was formal. Dress was formal. Structures were formal. Communication was formal. Everything at work was structured, just like childhood seemed to be.

Now let's move forward a generation, to the Baby Boomer generation. 5th grade for the first of this generation was in 1956. The birth years for this generation were from 1946-1964. America was booming and "Leave it to Beaver" land was in full swing. Many young people did jobs like mowing, delivering newspapers, etc. for their parents and neighbors. With the economy booming and fewer people making their living on the farm, your summer looks quite a bit different. You have time to play sandlot baseball with your friends after your chores are done. Parental roles were beginning to change some, but moms were still seen as the one that took care of the home. More moms were working outside of the home, but that was still the minority. Your life was much more stable than your parents' or even your grandparents' lives. You saw the possibilities in life and believed that you could do anything you put your mind to. You knew that you could be rich and successful if that was what you decided to do. You were the first generation in your family to plan on going to college and the first generation that would have the opportunity to break out of the socio-economic molds that previous generations of your family were in. You still worked hard, but you also played hard. Your family and your teachers conditioned you. They taught you that you would be what you did for a living.

The next generation to enter the scene is the Generation Xers. This generation grew up in a time where technology was crashing onto the scene. They went from only being able to see local news to knowing what was going on in other countries. MTv made a splash by allowing people to see their favorite bands performing their songs. Cable boxes (12 whole channels at first) connected this group with the rest of the world and shortened the distance between geographical locations. From 1968 to 1972, the percentage of women in the paid labor force (their moms) went from 25% to 47%. During that same timeframe, the divorce rate rose from 25% to 45%. 1972 was the first year in US history for the divorce rate to be lower than the percentage of women in the paid labor force. As a result of the increase in working moms and the lack of "daycare" facilities, many of the young people from this generation simply went home to an empty house after school.

The term "latch-key" kids was created for this generation because they made it home with a key on a string around their necks for the latch. They grew up with a very broad freedom and independence because of the amount of alone time they had to themselves. This generation, born between 1965 and 1980, is the smallest of the generations in America. Their birth years cycle was shorter than other generations, as well as other social factors that reduced the number of births during these years. In total, there are 46 million people born into Generation X, which is 34 million fewer people than the baby boomer generation. Their values were things such as autonomy, freedom, independence, and time for themselves. They were the first generation NOT to define themselves by the work that they did.

Next comes the Millennial Generation. This generation has a very unique mix of parents. Some are Boomers married to Xers, Boomers remarried to Boomers, and Xers married to Xers. This generation grew up with a much more positive experience and a friendlier relationship with their parents. Their parents were often their friends, which is different than the majority of previous generational experiences. Their sports involvement changed, and the idea of teamwork over winning started floating to the surface. Interestingly enough, they were often rewarded for simply participating, yet their parents pushed them to excel in multiple activities simultaneously, including academics. Many of these young people grew up competing in two and three sports while striving to maintain status in the National Honor Society. This drive made them feel both pressured and driven, and yet many of them needed the safety-net of their parents' support and continuous recognition to keep going.

With 75 million people born into this generation between the years of 1981 and 2000, and the push of their parents to be in charge as quickly as possible, they jumped into work with an expectation that they would be recognized just like they were when they were competing as kids. This is likely the only way they could have seen the world, since this is the way they were conditioned to see the world. The very people who conditioned them to expect more for themselves than previous generations were often the loudest opponents to this type of thinking at work, from other people's kids, that is. Many parents of Millennial kids intended only their own kid to be further ahead than the others. They were also very frustrated when other people's kids had that expectation to move up… NOW. This generation, just like the others, is simply a product of how they were raised by parents, media, and society as a whole. They were taught to think a certain way.

The final of the five current generations is being dubbed Generation Z. This generation is still being born as of 2017, and they are estimated to be as large as the Millennial generation by 2020. Their birth years began in 2001. This generation has faced an even greater challenge than the

Millennial generation did in the formation of their values. This challenge will most definitely impact their work as well as society. The challenge they face is that of a lack of accountability. Just a few examples that were submitted in the research for this book include…

- A 6th grader's parents selling their house and moving to a new town in order to keep their kid from facing discipline for pulling a fire alarm at school
- A 5th grader's parents moving to a new part of the district to avoid their daughter being punished for bringing Vodka to school and sharing with other 5th graders
- A 9th grader's parents threatening to sue the school district if they punished their daughter for stealing a test from a teacher and helping other students cheat
- A 3rd grader's parents suing the school district because their child was made to sit in the corner after acting out in class
- A 4th grader's parents launching a campaign to remove a principal for "giving excessive tardies" to their child when he was consistently late to school more than 10 times in 20 days.
- A 4th grader's parents lobbying to get a teacher fired for counting off on homework that was turned in obviously done in the Mother's handwriting.

Each generation is different than the one before them. Each generation is shaped by both the experiences of their youth and the meaning assigned to those experiences. If a child is overprotected by their parents or anyone for that matter, they are less likely to be accountable as adults. The challenge of creating a belief in accountability is a tough one and requires tremendous skill as a supervisor. Being able to modify beliefs is at the core of what a supervisor will have to do for the rest of their career. Each generation of leaders has been faced with developing the right beliefs in the next generation of workers. This will continue for generations to come.

1

Values Based Diversity…

JODY HOLLAND
· Educator · Entertainer · Motivator ·

3

Learning Objectives

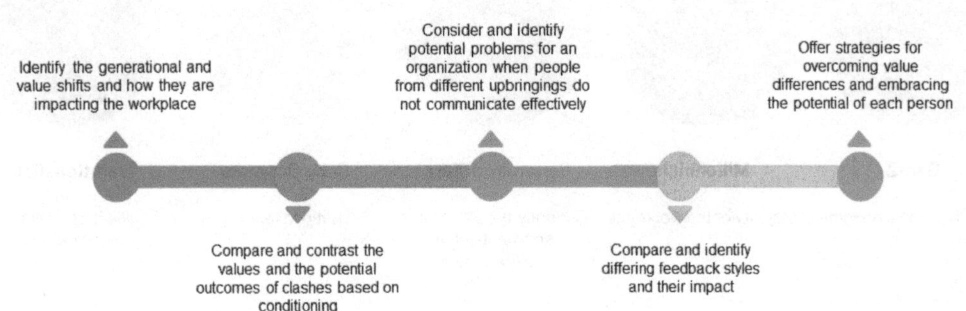

JODY HOLLAND
· Educator · Entertainer · Motivator ·

What Is A Generation?

- Strauss and Howe observe, "As a social category, a generation probably offers a safer basis for personality generalization than such other social categories as sex, race, religion, or age". (1991, Straruss & Howe)

- Generational categories are simply a manner of grouping a set of experiences together in order to understand what has shaped people.

JODY HOLLAND
· Educator · Entertainer · Motivator ·

Mixing & Matching 4 Generations At Work

5

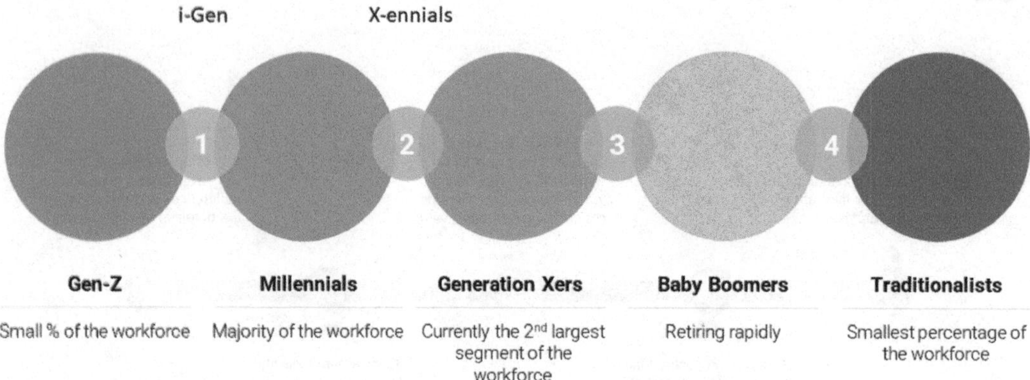

JODY HOLLAND
· Educator · Entertainer · Motivator ·

6

Discussion

Is it the time-period a person is born into or the labels of their experience that shapes the person? And, can people be different even with the same experiences?

JODY HOLLAND
· Educator · Entertainer · Motivator ·

Why Do We Have Conflict

Many organizations experience generational conflict. Older leaders have a hard time understanding, and therefore trusting, younger ones who are anxious to find their role in leadership. The latter often can't understand why older leaders believe and do what they do, and their questioning may lead to conflict.

JODY HOLLAND
· Educator · Entertainer · Motivator ·

8

Generational Tensions

Most of this tension results from generational differences that exist because of contrasting values. We make choices and decisions based on our value system, and differing values often lead to misunderstandings and misinterpretation. This, in turn, hampers our relationships and lessens the effectiveness of our work together.

JODY HOLLAND
· Educator · Entertainer · Motivator ·

Why Learn About Generations?

9

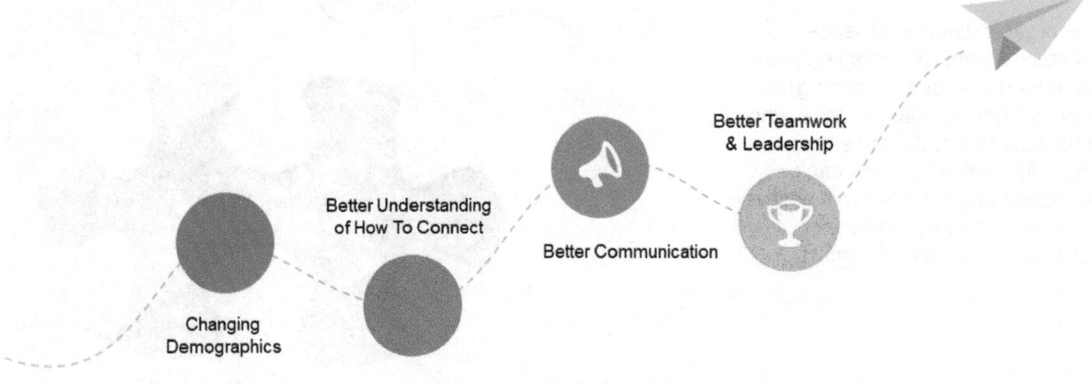

JODY HOLLAND
· Educator · Entertainer · Motivator ·

Who You Are When...

10

It's not just what you do that matters.

It is who you are while you are interacting with others that matters.

JODY HOLLAND
· Educator · Entertainer · Motivator ·

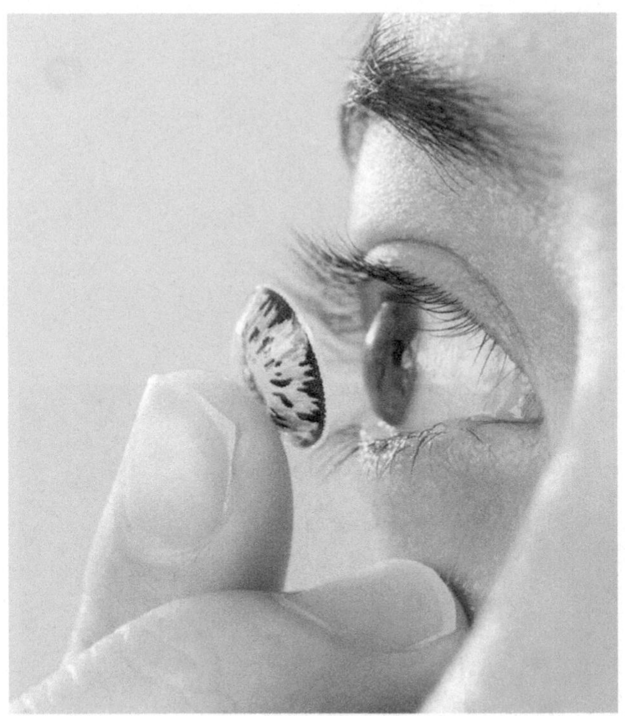

11

You Are Your Thoughts

The events and conditions that happened during our formative years helped to shape the world-view that we adopted.

Because of the labels that we place on those events and experiences, we end up seeing the world through that filtered lens.

JODY HOLLAND
· Educator · Entertainer · Motivator ·

Stages To Being You

Dr. Morris Massey stated that there are **3 stages** of development that each of us goes through to become who we are.

JODY HOLLAND
· Educator · Entertainer · Motivator ·

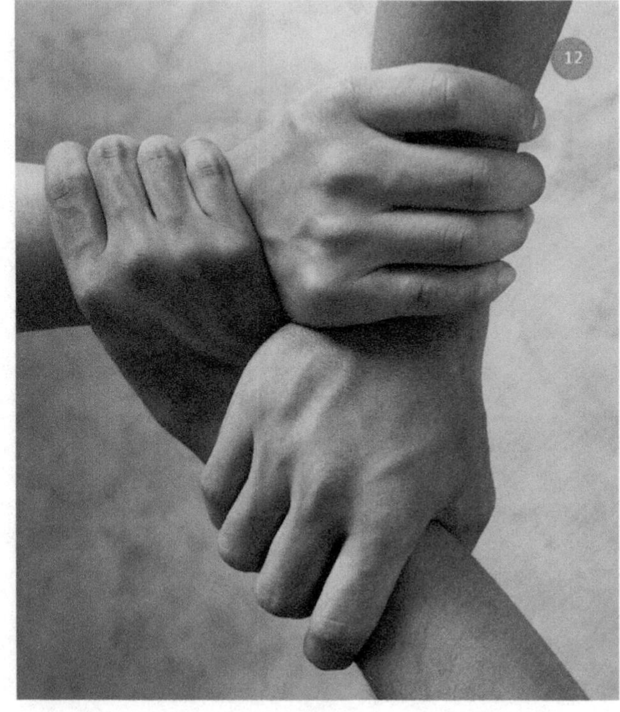

12

13

Imprinting – Stage 1

Up To Your 7th Birthday...

- Your brain operates differently.
- You develop personality.

JODY HOLLAND
· Educator · Entertainer · Motivator ·

14

Modeling – Stage 2

From 7 to our 14th Birthday...

- We develop values and beliefs
- We model others.

15

Socialization – Stage 3

From 14 to 22ish...

- We test our values.
- We learn critical thinking, decision-making, and accountability.

JODY HOLLAND
- Educator - Entertainer - Motivator -

Discussion

What are 2 or 3 experiences that shaped the way you look at work, leadership, and success?

JODY HOLLAND
- Educator - Entertainer - Motivator -

17

Why People Work The Way They Do…

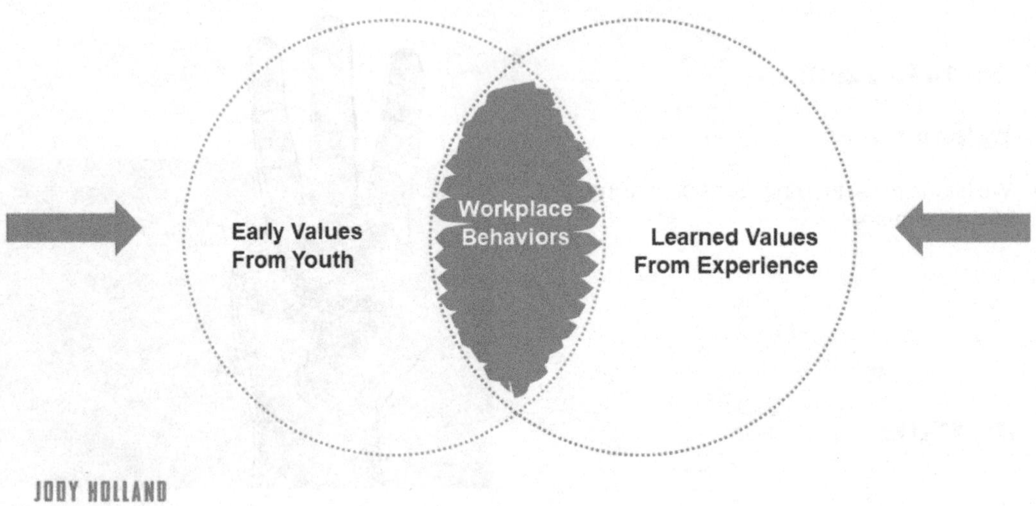

JODY HOLLAND
· Educator · Entertainer · Motivator ·

18

Momma Always Said…

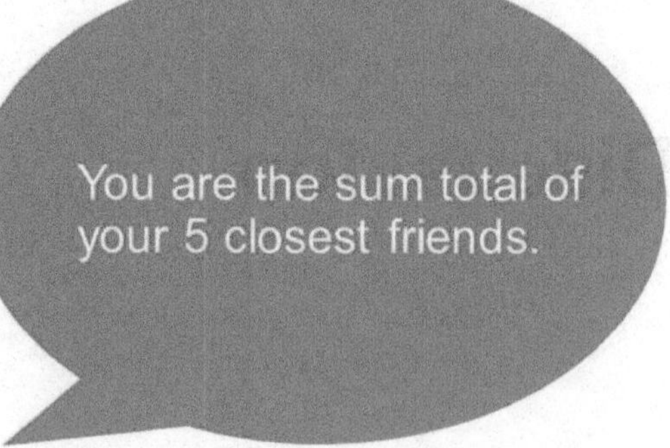

JODY HOLLAND
· Educator · Entertainer · Motivator ·

Traditionalists

- Born between 1922 and 1945
- Experienced the Great Depression and World War II
- Valued financial security, teamwork, sacrifice, delayed gratification, and the government which got them through these ordeals
- Their values more closely resembled biblical values; extended families were close, and marriages lasted a lifetime

JODY HOLLAND
· Educator · Entertainer · Motivator ·

Baby Boomers

- Born from 1946-1964
- Arrived to postwar affluence and the indulgence of parents who wanted them to have a better life than theirs
- More aware of political and social issues and became more and more disillusioned with government, big business, traditional religion, and parents
- Values included self-fulfillment, individualism, and material wealth
- 80 Million People

JODY HOLLAND
· Educator · Entertainer · Motivator ·

21

Generation Xers

- Born between 1965 and 1980
- The 1st Generation To Enter The Workforce after Corporate Downsizing
- Grew up independent
- They work hard and play hard and define themselves by things outside of work.
- 46 Million People

JODY HOLLAND
· Educator · Entertainer · Motivator ·

22

Millennials / X-Ennials / Gen-Y

- Born between 1981 and 2000
- Much more positive relationships with parents
- First generation to be raised with "positive psychology" and affirmation before struggle principles
- Incredible at juggling information
- 75 Million People

Don't Define Me!

JODY HOLLAND
· Educator · Entertainer · Motivator ·

23

Generation Z

- Born between 2001 and 2020 (estimated)
- More protected than previous generations
- Lived with significantly more structure than previous generations
- Started working in 2016 (first wave)
- Estimated 76 Million People
- Raised with preventive accountability principles

JODY HOLLAND
· Educator · Entertainer · Motivator ·

24

Unconscious Bias

- We are the result of our conditioning
- You think, feel, and act according to the conditioning you experienced through influential exposure
- Your beliefs create your thoughts.
- Your thoughts create your actions.
- Your actions create your results.

B.T.A.R.

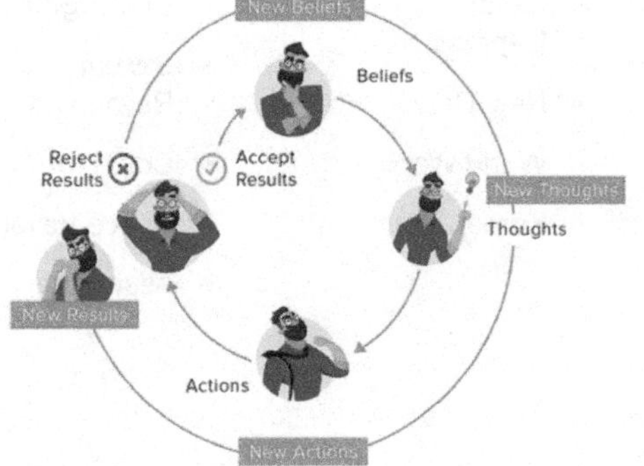

JODY HOLLAND
· Educator · Entertainer · Motivator ·

Generational Experiences

- Experience influences behavior
- It doesn't determine behavior
- Everyone has free will
- Ultimately, it is the label that we create for the event, not the event itself that matters.

JODY HOLLAND
· Educator · Entertainer · Motivator ·

Events & Experiences

Traditionalists:
- Great Depression
- New Deal
- World War II
- Korean War

Boomers:
- Civil Rights
- Sexual Revolution
- Cold War
- Space travel
- Assassinations

GenXers:
- Fall of Berlin Wall
- Watergate
- Women's Liberation
- Desert Storm
- Energy Crisis

Millennials:
- School shootings
- Oklahoma City
- Technology
- Child focused world
- Clinton / Lewinsky

JODY HOLLAND
· Educator · Entertainer · Motivator ·

27

Generational Values

Traditionalists:
- Hard work
- Dedication & sacrifice
- Respect for rules
- Duty before pleasure
- Honor

Baby Boomers:
- Optimism
- Team orientation
- Personal gratification
- Involvement
- Personal growth

Xers:
- Diversity
- Techno literacy
- Fun and informality
- Self-reliance
- Pragmatism

Millennials:
- Optimistic
- Feel civic duty
- Confident
- Achievement oriented
- Respect for diversity

JODY HOLLAND
· Educator · Entertainer · Motivator ·

28

What Generations Want

Baby Boomers:
- Recognition without reminders
- Be respected for their contribution
- Be rewarded for their success

Generation Xers:
- Work independently
- Be respected for results
- Be able to leave when the work is done
- Be relaxed

Millennials:
- Work as a team
- Be trusted to get the job done
- Be trained in the job and other skills
- Be very casual

Gen-Z:
- Work from anywhere
- Be given a chance
- Be trained on jobs and interests
- Be very casual
- Learn to succeed on their own

JODY HOLLAND
· Educator · Entertainer · Motivator ·

Discussion

What values do you believe guide Generation Z?

JODY HOLLAND
· Educator · Entertainer · Motivator ·

Making Sure We Are Clear...

Each person gets to shape and reshape themselves throughout their lives. You are responsible for you!

JODY HOLLAND
· Educator · Entertainer · Motivator ·

31

Making Sure We Are Clear…

Every employee should be held to the same standard. No adaptation should be made that compromises the integrity of the job or diminishes the effectiveness of your department to carry out its mission.

All employees should comply with policies and procedures set forth by their department and company.

JODY HOLLAND
· Educator · Entertainer · Motivator ·

32

VALUES IN…	TRADITIONALISTS	BOOMERS	GENXERS	MILLENNIALS
MOTHER	Homemaker	Working Mother	Single Mother	Single Mother/ Father
FAMILY	Close Family	Dispersed Family	Latchkey Kids	Looser Family Structure
MARRIAGE	Married Once	Divorced/ Remarried	Single Parent	Undetermined
HAIR	Short Hair	Long Hair	Any Style Hair	Bleached/ Spiked
CLOTHES	Formal	Casual	Bizarre	Anything Goes
MUSIC	Big Band/ Swing	Rock 'n' Roll	Alternative, Rap	Very Diverse
MONEY	Save It Now	Buy It Now	Want It Now	Get It Now (online)
PURCHASING	Purchase w/ Cash	Purchase w/ credit card	Struggling to Purchase	Purchase Online
MARKETING	Ford Marketing Concept	GE Marketing Concept	Ignored Market	Interactive Global Market
HIGH-TECH	Slide Rule	Calculator	Computer	Internet
WORK STYLE	Teamwork	Personal Fulfillment	Tentative/ Divided Loyalty	Networking
WAR	Win a War	Why a War?	Watch A War	Winless War
MORALS	Puritan Ethics	Sensual	Cautious	Tolerant

JODY HOLLAND
· Educator · Entertainer · Motivator ·

33

What Is A Values Gap?

- When people are raised with different beliefs and those differences result in an inability to work effectively together.
- When people are unable to communicate effectively as a result of differences in beliefs and thoughts.

JODY HOLLAND
· Educator · Entertainer · Motivator ·

34

Where Drama Comes From

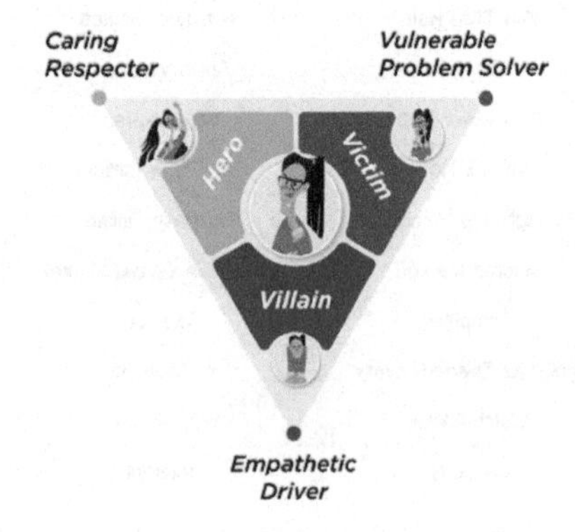

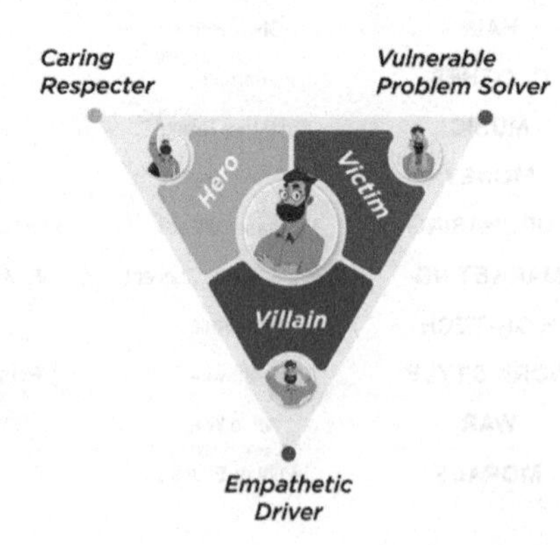

JODY HOLLAND
· Educator · Entertainer · Motivator ·

Why Do People Leave A Job?

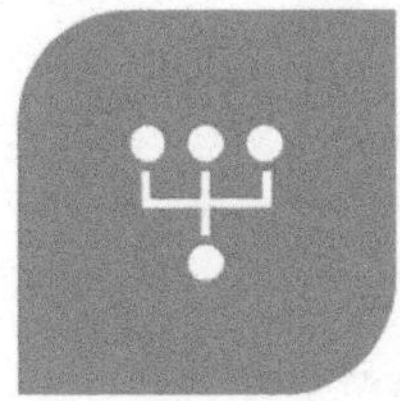

81% IS THEE RESULT OF A POOR RELATIONSHIP WITH THE SUPERVISOR OR LEADERSHIP

10% IS THE RESULT OF A POOR RELATIONSHIP WITH COWORKERS AND/OR EMPLOYEES

9% IS EVERYTHING ELSE INCLUDING PAY

JODY HOLLAND
· Educator · Entertainer · Motivator ·

36

How Do You Get People To Stay?

01

DEVELOP THE POTENTIAL OF YOUR SUPERVISORS AND LEADERS

02

ENSURE THE RIGHT HIRING AND ONBOARDING PROCESSES ARE IN PLACE

03

LEARN FROM THOSE WHO LEAVE

JODY HOLLAND
· Educator · Entertainer · Motivator ·

37

A Half Century of Change… And what is next?

1956

- Domestic Economy
- Working 9 to 5 with holidays off
- Formal / Professional Dress
- Work at the "office"
- Corporate Ladder

2006

- Global Economy
- Working 24/7 – 365
- Casual / Trendy Dress
- Work at the "coffice" or anywhere
- Corporate Labyrinth

JODY HOLLAND
· Educator · Entertainer · Motivator ·

38

These demographic changes will have profound impacts on organizations.

Consider the areas that must be developed and/or changed…

- Training & Development Will Be On-Going
- Recruitment Strategies Vs Screening Strategies
- Talent Development / Talent Planning
- Work-life balance
- Coaching & Mentoring

39

What Does This Mean To You?

The world of work as it was in 2000 will not exist again.

Recruiting is different

Managing is different

Diversity is different

JODY HOLLAND
- Educator - Entertainer - Motivator -

40

Managing Generational Diversity

Old Model

- Loyalty to institution
- Rank, hierarchy and following rules
- System and process
- Safety, security, don't rock the boat
- Career and advancement

New Model

- Free agency
- Autonomy and independence
- Action and results
- Challenge, risk and innovation
- Work-life balance

JODY HOLLAND
- Educator - Entertainer - Motivator -

41

How Do You Attract New Talent Now?

MINIMIZE BARRIERS TO ENTERING THE WORKFORCE

HAVE CONSISTENT TRAINING & DEVELOPMENT

CREATE A FUN ATMOSPHERE

DO THINGS THAT BUILD RELATIONSHIPS BETWEEN YOUR WORKERS... OUTSIDE OF WORK

JODY HOLLAND
· Educator · Entertainer · Motivator ·

42

A Few Generational Clashes...

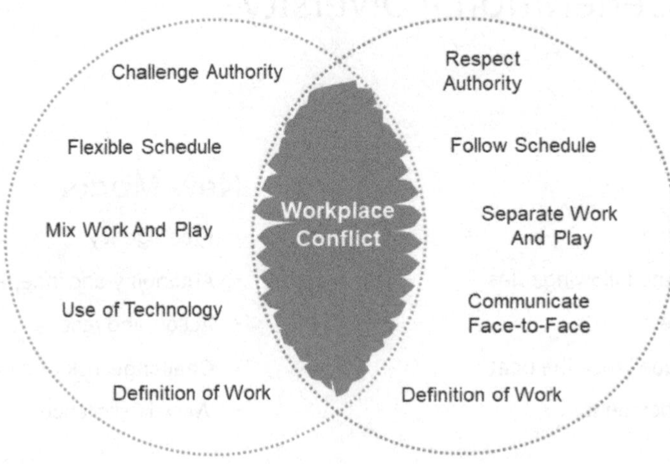

JODY HOLLAND
· Educator · Entertainer · Motivator ·

Creating Generational Harmony...

JODY HOLLAND
· Educator · Entertainer · Motivator ·

Communication Expectations

Traditionalists	Boomers	Gen Xers	Millenials
No news is good news!	Feedback once a year with documentation	How did I do on this project?	How did I do today?

JODY HOLLAND
· Educator · Entertainer · Motivator ·

Create Understanding

47

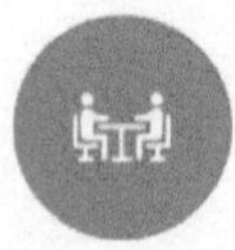

UNDERSTANDING OTHER POINTS OF VIEW AND ALLOWING FOR DIFFERENCES HELPS PEOPLE COMMUNICATE AND GET ALONG.

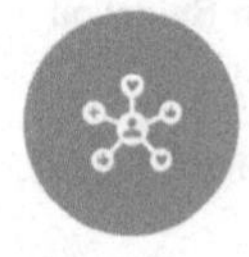

DON'T JUMP TO CONCLUSIONS ON OTHERS!

SEEK TO UNDERSTAND THEIR PERSPECTIVE.

SPEND TIME WITH PEOPLE WHO ARE DIFFERENT FROM YOU.

LISTEN!

JODY HOLLAND
· Educator · Entertainer · Motivator ·

Feedback Styles Differ

45

Some prefer not to get feedback.

Some prefer to get consistent feedback.

Some need affirmation mixed with their feedback.

Some come across as harsh or overly direct.

Some come across as soft or too easy.

What is your style? How do others respond to it? Where did you learn it?

Traditionalists seek no applause but appreciate a subtle acknowledgement that they have made a difference.

Boomers are often giving feedback to others but seldom receiving, especially positive feedback. Xers need positive feedback to let them know they're on the right track.

Millennials are used to praise and may mistake silence for disapproval. They need to know what they're doing right and what they can improve on.

JODY HOLLAND
· Educator · Entertainer · Motivator ·

Resolving Differences

Give every generation a voice

Invest in the success of all of your people

Build relationships

JODY HOLLAND
· Educator · Entertainer · Motivator ·

Create Understanding

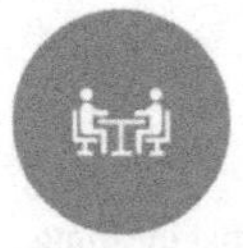

UNDERSTANDING OTHER POINTS OF VIEW AND ALLOWING FOR DIFFERENCES HELPS PEOPLE COMMUNICATE AND GET ALONG.

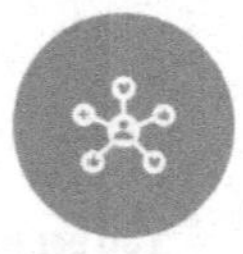

DON'T JUMP TO CONCLUSIONS ON OTHERS!

SEEK TO UNDERSTAND THEIR PERSPECTIVE.

SPEND TIME WITH PEOPLE WHO ARE DIFFERENT FROM YOU.

LISTEN!

JODY HOLLAND
· Educator · Entertainer · Motivator ·

Accept People Where They Are

Acceptance is crucial to every relationship, and a basic need for healthy self-esteem.

Acceptance of someone doesn't mean we have to approve of what he/she believes or does.

We can accept someone as having worth, even if we can't always agree.

Sometimes acceptance involves trust and even some risk.

JODY HOLLAND
· Educator · Entertainer · Motivator ·

Forgive & Choose Your Labels

People often hold on to grudges and prejudices far longer than they should.

If someone from another generation has "wronged" you, understand that it was one person

You get to decide what meaning you assign to things in your life, and ONLY you!

JODY HOLLAND
· Educator · Entertainer · Motivator ·

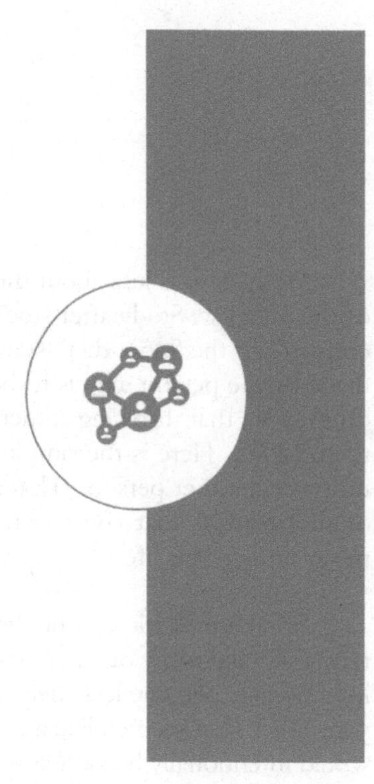

Embracing Diversity

• Each of us has our own unique characteristics. It is our differences that make our lives together interesting and rewarding.

• Everyone has something to contribute. We all need to remember to accept others for who they are and look for the best that they have to offer. That is what valuing diversity is all about!

3 MOTIVATING EMPLOYEES

Motivation is less about the carrot and the stick and more about the often unseen pot of gold at the end of the rainbow. Study after study has shown that it is not the "if-then" statements that matter the most. It is consistently the "now-that" statements that make the difference. Motivation itself is simply a decision that is made by the person who is to be motivated. Unfortunately, we have built program after program predicated on the idea that throwing something out in front of a person will motivate them to want to do what we want them to do. Here is the simple and yet painful truth. There isn't anything that you can do that will directly motivate another person. That's right. I can't motivate you! You can't motivate me! Now, the second side of that truth is that you can motivate you and I can motivate me. Each of us is in control of our own motivation in this life.

Abraham Maslow, who has been referred to as the "Father of Motivation" explained motivation in terms of a hierarchy or a pyramid that builds from base level motivation to self-actualization. He said, "If you intentionally become less than you are capable of being, then I warn you; you will be unhappy for the rest of your life." That seemed like an odd statement to me the first time that I read it. I thought, "who in the world would intentionally become less than they were capable of being?" Then I thought back to my parents telling me that I could be anything that I wanted to be if I was willing to work at it. I could be president of the United States, or a General in the Army, or an astronaut, or a police officer, or an entrepreneur, or a writer, or literally anything that I wanted to be. The question was… what was I capable of?

In Maslow's Hierarchy of Needs, he describes the five levels as each being dependent on the fulfillment of the previous level. For example, someone who is starving to death is not going to care about self-actualization. In order, Maslow indicated that we must take care of our base needs, such as physiological needs including food and sex. Once our base level needs are taken care of, then and only then can we move toward ensuring our safety. We strive to feel safe physically, mentally, and emotionally. Your brain does not distinguish between types of danger. In fact, you will experience emotional fear in the exact same way as physical fear. This is part of how we can explain the fact that many people have a greater fear of public speaking than they do of drowning. Once we feel safe, we move towards creating social connections. Our social needs include our friends and developing depth in our personal relationships. We need to have people around us that support us, inspire us, challenge us, and help us to move our lives forward. Once we have that, we then are able to truly focus on esteem needs. Our esteem needs will play into both the internal perspective and the external perspective that we have on reality. Achievement and personal success tie into this area. We judge ourselves based on our accomplishments as measured against our beliefs about self. Finally, once we have achieved our definition of success, then we can search for true meaning in life. We begin the self-actualization process, searching for who we are, why we are here, and how we can give back to make the world a better place.

A friend of mine sold one of his companies for a very nice sum of money. He made enough that he would never have to work again. With millions in the bank, he looked me in the eye one day and told me that he had realized that it was never about the money. He wanted to do something that made a difference in the world. I looked him straight in the eye and asked if he would give me all of his money. This caught him off guard and he cocked his head to the side a little, then said, "If I give you all of my money, I will have to work back to this point where life is no longer about money." That statement was full of truth. It was true because life is not about money when you have plenty of it. When you are struggling to make it up the ladder of success and to achieve your definition of success, you are passing through the phases of motivation until you reach self-actualization. Once a phase is satisfied, our focus shifts to the next level. Maslow simply said that one must hit each rung on that ladder as they climb their way to the top. We are motivated to move up the ladder of motivation. We are motivated to live into a vision that we have for ourselves. It is just that some people have a clear vision that they pursue, while others have a distorted and often wrong vision that they pursue. You will have to decide which is which in your own life.

The challenging part for many of us is that we have tried to live life without taking proper care of ourselves. We have tried to live as someone that we are not, in the direction that we shouldn't go, for purposes that really aren't ours. When we do that, we live our lives in the misery of no motivation. We live without an inspiring purpose for the actions that we are taking. That doesn't work. It doesn't work because we don't actually want it to work. The only thing that works is what we decide absolutely will work. I think that this explains why people have hobbies and do so much volunteer work. They volunteer to do things that they would pay someone to do at their own house. They do it and they love it and they work their tails off. When I was early in my life, I worked for a non-profit organization. I was responsible for recruiting volunteers, training them, and inspiring them to do great work. One of my duties was helping to ensure that our camp was funded, fixed, and functional. I had doctors, lawyers, dentists, nurses, teachers, preachers, business owners, and minimum wage employees all working for free to help with plumbing, construction, painting, tree-trimming, and anything else that was needed. In fact, many of them were paying for the chance to work in the heat, without pay, while singing a song, and helping one another. They were extremely motivated and there were no "if-then" statements involved at all.

What I had to understand as an executive was that people loved the opportunity to simply be motivated without any strings attached. They loved the chance to be self-actualized because money was off the table. I think that money itself has hurt motivation more than it has ever helped it. I'm not saying that I want to work for free from this point forward, but I am saying that I work my tail off to do the things that I love to do. I am also saying that I love to write and speak and make a difference in the world. I would do those things regardless of whether I could ever make money at them or not. I am simply blessed that I get to do what I am passionate about and people offer to pay me for it. I wrote and spoke before there was ever money on the table, though. I operated on the "now-that" premise. Now-that I have studied for decades and written books and spoken thousands of times, people want to pay me to keep doing what I love to do! That is truly awesome! And, awesome is how I want to live my life. I think it is how everyone wants to live their lives.

Below, you will find a variation of Maslow's Hierarchy of needs. It is normally presented in a pyramid format and in the order that I described it earlier. I wanted to make it a little more personable for you, though. So, take a look at the picture and think about how you are fulfilling each of those five areas. Many of us are not really taking care of the top two, or at least not very well. However, they are possible. In fact, other great minds have seen that the order can be reallocated or even rearranged based on a person's values and beliefs.

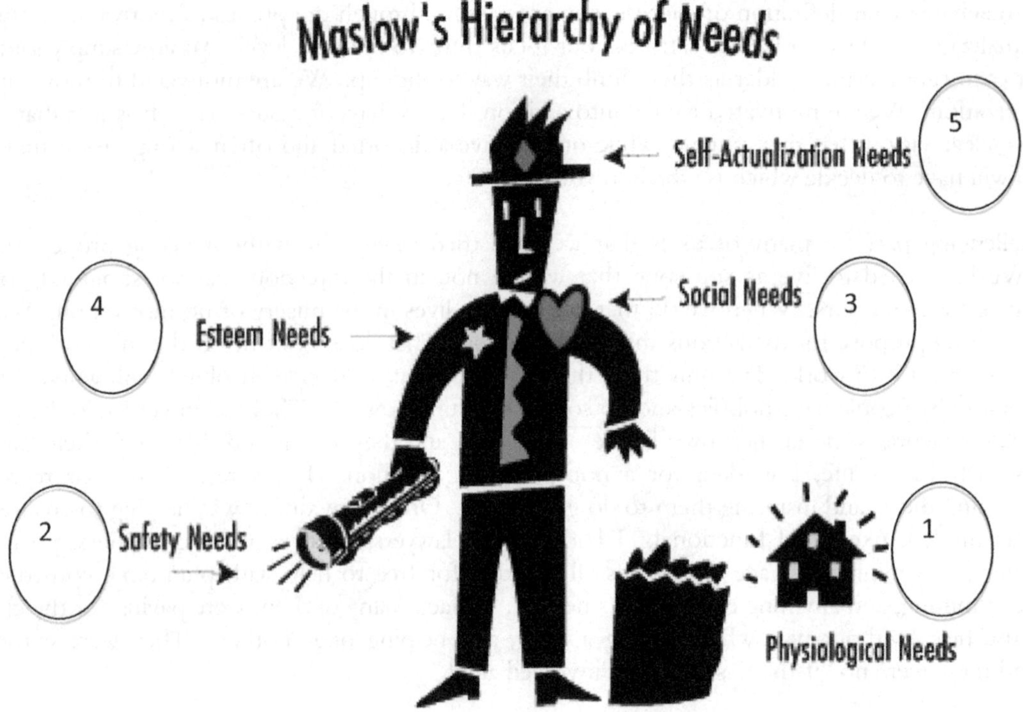

You have to ask yourself the question… *What motivates me?* For you, it is likely something different than it is for me. The core of society would tell us that we should be motivated by money and power and moving up in the world. What if that wasn't what drove you, though? What if you were driven to help people, like Mother Theresa? What if your calling was to be the best taxi cab driver in your city and that is what you love to do? What if you were designed to stay at home and raise kids? What if you were designed to preach or teach or start businesses? Whatever it is that you were designed to do, you will find that you are only fulfilled when you are doing that thing. I believe this is the reason that other theorists started to realign Maslow's Hierarchy of Needs.

Daniel Pink has written some great works on the science and art of motivation. Pink says that using carrots and sticks is "so last century." It is now more about autonomy, mastery and purpose. (Drive, by Daniel Pink) This author could not agree more with what Pink has to say. In fact, as a consultant, this author has seen more top level executives quit their post and move on because of a lack of autonomy, mastery and purpose than for any other reason. Employees at all levels desire the opportunity to participate in directing their career or even their job path. They want a say in what they are doing. They want a challenge that enables them to stretch and grow and become better than they were yesterday. And finally, they want to know that they are making a difference. Adeco, in 2015, indicated on Fox News that more than 80% of people who were employed, did not like their job and were disengaged at work. This would indicate that 8 out of every 10 people could produce more at work if they were simply motivated to do so.

Cocktail Party Summary of Drive, as stated by Dan Pink on www.DanPink.com…

COCKTAIL PARTY SUMMARY

When it comes to motivation, there's a gap between what science knows and what business does. Our current business operating system–which is built around external, carrot-and-stick motivators–doesn't work and often does harm. We need

an upgrade. And the science shows the way. This new approach has three essential elements:
1. Autonomy – the desire to direct our own lives.
2. Mastery — the urge to get better and better at something that matters.
3. Purpose — the yearning to do what we do in the service of something larger than ourselves.
(Buy The Book at: http://bit.ly/drivedanpink)

Pink goes on to say that rewards and incentives work for basic mechanical tasks or physical work. The moment that even rudimentary cognitive skills are required, however, the incentives no longer work. In fact, they have an inverse correlation to performance. Pink looked at research over a 70 year period and discovered that science has known for a very long time that motivation hasn't had anything to do with carrots and sticks in, well, at least the last 7 decades. He clarified that if-then statements work for physical tasks that do not require creative thought. If a person even has to do something as simple as putting together a puzzle, though, the if-then statements no longer work.

Pink goes on to say that what must be employed is the use of now-that statements. When a person is rewarded for something that they already did and they were unaware that a reward was a part of the effort, then the reward garners greater levels of loyalty and motivation. This means that we must be vigilant in watching our people and in appreciating the work that they do, as they do it.

So, there are two basic questions that most people want answered. The first is… What is Motivation? The second is… How do I motivate others?

What is Motivation…

Motivation is a state of focus where an individual chooses to perform at their best, and chooses to do more than is asked of them. When a person is motivated, they begin to look for ways to contribute. They willingly give of their talents in order to help their supervisor, their coworkers, their company, society, or some combination of those. Motivation is a feeling as well as a mental construct. According to Zig Ziglar, motivation is preceded by action. According to Steven Pressfield in The War of Art, motivation shows up after the person does. The reality is that motivation is a state of mind that follows a state of action, which was stimulated by a choice to act. The choice to act in the right direction can be a simple one if the conditions for work are right and the skills of the leader are sharp. It can be a very difficult choice to act in the right direction if the supervisors, managers, and/or leaders have not created the right culture.

While it is definitely possible to remain or become motivated with managers and leaders that are not creating the right culture, it is an incredibly self-disciplined choice when the culture is wrong. A great culture can make a mediocre employee strive to be a top performer. A poor or bad culture can make a top performer strive to destroy the success of the company. As leaders, we set the tone for those choices. We make it easy to be motivated or difficult to be motivated. We must accept the responsibility to create the right culture and we must accept responsibility if that culture has not been created thus far.

So How Do You Motivate Others?

I just shared with you that you are responsible for creating the right culture as a leader within your organization. Here comes the tough reality. You cannot directly motivate anyone. People are motivated internally, or intrinsically. There is no magic potion that you can put in the water cooler or the coffee. There is no chant or dance or music that will automatically lead to a motivated staff. You can, however, create a culture where the choice is easy. So, the answer to the question is this… Motivation follows developed and implemented management and leadership skills. As you learn the skills of a great manager and a great leader, and yes they are two different skillsets, then others will simply begin responding to the better culture that you are creating. They will slowly but surely become motivated. They will wake up a little more excited each day to be a part of your team and to make a positive impact.

You motivate others by being motivated, by developing and enhancing your skills on a continuous and never-ending basis, and by being a great manager **and** leader. People will follow you if you have and implement the skills of someone who is worth following. Please notice that I keep referring to skills and not to titles. People are not motivated to follow you if you are mean, unappreciative, arrogant, intimidating, gruff, unhappy, and definitely not just because you have a bigger and fancier title than them.

You create the environment that your employees have to make their choice inside of. It is that environment, that culture, that will ultimately lay the groundwork for the choices they will make. So, before you lay blame solely on an employee for not being motivated, take a look at the framework within which they make that choice. What would you choose, honestly, if you were being managed and supervised the way that they are? Put yourself in their shoes and try to see the world the way that they do, with their circumstances, with their reporting structure, with their rules and restrictions. Then determine what would be best for you, in order to stay motivated if you were in their shoes.

The Law of Reciprocation in Motivation

The law of reciprocation says that when a person receives something, they automatically feel an obligation to return something of equal or greater value, but only when the expectation of reciprocation is not requested by the original giver. Consider the following…

When an employee goes to work for an organization and their supervisor goes out of their way to compliment them on positive behaviors without asking for anything in return, the employee will consistently provide more of the positive behaviors. Additionally, when a supervisor provides a small gift, say an embroidered hat that is not standard, then indicates that they are just excited about the employee's future at the organization, the employee feels a psychological compulsion to prove the supervisor right. The issue only arises when a supervisor provides a gift or a compliment and then follows with, "Now, I expect better performance in return for this." This makes the appreciation… well, not appreciation.

It is in making the original gift to the employee actually a gift, with no implied obligation, that the obligation is in fact, made automatic. Perhaps it is in the societal expectations that we have been taught that the secret exists. When we were young, particularly when developing our value structures, we were taught that we were supposed to do something nice for people who were nice to us. We were also taught that there was no such thing as a "free lunch." In the present, this implication would indicate that we are obligated to be nice and to return a favor when one is done for us. Rooted in our psychological need for compliance to this unwritten rule of reciprocation, we attempt to equal, and often to out-give the original gift. That is simply human conditioning.

There are a number of employees that work extra hours, stay wholly devoted to, and stay loyal to a leader because they are nice. When a supervisor remembers to do things like writing birthday cards, buying presents for the employee's family, etc., then the employee has trouble leaving the organization. To be fully correct, the employee has trouble leaving the supervisor, not really the company. There are so few supervisors that have been taught correctly to be nice and respectful that when an employee experiences one, they are baffled and at the same time devoted. In some of my conversations with employees who work for a company that appears to not care about them as a person at all, who remain devoted, I have found it is their devotion to their direct supervisor who does care, that keeps them there.

Hawthorne Effect

Workplace conditions were studied at Hawthorne Works in Cicero, Illinois between 1924 and 1932. Elton Mayo was in charge of the research and the research itself was conducted by young male researchers. One of the intents of studying working conditions was to determine the effects of lighting on the overall productivity of factory workers. The idea, by Western Electric, was to determine if increasing lighting in factories would make the workers more productive and more successful on the job. Additionally, they experimented with changing up breaks, break times, work structure itself, and a few other components of work. In typical research fashion, three groups were set up. In one group, the lighting was increased. In another, the lighting remained the same. In the final group, the lighting was actually decreased. The research method involved young men in white coats, interacting with, observing, and taking notes on the work behaviors of the employees. As I stated, it wasn't just the lighting, but the conclusions from the study were fairly consistent regardless of the change that was made.

The overall conclusion was that it was in the act of observation that a temporary positive effect could be accomplished. The act of observation was actually driving behavior more than the changes. If a change was made and no observation was made, the impact was barely noticeable or was negative. If observation happened, with or without change, a positive change happened. The results of the studies were initially labeled as "the observer effect." Henry Landsberger, in reviewing the studies in 1958, dubbed the positive impact that was achieved through simple observation as "The Hawthorne Effect."

This effect can be used incredibly well to influence a team to move in the right direction. For example, when an outside trainer is brought in to teach leadership to all of the supervisors, managers, and the leaders, the entire organization will begin to look for the new leadership characteristics within the participants. This creates a new focus in the workers because they see both hope for better management and a lessening of their focus on what is wrong. This is particularly effective when coupled with an employee survey prior to announcing the new training series that will be implemented. In this case, the survey is implemented and the results reviewed at a high level with the entire staff. Based on the results, the training topics are introduced and then implemented. This provides a level of ownership in the minds of the employees for choosing what direction to take and therefore an obligation to be positive about the direction.

Many times, it is the simple act of changing focus that is needed to spur an employee, or an entire staff, in the right direction. They need to shift their focus in order to see the good that is happening. They become motivated to make it work because, after all, it was their idea.

Holland's Theory of Value-Based Drive

My theory is one of value-based drive. Holland's Theory of Value-Based Drive states…

We are motivated first by creating an image of the world. We assign meaning to everything around us. So, the first tenet of the theory is that nothing has meaning except that which I give it. Each of your employees are assigning meaning to every interaction that they have with their supervisor and/or leader.

They are motivated second by working with people and in a position that fits their definition of the world around them. When we are doing something that we would want to do, even if we didn't get paid, then we have found our fit. This is the part where they are allowed to operate inside of their personal area of brilliance.

And the third tenet of the theory is that our definition of success must be attainable through the vehicle (work) that we have chosen. If what we do and who we see ourselves as conflicts, we will experience stress and dissatisfaction… low motivation.

It is fairly easy to tell when people are not living within this motivational model. When a person's labels for reality are wrong, or when they are in the wrong job, or when they realize that they will not achieve their definition of success on the path that they are on, they become demotivated. This misalignment is the cause for a great deal of depression, anger, and seeking out of coping mechanisms. It is also the cause for people living their lives in quiet desperation instead living as fulfilled and happy people.

Over the years, I have had the chance to test the personalities of thousands of people. I have observed their behavioral patterns, which are quite predictable, based on their personality. I have also had the chance to see that people will modify their temperament, or their portrayal of personality to the rest of the world, when they have a shift in values. I have seen that values strongly influence what a person does with their inner drives and feelings. From a simplified standpoint, we can modify our motivation with some very simple questions.

1. What would I have to believe to be motivated in this situation?
2. Is that something that I can believe if I want to?
3. Do I want to?

I realize that this may sound very simple, but it is incredibly effective in helping you see the world in the image that it needs to be. When you are asking yourself what you would have to believe in order to be motivated, or happy, or driven, or satisfied, or any other emotion, you are asking what the image of the world needs to be in order to achieve the emotional state that you desire.

With the second question, you are then identifying the viability of the belief in your own mind. In James Allen's Book, As A Man Thinketh, he explains that the mind creates your world, not the other way around. He states, "The mind doth make heaven of hell and hell of heaven." It is possible to believe anything if that is what you absolutely choose. The trick is to choose your beliefs so that you live your life the way that you want to live it. You choose motivation by choosing to believe that you are motivated. When you believe that something is possible, then it is possible.

This is simply a question of desire when you get to the third question. Do you want to be motivated? Do you want to believe in the direction that you need to go? Do you want to? When you confidently say, "YES," then it becomes easy to create the right drive in yourself. When you say "NO," then it is virtually impossible to move forward. Everything comes down to creating the image, affirming its possibility, and then choosing it. You are in control.

You can operate in other people's definition of who you should be for a while, but not forever. I have had the chance to meet a number of very unhappy, financially successful people during my life. I have met CEOs that really wanted to be bartenders. I have met CPAs that wanted to be engineers and engineers that wanted to be teachers. The list goes on and on. The point is that when a person tries to live in the image of the world that their parents or their friends or society in general has for them, they are unhappy. They can be disciplined without being motivated. When a person lives their life in the image that fits how they see happiness, then they are happier and more motivated.

As a caution, there are a number of people that cannot or have not created an image of what the world should be. These are the people that struggle with what reality should be, that self-sabotage, that self-medicate, because they are trying to determine what should be and they are coming up blank. Motivation to succeed stems from believing in a world where they are successful. Never underestimate the power of belief. Belief creates thoughts. Thoughts create actions. Actions create results.

What would you have to believe to love learning about being a great supervisor?

____

____

____

____

Additional notable theories that you may want to research…

**Clayton Alderfer's ERG Theory (Existence Relatedness and Growth) And the Frustration Regression Principle

**McClelland's Learned Needs (Power, Affiliation, Achievement)

**Herzberg's Two-Factor Theory (Satisfiers versus Dissatisfiers, or Hygiene versus Maintenance)

**Albert Bandura – Self-Efficacy Theory

Learning Objectives

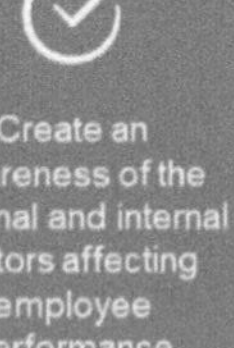

Create an awareness of the external and internal factors affecting employee performance

Understand your own motivation and what motivates others

Enhance your knowledge of various motivational theories

Apply these theories to the workplace

Expand your skills and your perspective

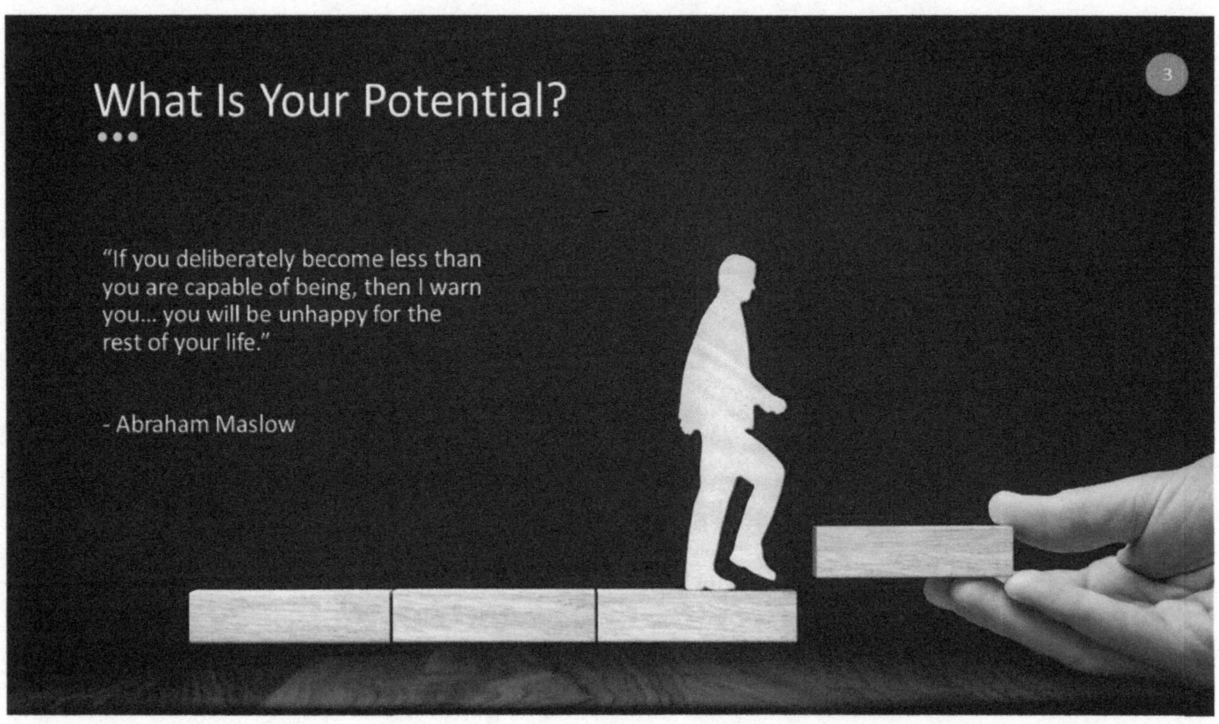

Our research has shown that a motivated workforce...

4

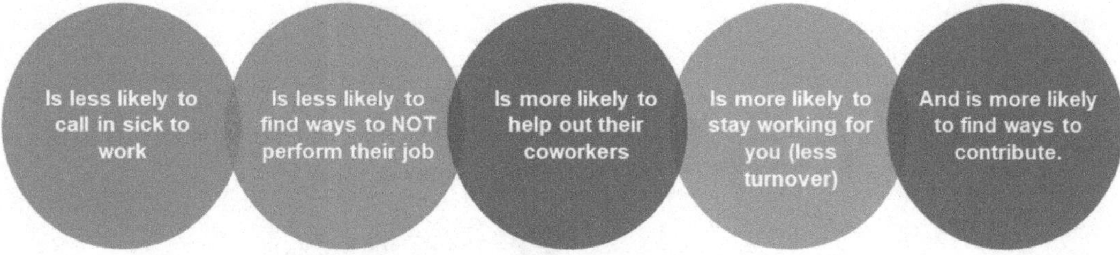

What Has Been Observed?

JODY HOLLAND
- Educator - Entertainer - Motivator -

Why did you come to work today?

5

Question?

Are your reasons different than your employees' reasons?

JODY HOLLAND
· Educator · Entertainer · Motivator ·

Job Performance Has A Few Components

- Job Performance equals
- Job Fit multiplied by
- The Person's Training & Ability To Do The Job multiplied by
- The Person's Motivation

JODY HOLLAND
· Educator · Entertainer · Motivator ·

7

Life Cycle Of Employment Motivation

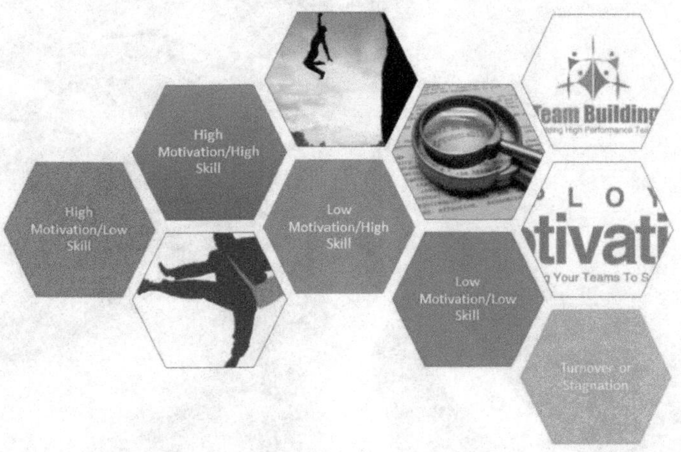

JODY HOLLAND
· Educator · Entertainer · Motivator ·

8

SHRM's Top Components of Engagement

After declining between 2009 and 2013, job satisfaction is again on the rise. What makes employees happy in their jobs?

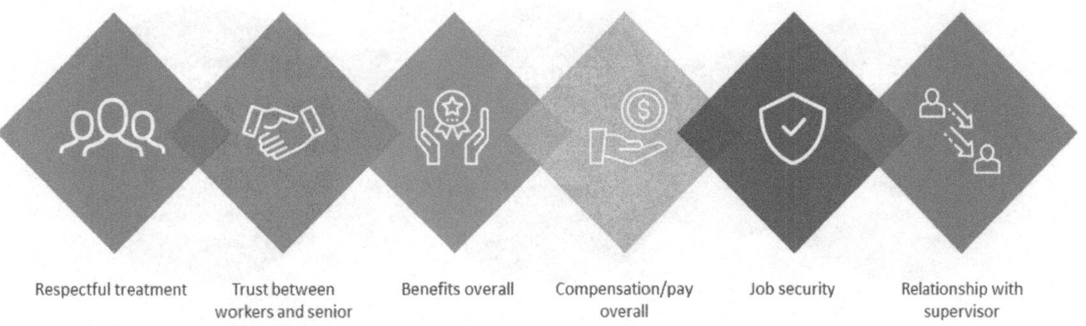

JODY HOLLAND
· Educator · Entertainer · Motivator ·

How Do We Motivate Long-Term?

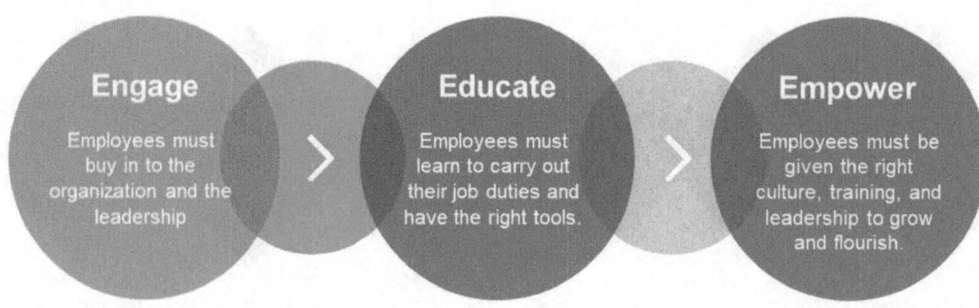

JODY HOLLAND
· Educator · Entertainer · Motivator ·

11

Maslow's Hierarchy of Needs

JODY HOLLAND
· Educator · Entertainer · Motivator ·

12

Clayton Alderfer's ERG Theory

ERG theory (Existence, Relatedness, and Growth), and was created to align Maslow's motivation theory more closely with empirical research.

~ Clayton P. Alderfer

JODY HOLLAND
· Educator · Entertainer · Motivator ·

G – R – E

13

- Growth
- Self-Actualization
- External Esteem Needs

- Relatedness
- Internal Esteem Needs
- Social Needs

- Existence
- Safety Needs
- Physiological Needs

JODY HOLLAND
· Educator · Entertainer · Motivator ·

How Alderfer Was Different

14

Alderfers ERG theory demonstrates that more than one need may motivate at the same time. A lower motivator need not be substantially satisfied before one can move onto higher motivators.

The ERG theory also accounts for differences in need preferences between cultures better than Maslow's Need Hierarchy; the order of needs can be different for different people. This flexibility accounts for a wider range of observed behaviors. For example, it can explain the "starving artist" who may place growth needs above those of existence.

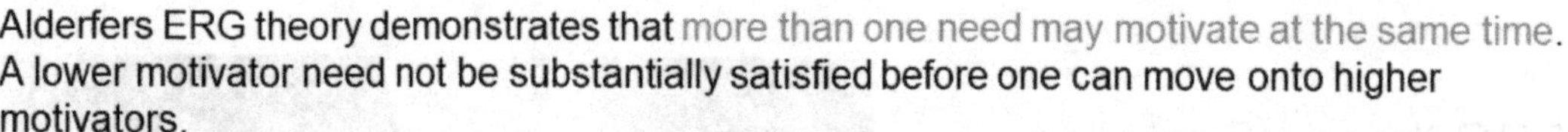

The ERG theory acknowledges that if a higher-order need is frustrated, an individual may regress to increase the satisfaction of a lower-order need which appears easier to satisfy. This is known as the *frustration-regression principle*.

JODY HOLLAND
· Educator · Entertainer · Motivator ·

15

Leadership Lessons Learned

Managers must recognize that an employee has multiple needs to satisfy simultaneously. According to the ERG theory, leadership focused exclusively on one need at a time will not effectively motivate.

The frustration-regression principle impacts workplace motivation. For example, if growth opportunities are not provided to employees, they may regress to relatedness needs, and socialize more with co-workers. Or, the inability of the environment or situation to satisfy a need for social interaction might increase the desire for more money or better working conditions. If Leadership is able to recognize these conditions, steps can be taken to satisfy the frustrated needs until the subordinate is able to pursue growth again.

JODY HOLLAND
· Educator · Entertainer · Motivator ·

16

Herzberg's Two-Factor Theory

Satisfiers

- Achievement
- Recognition
- Nature of Work
- Responsibility and Advancement

Dissatisfiers

- Company Policy
- Bad Administration
- Incompetent Supervisor
- Poor Working Conditions

JODY HOLLAND
· Educator · Entertainer · Motivator ·

Learning Objectives

17

Frederick Herzberg

(18 April 1923 – 19 January 2000)

- "Father of job enrichment principle"
- WWII Nazi Dachau Concentration Camp witness, Germany
- 1946 Graduate, City College
- 1950 Ph.D., University of Pittsburgh
- 1951 Research Director, Psychological Services of Pittsburgh
- 1957 Professor of Psychology, Case Western Reserve University, Cleveland
- 1972 Professor of Management, University of Utah

1959 book release:
"The Motivation to Work"
Focuses on a particular motivation theory which based his future publications.

1968 publication on motivation:
"One More Time, How Do You Motivate Employees?"
1.2 million reprints in 1987
Most requested article from Harvard Business Review

JODY HOLLAND
· Educator · Entertainer · Motivator ·

Learning Objectives

18

"The Motivation to Work" 1959
Motivation study

Interview
Accountants Engineers
Pittsburgh

One question:
"Think of the time when you felt exceptionally good, or exceptionally bad about your job; either your present job or any other job you have had..."
Tell me what happened.

I like my job!
- Achievement
- Recognition
- Nature of work
- Responsibility and advancement

I don't like my job!
- Company policy
- Bad administration
- Incompetent supervisor
- Poor working conditions

JODY HOLLAND
· Educator · Entertainer · Motivator ·

19

Two-factor motivation

Promote

Motivators
Job content

The absence of these conditions **doesn't necessarily dissatisfy**. But when present, they build strong levels of motivation that result in good job performance.

Improve

Hygiene factors
Job context

The presence of these conditions to the satisfaction of the employee **doesn't necessarily motivate**, but their absence results in dissatisfaction.

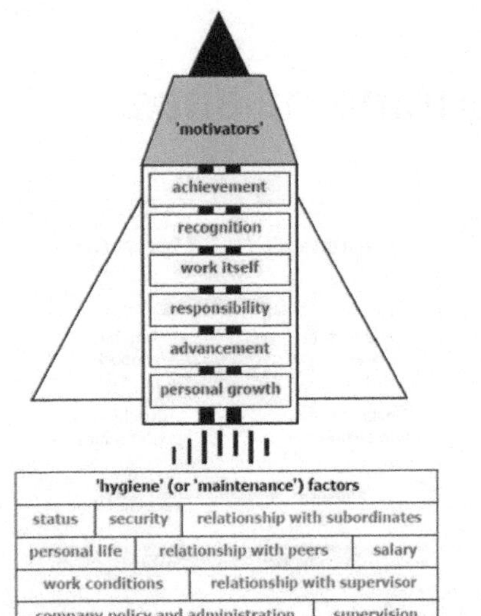

Hygiene factors are merely a launch pad - when damaged or undermined we have no platform, but in themselves they do not motivate.
The contrast is true for motivators.

JODY HOLLAND
- Educator - Entertainer - Motivator -

20

How to implement Hygiene-Motivator?

Motivators

- Give more recognition or rewards for good performance
- Offer opportunity to obtain more experience and knowledge
- Give a sense of reliance for the employee's performance
- Give room for "improvisation"

Promote

Improve

- Improve safety standards at work
- Offer flexibility in working hours and location
- Improve working environment (better air conditioning, water dispenser, clean toilet)
- Provide security via health benefits, etc.

Hygiene factors

JODY HOLLAND
- Educator - Entertainer - Motivator -

Determine balance

21

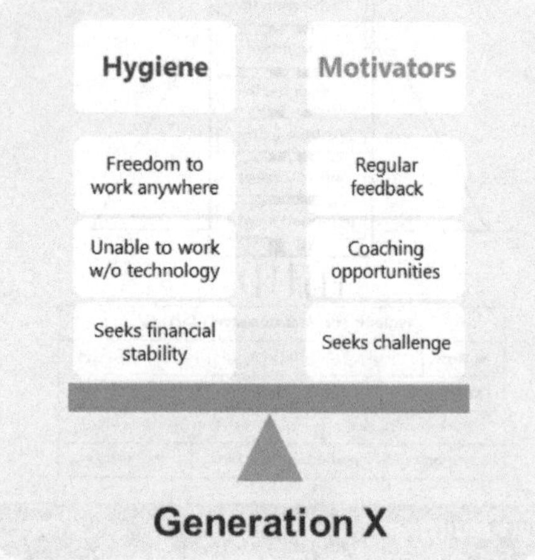

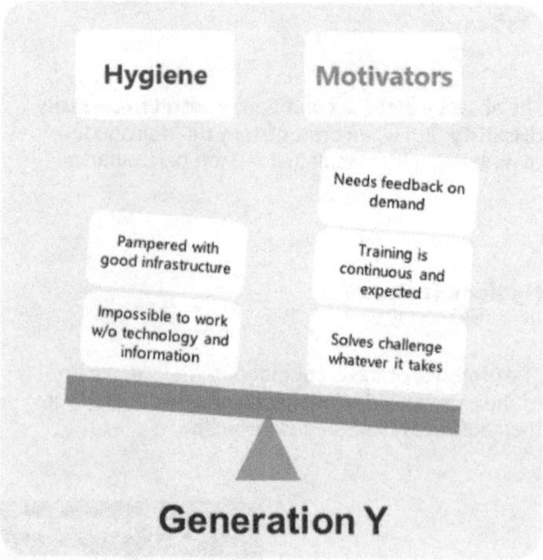

JODY HOLLAND
· Educator · Entertainer · Motivator ·

Propose motivation program

22

Gen X :

Team Building

Training Opportunities

Flexible Work Schedule

Increased Pay

Increase promotional opportunities

Gen Y :

Communication

Multitasking preferred

Give them a team

Establish clear expectations & rewards

Help them grow and Learn

Feedback

Flexibility

Expect them to go

JODY HOLLAND
· Educator · Entertainer · Motivator ·

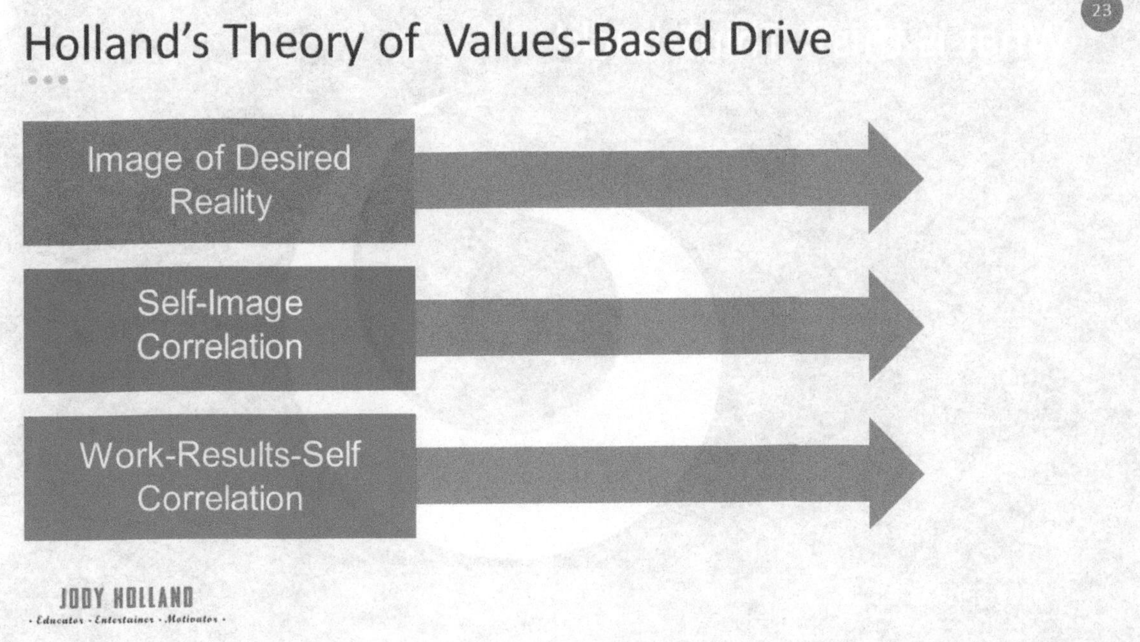

24

Image and Perception

The act of perceiving; cognizance by the senses or intellect; apprehension by the bodily organs, or by the mind, of what is presented to us; discernment; apprehension; cognition.

The quality, state, or capability, of being affected by something external; sensation; sensibility.

(Hearing, seeing, tasting, touching, smelling)

JODY HOLLAND

· Educator · Entertainer · Motivator ·

Apperception

26

Apperception means making sense of a new perception by interpreting it in terms of our existing concepts, languages, beliefs, theories and our past experiences.

Our mental encyclopedia of pre-existing concepts, beliefs, ideas, theories has traditionally been termed our *apperception mass*.

Source: Karl Jung's definition of apperception

JODY HOLLAND
• Educator • Entertainer • Motivator •

27

Dan Pink – Drive

Autonomy

The desire to direct our own lives

Mastery

The desire to get better and better at something

Purpose

The yearning to do what we do in the service of something larger than ourselves

JODY HOLLAND
· Educator · Entertainer · Motivator ·

28

We simply assume that the way we see things is the way they really are or the way they should be. And our attitudes and behaviors grow out of these assumptions.

~ *Stephen Covey*

WHAT DID YOU SEE?

31

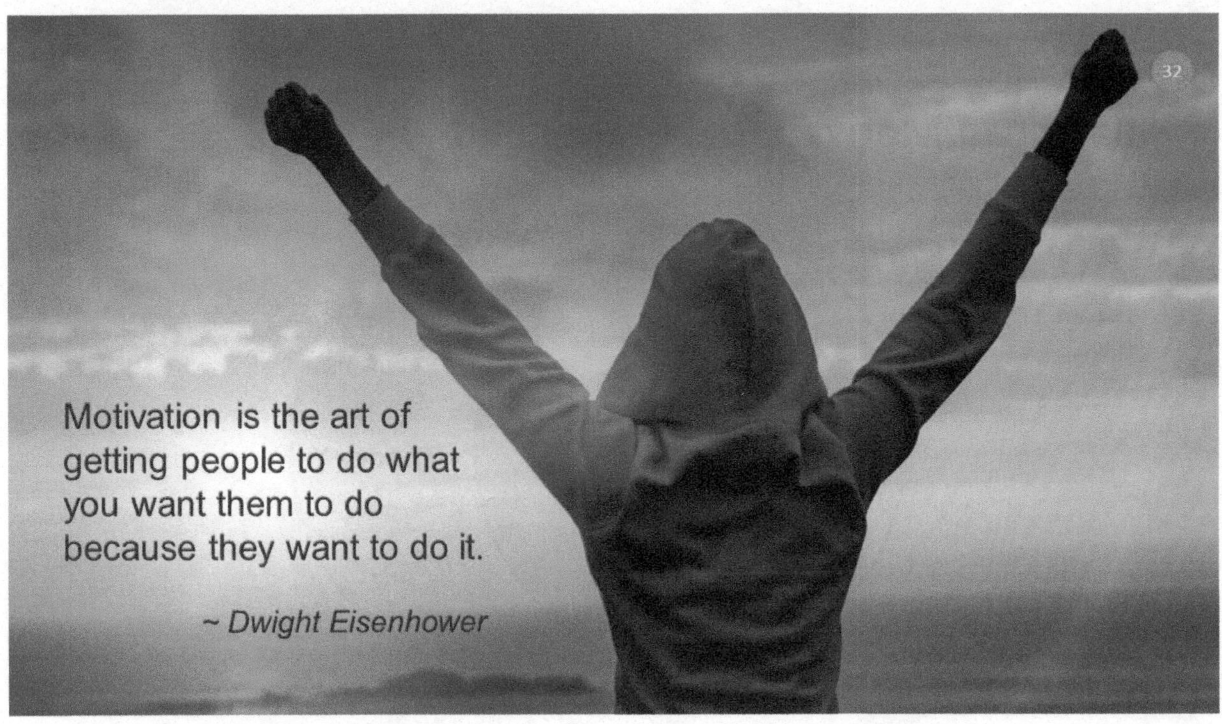
32
Motivation is the art of
getting people to do what
you want them to do
because they want to do it.
~ Dwight Eisenhower

We Manage To Our Apperceptions Douglas McGregor – Theory X / Theory Y

33

- Autocratic
- Strong Control

Theory X

Democratic Middle

- Listens More
- Maintains Final Say

- Laissez-Faire
- More Trusting

Theory Y

JODY HOLLAND
· Educator · Entertainer · Motivator ·

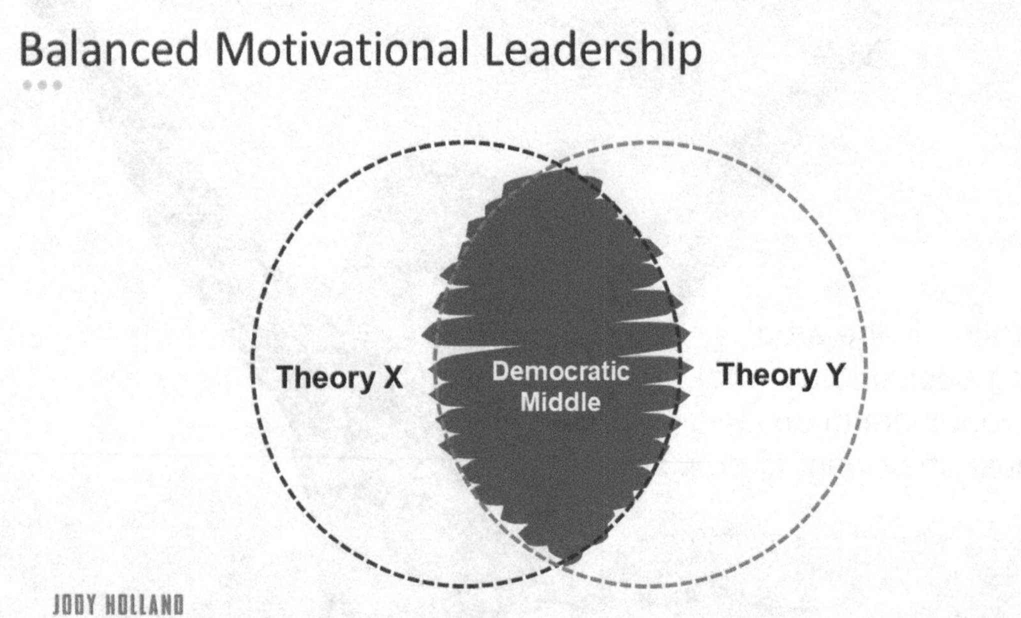

WHY WOULD ANYONE VOLUNTEER FOR THIS JOB?

Men wanted for hazardous journey. Small wages, bitter cold, long months of complete darkness, constant danger, safe return doubtful. Honor and recognition in case of success.

Explorer Ernest Shackleston in a 1890 job ad for the first Antarctic expedition.

JODY HOLLAND
· Educator · Entertainer · Motivator ·

Think about your own experience

What are the things that drive you to stay motivated?

What are the things that you have seen work for your team?

JODY HOLLAND
· Educator · Entertainer · Motivator ·

37

Motivation is the driving force behind all actions of human beings.

Motivation is often based on emotions, not factual logic.

We all search for positive emotional experiences and the avoidance of negative ones.

JODY HOLLAND
· Educator · Entertainer · Motivator ·

38

Motivation Is...

an internal state or condition that activates behavior and gives it direction;

desire or want that energizes and directs goal-oriented behavior;

influence of needs and desires on the intensity and direction of behavior.

JODY HOLLAND
· Educator · Entertainer · Motivator ·

39

What is it that employees want?

- To know the organization has purpose and is moving in the right direction
- A good supervisor
- Personal development
- Efficient work systems
- Tools and equipment or to know why not available
- Appreciation
- Good interdepartmental relationships

40

The numbers are a bit scary at times…

70% of your employees are less motivated today than they used to be.

80% of your employees could perform significantly better if they wanted to (had the emotional desire).

50% of your employees only put enough effort into their work to keep their job.

Statistics are from the book Super Motivation by Dean Spitzer, 1995.

JODY HOLLAND
• Educator • Entertainer • Motivator •

41

"The only happy people I know are the ones who are working well at something they consider important."

~ *Abraham H. Maslow*

JODY HOLLAND
· Educator · Entertainer · Motivator ·

42

Always Start With Why

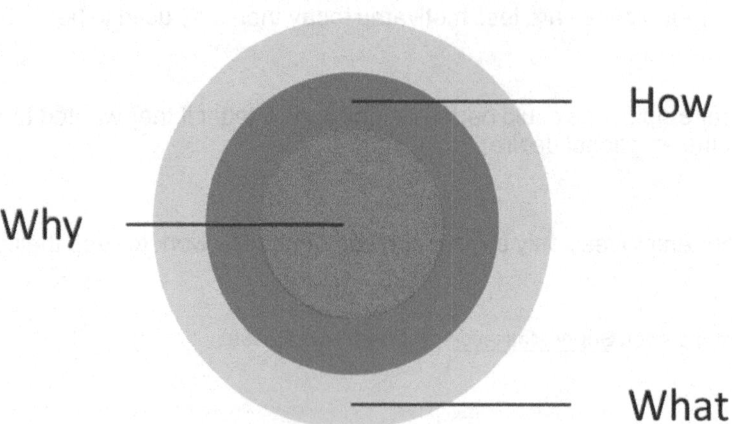

JODY HOLLAND
· Educator · Entertainer · Motivator ·

What Motivates Your Team?

Make a list of three things that motivate each of your employees.

- Career Development / Success
- Comfort / Relaxation
- Health / Balance / Energy
- Influence / Leadership
- Learning / Knowledge / Discovery
- Materials / Possessions
- Recognition / Praise
- Security / Money / Home
- Social / Affiliation / Popularity / Acceptance
- Status / Prestige / Stand Out / Reputation
- Task Accomplishment / Problem Solving / Achievement
- Teaching / Guiding Others
- Vitality / Energy
- Others?

JODY HOLLAND
· Educator · Entertainer · Motivator ·

49

Theoretical Perspectives

Content Theories
- Maslow's Hierarchy of Needs
- Herzberg's Two-Factor Theory
- McClelland's Three Needs Theory
- McGregor's Theory X and Theory Y
- Alderfer's ERG Theory
- Mayo's Motivation Theory
- Holland's Value-Based Theory

Process Theories
- Adam's Equity Theory
- Vroom's Expectancy Theory
- Taylor's Motivation Theory
- Bandura's Self-Efficacy Theory
- Skinner's Reinforcement Theory
- Locke's Goal Setting Theory

JODY HOLLAND
· Educator · Entertainer · Motivator ·

4 COMMUNICATION

One of the greatest struggles that we face in communication is actually connecting. In my book, Authentic Communication, I describe what it means to be aware in communication. As a fitting start to this chapter, I wanted to include that here.

In this section, you will learn the five key components of awareness. For ease of remembering, I have organized them into the acronym, AWARE. A is for acceptance. W is for waiting for your turn to speak. A is for anticipating the needs of others. R is for responding instead of reacting. And E is for engaging fully in the interaction.

A

Acceptance is one of those words that we confuse between tolerance and simply giving up on a person. The truth, however, is that acceptance is about releasing your judgment of the person in the interaction and focusing on the moment. There are only three times in a person's life that exist and two of them are not real. There is the past, which is gone and cannot be changed. There is the future which is yet to be written, and there is the present which is where we should be fully immersed. As one of my friends, who is a business coach put it, "Wherever you are, be in that moment." When we accept a person, we are looking at them as an equal and as someone who is exactly who they are. We must accept them as they are, in order for them to desire to be anything more than they are. When we look at a person and give off the nonverbal signal that they are not good enough, they feel it. You, as the supervisor, will set the tone for whether or not your people see their own potential.

Acceptance is about being comfortable enough with who you are that it becomes okay for others to be who they are. When you don't accept others as they are, it is generally because you fear something. You may fear that they will hold you back or let you down or limit the potential of others. Whatever it is, let it go. Simply focus on the communication and let them be them.

W

Waiting isn't just about the physical act of waiting your turn to speak. It is also about the way in which you process information. People speak at an average of 125 words per minute, but the conscious mind has the ability to process between 400 and 600 words per minute effectively. This means that you have a little extra time floating around in your brain. Unfortunately, most people don't innately focus just on the person in front of them at that moment. They are always thinking, though. Cognition is the act of thinking. Meta-cognition is the act of thinking about what you are thinking. When you are listening, people often spend their time thinking about what they want to respond with instead of thinking about what the person is saying. In order to be effective at communication, particularly at listening, you have to wait both mentally and physically for your turn.

Waiting for your turn mentally means suspending judgment about the other person, about the situation, and about what is being said. You have to remove that judgment filter by accepting the person as they are, and then focusing on just the information at hand. Our tendency is to put our own meaning into the conversation based on our apperceptions. An apperception is a perception that we hold of someone or something with our past experiences serving as the filter for its current meaning. Do your very best to remove the filters of past experiences and allow the current experience to take precedence. Wait to make your judgment call until after you have taken time to listen to the person fully.

A

Anticipating the needs of others means thinking about their comfort as well as their interpretation of meaning. As you do your very best to suspend judgment, keep in mind that if you have filters, so do they. They have their own collection of past experiences that have helped to shape the way that they are viewing their situation now. The thought of anticipating how a person has labeled every event in their history can be a bit much, though. The most effective way to anticipate is to stay focused on the non-verbal reactions of the other person. Small movements, facial expressions, and even auditory reactions will tell you a lot about how they are filtering their interaction with you.

To anticipate the needs of the other person, you must imagine seeing the world through their lens, or their frame of understanding. When learning about emotional intelligence, this will be one of the most critical components of empathy. Not to be confused with sympathy, or feeling sorry for another person, empathy is all about trying to understand how the person came to the conclusion to label their world the way that they did. Empathy essentially says, "If I had seen the world the way that you do and had interpreted my experiences the way that you do, then I would agree with you." You have to remove your emotional attachment to your opinion and embrace the idea that there is always more than one way to look at things, then focus on trying to see the world the way that the other person does. The beauty of anticipating what a person needs by seeing from their perspective, is that it allows you to switch back and forth from your view to their view, giving you a more robust interpretation of what things could mean. So, try to see what they see. Try to look for ways to make things work for them as well as for you, and try to anticipate what they will need from you in order for the communication to be positive.

R

In every interaction that we have, we will have the opportunity to handle the other person either positively or negatively. We have the choice to make as to whether it is better to use the emotional side of our brain or the logical side of our brain, or somewhere in the middle. To respond is to think through what we are about to see and look for the following…

- What are the possible consequences, good or bad, of what I am about to say?
- If I were to switch places with the person that I am interacting with, what would I think of my actions and my treatment of them?
- How would I want to be communicated with if I were in their position?

By thinking through what you are about to do before you do it, you position yourself to more easily avoid reaction and embrace response. Reactions come from our emotions and don't involve thinking through what we are about to say. Reactions are about making the sender of the message feel better, or vindicated, or superior. They are not about making the communication more effective, nor are they about creating a win/win situation. Reactions generally lead to some level of misunderstanding, whereas responses generally lead to better understanding and better relationships. If you are unsure of which you are doing, ask yourself… "Are people generally better off after I interact with them or are they more frustrated, angry, or worse off?" That is the easiest way to determine which angle you have been taking. Reactions often damage relationships. Responses often strengthen them.

E

Engaging fully with another person or a group of people is about following the four golden rules of communication. These rules position you to avoid distraction and build trust with your team, your supervisor, or virtually anyone that you interact with. The four golden rules of communication are as follows…

1. Focus on the person that you are with. The American Psychological Association in an article in 2012

indicated that multi-tasking (truly divergent thought) was a psychological impossibility. This means that when you are typing on your computer and an employee comes up to talk to you, you cannot be fully engaged if you keep typing away on the computer. You have to stop what you are doing, look at the person, and keep your focus on them. Additionally, you are dealing with their perception of the situation, not just your belief about your psychological capacity for thinking in divergent directions. If they don't think that you are fully engaged with them, then you aren't. Stop what you are doing when you interact with them and focus on the person that is with you.

2. Respond non-verbally to the speaker. When interacting with an employee, coworker, or anyone else in a relationship, it is critical that they see your responses to their message. It is in using your facial expressions and body language to indicate your agreement, understanding, disagreement, etc. that a person is able to connect at a stronger level with another person. Try demonstrating that you disagree with something without saying anything. What would that look like? Try demonstrating that you are intrigued, or excited, or confused. Each of these emotions, as responses to a speaker will help the speaker to determine whether or not their message is being understood correctly. DO NOT STARE BLANKLY AT THE SPEAKER!
3. Ask good questions. As you are focused on the other person, responding non-verbally to their statements, the next step is to ask questions in order to gain understanding, clarity, and to spur on the conversation. Questions serve as a way of telling the speaker that you are interested in what they are saying and would like to have more information. From the perspective of the speaker, this act of asking questions to spur on information is a way of connecting deeper, gaining perspective and ensuring understanding.

Reflect the underlying intent of the message. This is perhaps the most difficult of the four golden rules of being a great communicator, but it is also the most important. It rests on the foundation of the other three, so it works only when used in conjunction with them. When a person is speaking with you, you want to look for the emotions that they are using. You also want to look for the meaning behind their message. As an example, if a person says, "I just don't know what I am going to do now," their meaning could be and your response could be, "You sound stressed and unsure." What you don't want to do is to repeat back to them exactly what they said. Instead, you want to paraphrase what they said and try to ensure that you understand the meaning behind the words. This aspect of reflecting takes into account their non-verbal behaviors as well as the message itself.

What is Communication?

1. Communication is transactional because it involves an exchange. There is always give and take. Whether you are in a group setting, at a staff meeting, interacting with your boss, or interacting with an employee, there is a flow that occurs in your communication. The basic structure of communication is that there is a sender, a receiver, and a medium (the way the messages are exchanged). Each sender will encode their message with underlying meaning that is derived from their personal experiences in life. Certain tones of voice, body language, and facial expressions are used when saying something in order to make it reflect the sender's beliefs. That "encoded" message is sent via the communication medium to the receiver. The receiver must then decode the message (assign meaning to it) via their own set of experiences and beliefs. Once the message is decoded, the receive responds non-verbally and verbally to the message, and then sends that response back to the original sender with their own encoding in the message. This process, or transaction, continues to flow back and forth until the communication itself is complete.
2. Communication is complex. As you can tell from the description given for the transactional description of communication, the process can become complex very quickly. This is the reason that it is so critical to study communication in-depth as a supervisor, manager, and/or leader.
    1. Communication is interactive. There are a number of processes involved in good communication, and even in poor communication for that matter. When we interact with another person, we are sharing a part of who we are with them and then receiving back a piece of who they are in return. There is a continuous ebb and flow of information and meaning between the two or more participants in the communication process.

2. Communication is symbolic. The encoding that each person does puts their own symbolism into the message. Mannerism, presentation style, and hidden meanings are all a part of communication. The challenge comes with the fact that symbols are open to interpretation. What might mean one thing to one person could mean something entirely different to another person.
3. Communication is both personal and cultural. Characteristics of overall communication such as personal space, clothing, jewelry and the like all have meaning to a person. Just like the symbols, cultural differences will mean different things to people of varying cultures. What might mean bravado to one culture could be seen entirely differently by someone of another culture. Each culture creates meaning in their manner of communication.
4. Communication is irreversible. Once something has been said, it cannot be un-said. A variation of the old saying about the impact of words, and perhaps a more true interpretation would be… *Sticks and stones may break my bones but words can scar forever.*
   One of the reasons that it is so critical to learn the proper presentation of messages is that every interaction that you have with another person will leave them either better or worse off. You can't ever take your words back!
5. Communication is circular. Messages are created and sent. Feedback is provided from the listener. The speaker confirms that the message was properly understood and interpreted or the loop begins again.
6. Communication is purposeful. There is always a reason behind a message even when that reason may be difficult to understand. Sometimes the meaning is to simply get things off of a person's chest. Other times it is about solving a problem. Other times still, it may be about deepening a relationship.
7. Communication is non-duplicable. Every interaction is unique in its own right. There are no two people that would encode a message in exactly the same way. By the same right, there are also no two people that would interpret or decode a message in exactly the same way.

3. Communication is unavoidable. It is impossible to NOT communicate in some way. The way that we dress (paralanguage), the way that we move our bodies (non-verbal), our tone of voice, our facial expressions, literally every aspect of who we are says something about us. These mannerisms provide a way for others to interpret and understand us. Being on time is a message. Being late to work is a message. Everything that we do says something about who we are to others.
4. Communication is continuous because it continues to impact your future, even after the transaction is complete. After you interact with others, they will continue to think about the meaning and interpretation of the interaction. Often times, significant interactions will last for years in a person's mind. Some interactions will impact the very belief system of a person and can change the way that they interpret future interactions with others. Because communication is layered with meaning and interpretation and emotion, you could compare it to the onion. Onions have layer after layer to them. In communication, you can peel back layer after layer of messages, encoding, and interpretation.
5. Communication can be learned and can always be improved. With the right mindset, that of understanding that one can always learn and grow, one can grasp that communication capabilities are ever evolving. We are not born communicators. Instead, we learn every aspect of communication through trial and error, reprimand, affirmation, and study. The best communicators realize that there is always something more to learn and they invest consistently in growing their personal skill-set.

Factors of Communication

As we exchange meaning through communication, we take into account a variety of factors, including…

- <u>Meaning</u> within communication involves thoughts, ideas, and understanding shared by communicators. Communication is interpreted through both verbal and non-verbal means with the majority of interpretation having to do with the non-verbal side. Impacting that interpretation is the apperception, or the filtering of meaning based on previous meaning that we have given to past experiences that could be considered similar.

- The channel of communication is also known as the medium of communication. This represents how we send and receive messages with others. Consider the significant shifts in communication channels over the last 50 years and how those changes have impacted relationships with others. Various channels could include voice, text, social media, email, messenger, morse code, P.A. system, face-to-face, etc.
- The context of communication impacts interpretation as well. Consider how you communicate when multiple things have gone wrong over a short period of time. Also consider how you communicate when everything is going your way. You may act one way around one group of people and another way around another group of people. The people you are around, the occassion, the task, even your outlook will all impact how you communicate.
- Physical environment also plays a part. The temperature, the place, and other environmental factors all play a part in the way in which you will communicate. We are continuously being influenced in our thought patterns based on the environment that we are in at the time.
- The climate of communication is often felt by all parties involved. There are times that you can feel the tension in the air or you can feel the love in the air from the people that you are communicating with. Think about the "vibe" that you give off while interacting with others. The more positive of a vibe that you give off, the easier it is for others to interact with you. Always do your best to set the right tone for interactions.

The 5 Types of Communication

1. Intrapersonal – Each of us has conversations with ourselves on a regular basis. Some are positive, encouraging the self that it can accomplish what it needs to. Some are negative, telling the self that it is lacking or not good enough. When we put effort into positive self-talk, we begin to build our skills and confidence and have a greater impact on those around us.
2. Interpersonal – This is where two or more people are interacting. This is used in the maintenance of relationships and the deepening of connections between people. When you are communicating with an employee one-on-one, when you are communicating with your significant other, or any other one-on-one relationship, you are practicing interpersonal communication.
3. Small Group – When interacting in a small group, such as a staff meeting, the group shares a common goal. Group cohesion and team compatibility rely on the idea that each member of the group shares an interest for group success. When the interest is not shared by even one person, the climate changes very quickly and the entire group is impacted.
4. Group or Public Speaking – This is where one person or a small panel of people are giving out information to a larger group of people. The interaction is primarily one way (speaker to audience) from a verbal perspective, but it is definitely two-way when non-verbal aspects are taken into consideration. The intent of this type of communication is to inform, motivate, persuade, and/or entertain.
5. Mass Communication – Our world is rich with mass communication. From social networks, to TV and radio, to billboards and a host of other modes of mass communication. People often feel that they are being communicated "to" or "at" instead of "with" in this type of communication. Technology is the backbone of this interaction, but people will still interpret intent and meaning into the way in which the messages are constructed.

Think about the various aspects of communication and how each of them plays a role in your interaction with others. Every time that you communicate with another person or with a group, you have an impact on them and they have an impact on you. Never forget the responsibility that you hold in making sure that you are a great communicator and that you are building up the success of those around you.

The quality of your communication is measured in the quality of the response that you get from those you are interacting with. If the response is not what you want, evaluate ways in which you can enhance your communication in order to improve that response. Below, write out three goals that you have for yourself related to improving your communication skills in the next 90 days.

1. ____

____

2. ____

____

3. ____

____

Authentic
Communication
JODY HOLLAND
· Educator · Entertainer · Motivator ·

Interacting With
Employees /
Interacting With Self

3

Learning Objectives

The objectives for this training are to:

1. Identify what constitutes effectiveness in communication
2. Identify common barriers to effective communication
3. Understand your personal strengths and weaknesses in communication
4. Utilize the key concepts to assist you in increasing your effectiveness in communication

JODY HOLLAND
· Educator · Entertainer · Motivator ·

4

Listening

The average person can listen at between 400 and 600 words per minute.

Listening is perhaps the most significant part of communication. We spend more time listening than any other aspect of communication.

JODY HOLLAND
· Educator · Entertainer · Motivator ·

5

How We Spend Our Time In Communication

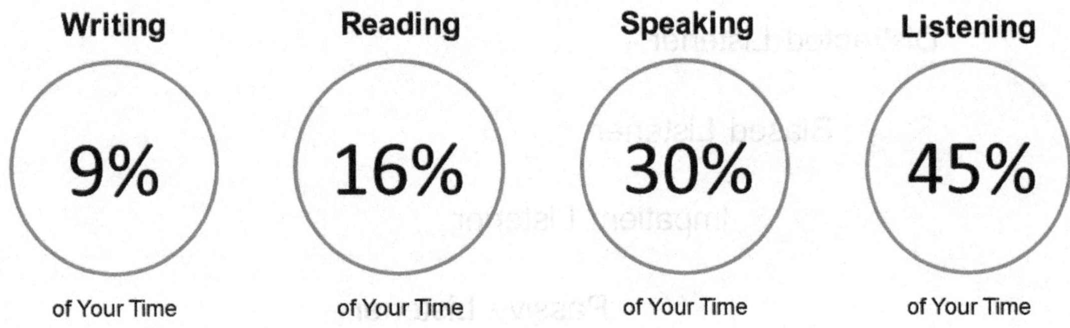

JODY HOLLAND
· Educator · Entertainer · Motivator ·

6

How Good Of A Listener Are You?

Sorry!
What did you say?

JODY HOLLAND
· Educator · Entertainer · Motivator ·

7

Types of BAD Listeners

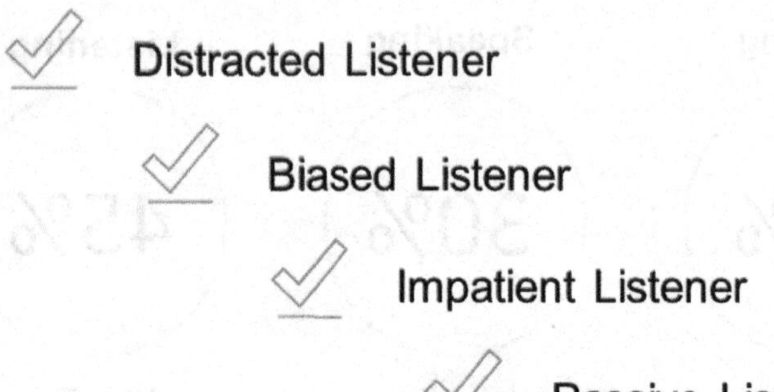

JODY HOLLAND
· Educator · Entertainer · Motivator ·

8

Types of GOOD Listeners

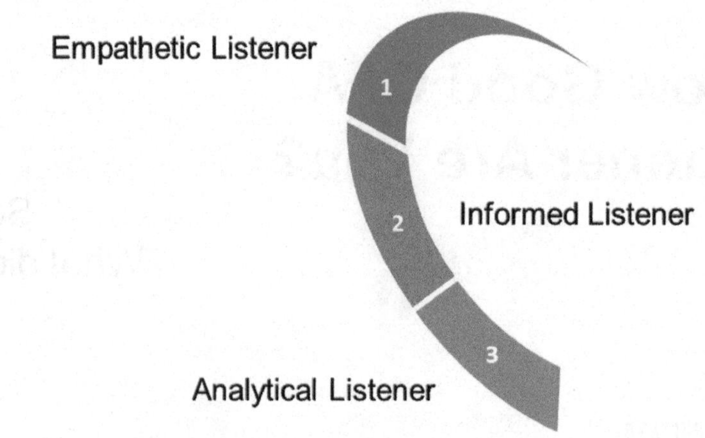

JODY HOLLAND
· Educator · Entertainer · Motivator ·

9

Listening With Empathy

Be attentive. You have to make an effort to listen carefully. Don't daydream and don't talk.

Think about the main point the speaker is trying to make. To remember it, write it down. If you are in class, write a summary of the information when the speaker has finished his/her presentation.

Paraphrase or restate in your own words what the speaker is saying.

Try to leave your reaction out when you're listening. Try not to make arguments in your mind. These things detract you from what the speaker is saying.

Ask for clarification if you don't understand a point the speaker is making. Be polite.

Avoid distractions. Sit close to the speaker, if possible.

JODY HOLLAND
• Educator • Entertainer • Motivator •

10

Steps To Empathetic Listening

Frederick Platt outlined the steps to listening with Empathy...

JODY HOLLAND
• Educator • Entertainer • Motivator •

11

Learning To Be Empathetic

Empathy is one's ability to recognize and properly interpret the feelings or emotions of others.

JODY HOLLAND
· Educator · Entertainer · Motivator ·

12

Connection Happens When...

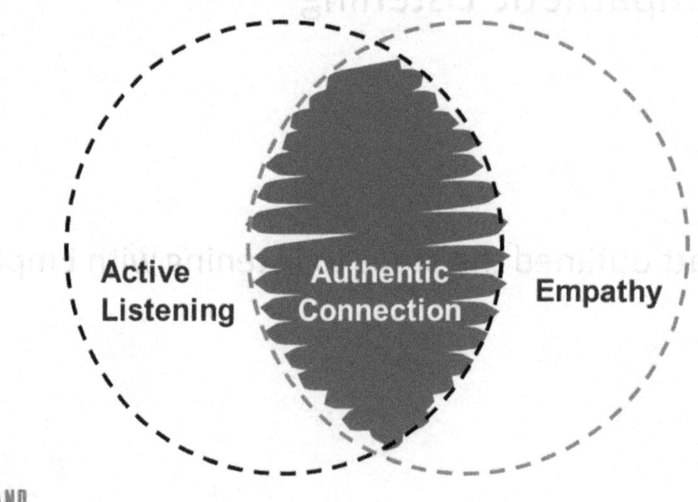

JODY HOLLAND
· Educator · Entertainer · Motivator ·

13

5 Principles of Communication

- Communication is **transactional**
- Communication is **complex**
- Communication is **unavoidable**
- Communication is **continuous**
- Communication is **learned and can be improved**.

JODY HOLLAND
· Educator · Entertainer · Motivator ·

14

Communication Process

2 Communication changes its meaning with context, environment, and the medium or channel of communication.

1 Communication involves a sender, receiver, and a message. All messages are encoded with meaning.

3 Communication is the process of creating and exchanging meaning through symbolic action that constantly moves and changes.

JODY HOLLAND
· Educator · Entertainer · Motivator ·

15

The Elements of Communication

In all aspects of communication, the various elements must be considered.

As two or more parties are involved, they each encode meaning into the messages that they send. The receiver must properly decode those messages in the midst of other elements of communication.

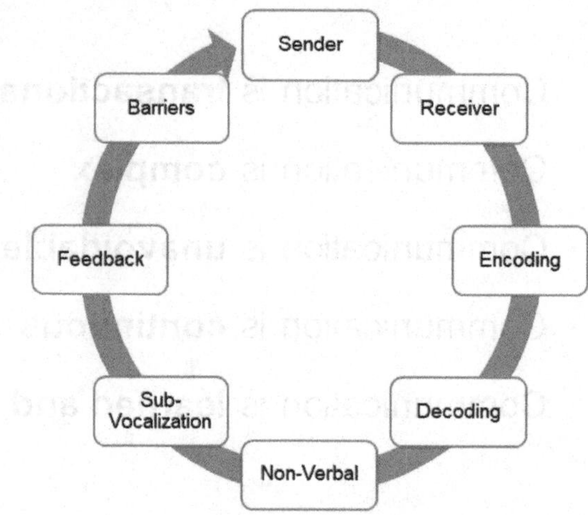

JODY HOLLAND
· Educator · Entertainer · Motivator ·

16

5 Types of Communication

1. **Intrapersonal** – Talking to Self (Feelings – Emotions)
2. **Interpersonal** – 2 or more people interacting – Maintenance of relationships
3. **Small Group** – Group Interaction – Common goal
4. **Group or Public Speaking** – Inform / Motivate / Persuade / Entertain
5. **Mass Communication** – Mass media to general public involving technology in varying sorts.

17

Intrapersonal Communication

Each of us participates in some degree of self-talk. We may talk about our fears, or build our own confidence, or tell ourselves what we can and can't do.

JODY HOLLAND
· Educator · Entertainer · Motivator ·

18

Interpersonal Communication

Communication between two or more people without the distraction of electronic mediums either builds up or tears down our relationships.

JODY HOLLAND
· Educator · Entertainer · Motivator ·

19

Small Group Communication

Things such as staff meetings, problem solving sessions, strategic planning sessions, and committee meetings fall into this category.

JODY HOLLAND
· Educator · Entertainer · Motivator ·

Group Communication or Public Speaking

This form of communication relies on an individual or a panel speaking to an audience with the intent to inform, inspire, and/or educate them. It is less interactive and more dependent on the single speaker.

JODY HOLLAND
· Educator · Entertainer · Motivator ·

21

Mass Communication

This communication happens through social media, TV, radio, newspaper, blogs, websites, and more. It is communication where the individuals involved are not directly connected and directly speaking to one another.

JODY HOLLAND
· Educator · Entertainer · Motivator ·

22

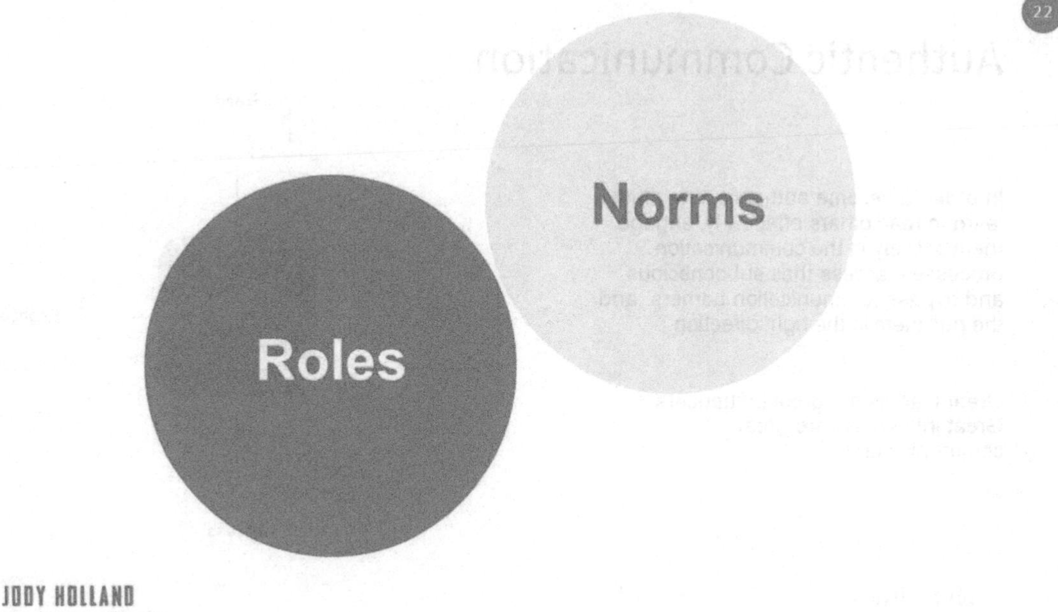

JODY HOLLAND
· Educator · Entertainer · Motivator ·

23

Reading People

JODY HOLLAND
· Educator · Entertainer · Motivator ·

24

Authentic Communication

In order to become authentic, one must learn to read others effectively, engage them actively in the communication processes, access their subconscious and bypass communication barriers, and the pull them in the right direction.

Great leaders are great influencers. Great influencers are great communicators!

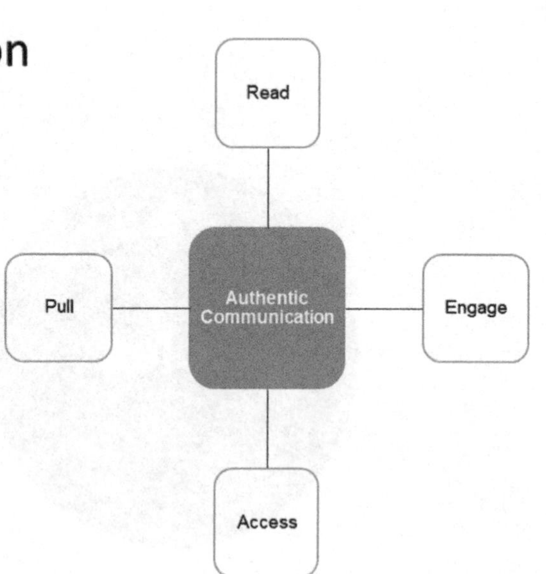

JODY HOLLAND
· Educator · Entertainer · Motivator ·

Read

A Person's Face Tells Quite A Bit

JODY HOLLAND
· Educator · Entertainer · Motivator ·

26

WHO ARE THEY?

WHAT DO THEY WANT?

WHERE ARE THEY GOING?

JODY HOLLAND
· Educator · Entertainer · Motivator ·

28

People Want To Be Heard And Understood

There Are 4 Levels To Listening

JODY HOLLAND
• Educator • Entertainer • Motivator •

Learn Their Story

- **Focus**
- **Non-Verbal Response**
- **Questioning**
- **Reflection**

JODY HOLLAND
· Educator · Entertainer · Motivator ·

30

Access

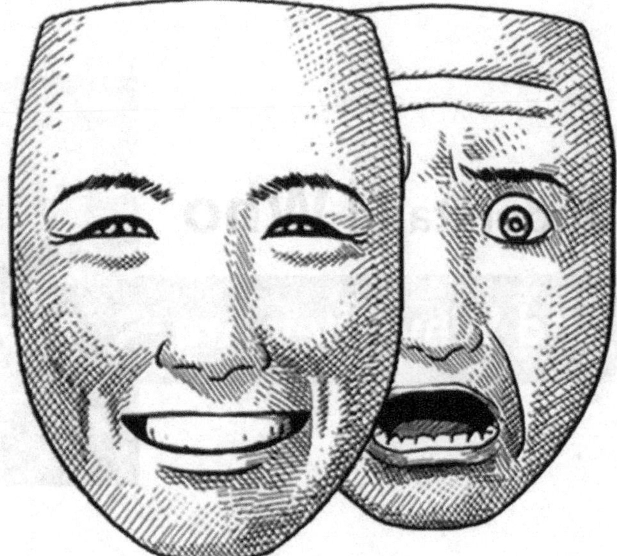

JODY HOLLAND
· Educator · Entertainer · Motivator ·

People Are Always Singing To The Beat Of Their Own Drum

Mirror Neurons

Leading

Inspiring

JODY HOLLAND
· Educator · Entertainer · Motivator ·

32

Understand Who

And Why They Are

JODY HOLLAND
· Educator · Entertainer · Motivator ·

PULL

JODY HOLLAND
· Educator · Entertainer · Motivator ·

34

Propose

Don't Direct

JODY HOLLAND
· Educator · Entertainer · Motivator ·

Use Their Own Words
It is about what they want, not what you want.
JODY HOLLAND
· Educator · Entertainer · Motivator ·

People Want
OPTION
2
1
Let Them Choose

37

Giving Great Business Presentations

As a leader in your organization, you are continuously needing to give presentations. Knowing the skills of a great presenter positions you to inspire your people to greatness!

JODY HOLLAND
· Educator · Entertainer · Motivator ·

The Art of Presenting

You Have To Show Up To Win

Jody's Trip To Austin with Mr. Grigsby…

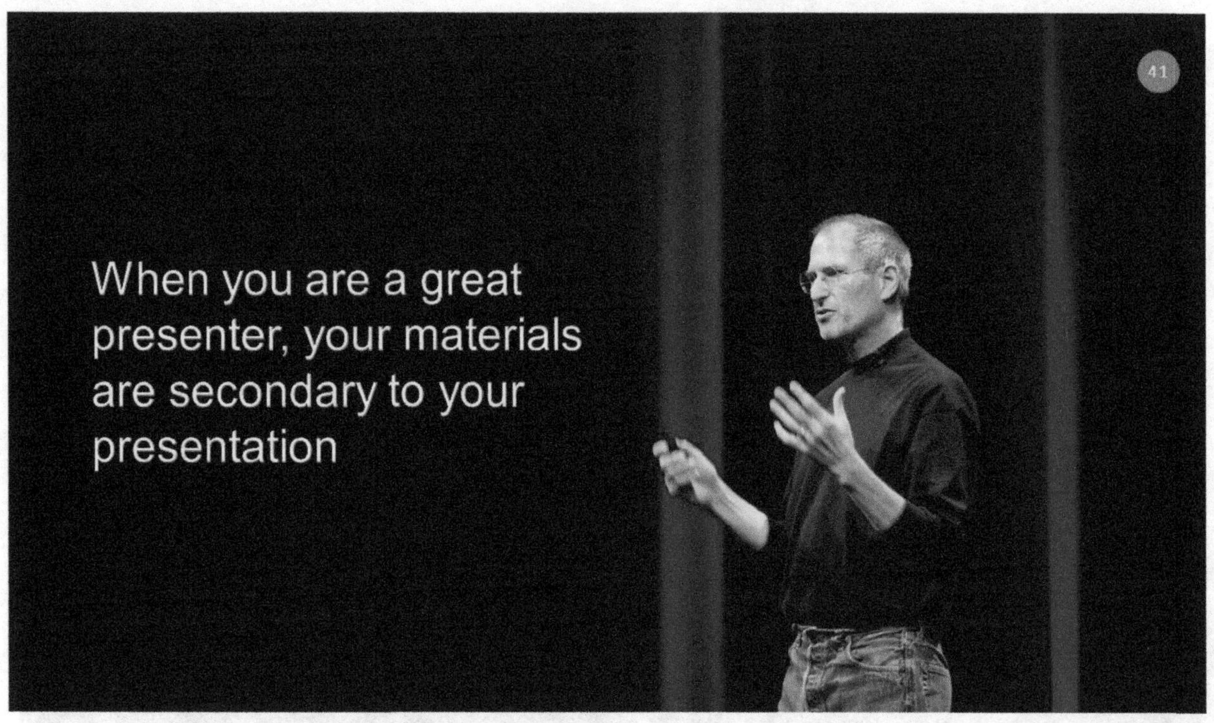
41
When you are a great presenter, your materials are secondary to your presentation

42
When you are good at presenting, you can do anything you want to do.

How do you
unleash the
great presenter
In you!
43

44
Learn to play the part
of the presenter

45

You are presenting as an actor or actress.

Not as yourself

JODY HOLLAND
· Educator · Entertainer · Motivator ·

46

JODY HOLLAND
· Educator · Entertainer · Motivator ·

47

Physiological separation from who you are......

To who you need to be right now

JODY HOLLAND
· Educator · Entertainer · Motivator ·

49

Skills come with practice

AND **PRACTICE**

AND PRACTICE

AND **PRACTICE**

JODY HOLLAND

· Educator · Entertainer · Motivator ·

51

You want to show them something awesome...

Not just tell them something awesome.

JODY HOLLAND
· Educator · Entertainer · Motivator ·

Watch the way your voice sounds.

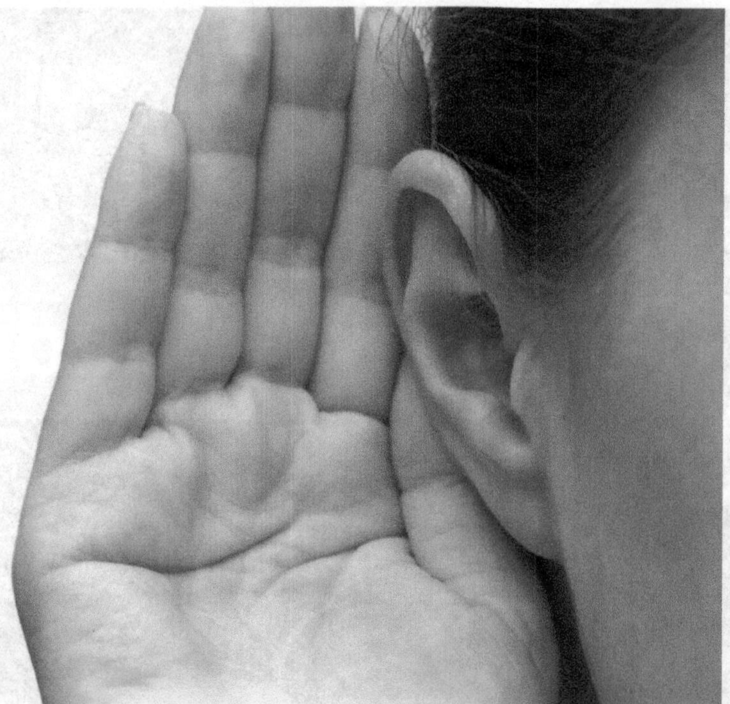

"That which I perceive is my reality."

William James

55
It's to simplify the complex!
JODY HOLLAND
· Educator · Entertainer · Motivator ·

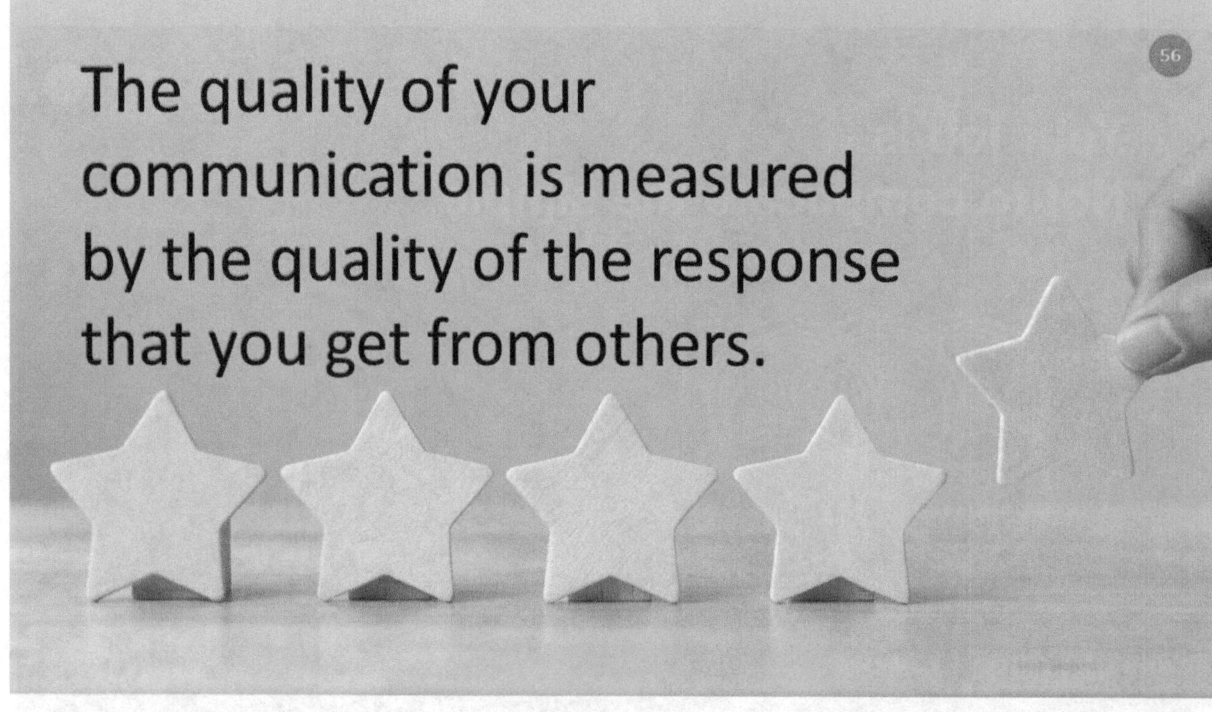
56
The quality of your communication is measured by the quality of the response that you get from others.

Look

Listen & Learn

How to create a connection in another person's mind

Leaders are Readers

"Not all readers are leaders, but all leaders are readers."

Harry S. Truman

JODY HOLLAND
· Educator · Entertainer · Motivator ·

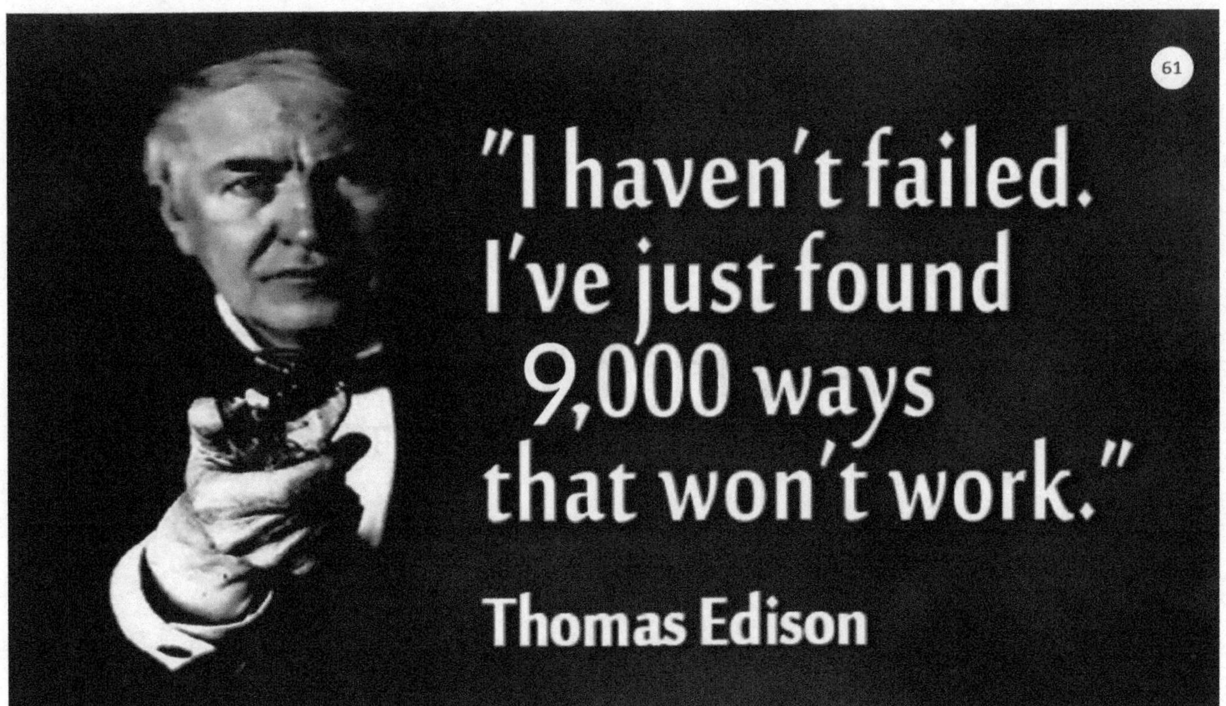
61
"I haven't failed.
I've just found
9,000 ways
that won't work."
Thomas Edison

Learn

Technology

62

63

UNLEASH YOURSELF

64

Keep Them Wanting More

5 COACHING FOR PERFORMANCE

Each of us as supervisors is called to coach our people toward success. Coaching, however, isn't just pushing people to do better or yelling when they make a bad call in business. It definitely isn't throwing chairs or breaking things. Coaching is the day-in, day-out process of observing one's team, knowing their strengths and their weaknesses, and then facilitating their adaptation of skills in order to move them forward. Being a great coach is about understanding each of your team members as individuals and drawing the best out of them. It is about your connection to your team and the respect that you have earned from your team. Within the model of coaching as well as in the models of leadership, there are four different types of authority that a person can have.

T – Title
E – Expertise
R – Relationship
C – Contract

Authority based on one's title is the model that many of the previous generations survived off of. They would receive a promotion and the structural hierarchy of the organization was respected enough that people would naturally respond to the "newly titled leader." In the traditional settings of moving up into a supervisory role, Baby Boomers and older would look at the person and say, "Well, they are in charge so I will do what they wish." True, it wasn't all people responding in that manner, but that response was much more common than it is now. Generation X and Millennial employees were taught when they were young to question authority and to speak up for themselves, even to their supervisor. This conditioning has rendered this type of authority almost pointless. Very few people will still respond to a person based solely on their title, particularly if their title is anything less than CEO. Even automatic respect for the CEO title is minimalistic at best.

Authority based on expertise has long been respected, dating back to the beginning of time. When a person has specialized training or specialized knowledge in an area, it is common for others to defer to them with questions. For example, someone who was great at operating an extruder in a manufacturing environment, who was promoted to a supervisor, would have an advantage in leading other extruder operators. It would be normal for others to go to that person with questions or for guidance. Other examples of this would be a nurse with a BSN and 10 years of experience working with a nurse with a LVN and 2 years of experience. It is normal and natural for us to seek out others that we believe are better equipped in an area and listen to their advice. A fascinating observation is that very few supervisors go out of their way to become expert supervisors. Just like any other skill, when this skill is mastered, people will naturally look to you to lead them. The skills and/or expertise must be demonstrated, though. It cannot be simply something that a person talks about and doesn't do.

Authority based on relationship has been the most solid form of respect that a person can receive since the beginning of time. Think about someone that you have a strong relationship with. Chances are high that you began to respect them for other reasons before you started to believe in them as a person. Once you began to believe in them, you started to trust them. Once you started to trust them, you then felt that you had a solid relationship with them. Relationship authority is earned through time, caring, and ethical standards. Relationships take concentrated effort. It takes a lot of work on the part of the supervisor to earn the respect of the employee. I can almost hear your thoughts here… "But aren't they supposed to earn my respect!?" In the old model of supervisory success, the authority started with a title and evolved into a relationship. In today's world, however, where young people were taught NOT to automatically respect authority, it requires that you take the first step toward building trust. Your skills as a communicator will lay the ground work for your success in building relationships. Make no mistake, the relationship now comes first!

The model that is effective in building the relationship, and moving people toward their goals, is based on the following steps…

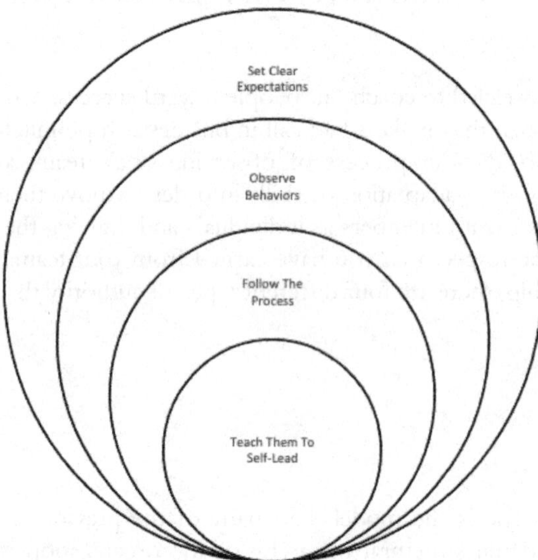

The S.O.F.T. Approach (Set expectations, Observe behaviors, Follow the process, Teach them to self-lead)

From the outset, it is critical that you, as a coach, set clear expectations for your team. One of the primary complaints that employees have expressed in employee surveys is that of "simply not knowing what my supervisor wants." Knowing that "not knowing" is one of the bigger challenges that is faced by employees helps supervisors to understand that they must step back and ensure that they are presenting the three most critical components of an assignement. Those three components are…

1. What would you like done?
2. When would you like it completed?
3. How will you measure the success of its implementation?

This seems simple enough but it is very seldom followed by supervisors. More often, a supervisor will say that they need an employee to "work harder" or they need something done ASAP, or that the employee will know that it is done right because the supervisor will be "happy." Those are not predictable measurements, and as such, cannot serve as valid metrics (measurements) of the success of the employee. I have seen lots of people "work hard" by their own definition, but not by their supervisor's definition. I have seen a number of interpretations of when exactly ASAP is referring to. I have even seen both happy and unhappy supervisors with successful employees.

In being clear on expectations, describe the outcome that you are looking for from the employee. Make sure that the employee is clear on what you are attempting to achieve through their efforts. Next, set an actual deadline for the project or task. This means that if you need it by Tuesday at 1PM, you say that you need it by Tuesday at 1PM. Be aware that supervisors have, at times, given more assignments to an employee than are physically possible for them to accomplish. Be willing to ask your employees if they will be able to accomplish that task. If they say that they are not sure, have a conversation with them about what might prevent them from accomplishing the task by the prescribed deadline. Sometimes, employees may have to shift other tasks off of their priority list if the new task is more important. Finally, let them know how you will measure the success of the task being performed. In other words, you might say something to the effect of, "what I am looking for in the end is that the xyz committee will have all of the information that they need in order to compare product a and product b, and be prepared to make a decision." Describing what success looks like makes it significantly more likely that the person will be able to succeed for you, their supervisor.

The second component of effective coaching is to observe the behaviors being exhibited by your employees, each of them, that is. In watching the way an employee behaves, you are continuously looking for any abnormalities that they might exhibit. For example, if an employee is generally in a good mood, and one day they are not, it is a good idea to approach them and simply ask if everything is ok. You would then let them know that you observed them coming across much differently than usual. Noticing these subtle changes in a person lets them know that you are paying attention and that you do care about what is going on in their world. Remember the Hawthorne Effect… the simple act of observation increases performance.

The behaviors that a person exhibits are the signals that help you, their supervisor, understand what is going on with them. Your objective is to understand what is happening beneath the surface rather than just on the surface. The behavior itself is the "above the surface" piece. The thoughts are just below the surface and the beliefs of that person are way below the surface. Behaviors are just the tip of the iceberg, and as a coach, you need to know what you are dealing with beyond just what you observe. The only way to get there, however, is to start with what is known. By observing behaviors closely, and then dealing with the behaviors that are witnessed, you open the door for greater levels of conversation about the rest of what is happening. Never discount the importance of noticing subtle differences in a person's behaviors. They are the pathway that leads to the root cause of a problem. They are also the conduit that helps you know who the person is, deep down inside.

You have to Follow "The Process" of coaching in order for it to work. One of the great challenges that we face is that supervisors are not really following a process. Instead, they are simply doing their best, albeit their unprepared/untrained best, but still their best. By having a specific model to follow in coaching, you mitigate the risk of letting employees steer you off course from what needs to be accomplished. The 4-S Model will guide you through the conversations that you need to have with employees in order to keep them on track.

Set the stage (positive action)
Stepped Walk-Thru of what happened
Seek a point of attribution
Set up their ownership of the future

Setting the stage for positive action means letting the person know that you value them as an individual and you sincerely want to help them succeed at work. This takes a little conditioning on your part because you will have to suspend any negative judgments you may have about the person and focus on truly desiring for them to be successful. In addition to reassuring them that you want them to succeed, you will also let them know that you understand that their performance is ultimately their choice. You will let them know that your focus will be on facilitating their success, but their success or lack thereof will be a direct result of what they choose to do moving forward. By making sure that they know you are not there to "make them" do something and that you relinquish any attempt to control them, you shift their mental focus. They now know that they are in control of their future and you are not attempting to do anything but help.

The Stepped Walk-Thru is a non-judgmental way of hearing the steps that the person followed in order to get to the place that they are right now. You would ask it in a calm and even-toned way, truly desiring to know the series of choices that were made that ended up with the result that they now have. I normally say something like, "Walk me through the steps that you took that got us where we are right now." If they use very little detail, then ask for more detail. You want to make sure and facilitate the conversation so that they explain all the way from step 1 to the end result. Don't correct or judge any of the steps. Instead, accept the steps as presented, verify that you heard the information correctly, and summarize what they have said. By doing this with an even tone and by not passing judgment, people will naturally be more open with you. Remember, your point in doing this is to help them discover a better way to move themselves forward and find the success that you wanted for them the entire time. After all, the more successful they are, the less stressed out you are. In addition, others tend to follow the behaviors of an influencer. By investing in one person, you begin to invest in the team. They could end up being a great example, instead of a flawed one, for the rest of the team to model.

Next, you will seek a "Point of Attribution." When you hear the word attribution, simply think explanation. You are looking for the point at which the person could have made a different and a better decision. You will simply ask them something to the effect of, "At what point in the process could you have made a different decision that would have gotten us the result that I was looking for instead of the result that we currently have?" Again, it is very important not to be sarcastic, condescending, or in any way derogatory to the employee. You want to remain as non-emotional as possible through this process. That makes it much easier for the employee to be honest and it keeps their emotions low. We, as humans, tend to mirror the emotional patterns of others. If you are intentional about it, they will mirror you in a good way.

Finally, you will Set Up Ownership for their future. The hook that helps the employee grow and develop into a better version of themselves is in the last step. This is a simple question that ties to their answer in the previous question. You will simply ask, "What are you going to do or put into place in order to ensure that you achieve the result I am looking for next time?" You are asking the person to commit to being accountable for better results moving forward. In doing this, you will make it impossible for them to blame you or to reject accountability. When a person comes up with their own idea on how to overcome a challenge or solve a problem, it is truly theirs. When we, as supervisors, tell them what to do, the idea isn't likely to ever be theirs.

Teach Them To Self-Lead

Leadership is more about owning who we are than it is about creating something inside of someone else. I once had a CEO ask me how to teach his team to lead themselves. He was frustrated with having to so closely manage them and continuously having to remind them of things they were supposed to do. He was frustrated with telling them to be a certain way, or believe a certain set of values, or look at their people in a certain way. Teaching your team to self-lead means teaching them to accept responsibility for their personality, claim responsibility for their actions, and choose the path that leads to success. The tough part for most of us is that it also requires us to allow them to fail from time to time, which can reflect poorly on our work performance.

Self-leadership starts with an awareness of who is impacting you and who you are impacting. It begins by setting up your circles of influence in such a way that you are surrounded with the right people whom you want the best for and who want the best for you. When someone is in your circle that doesn't seem to want the very best for you and for the company, you have to determine if you can fix the relationship and what it would take to fix it. On the next page, you will see a relationship circle, or a relationship wheel. Take out your pen or pencil and write in the names of the five most influential people on your thinking at work in the first one and the five most influential people on your thinking in your personal life in the second one.

Once you have their names in place, think about one thing that you could do with each of them that would make the relationship better. It could be that you need to deal with something that has kept you or another person upset. It could be that you need to spend more time coaching them or being coached by them. It could be that you need to simply smile at them every day or give them a compliment every day. Whatever it is, write down the one thing that you feel would make the relationship better. Do this for each of the relationships.

The Relationship Circles

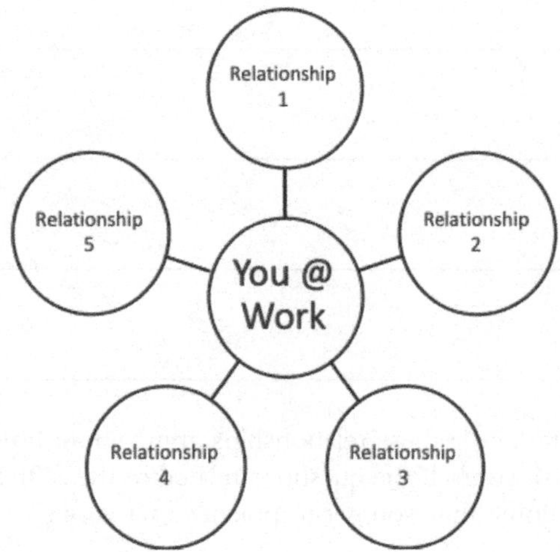

Relationship 1: ____________________

Relationship 2: ____________________

Relationship 3: ____________________

Relationship 4: ____________________

Relationship 5: ____________________

Relationship 1: ____

Relationship 2:____

Relationship 3:____

Relationship 4:____

Relationship 5:____

Now that you have made notes about these relationships, think about how you would coach yourself through making the relationships better. Ask yourself the questions related to the SOFT approach and interact internally as if you were your own coach. By doing this, you get to practice in a very safe enviornment the way in which you should talk to others.

Coaching is an incredibly powerful process of unlocking the potential in another person. You are reaching into their life and helping them to see ways to improve themselves that they often can't see on their own. By tuning in to the needs of each of those key relationships, you effectively maximize the potential that each employee has. You grow and expand your own influence by growing and expanding the possibilities for success in your team. Never forget the power of coaching to bring out the very best in another person.

LEADERSHIP

LEARNING OBJECTIVES

- Define Professionalism at Work
- Identify what is interpreted as unprofessional vs professional
- Define the difference that coaching makes in the workplace
- Review the SOFT Model for Coaching.
- Define and Discuss why some people perform and others do not

Learn2Lead

LEADERSHIP

WHAT DOES IT MEAN TO BE PROFESSIONAL?

Professionalism In The Workplace & Unconscious Bias

LEADERSHIP

PROFESSIONALISM

A set of normalized attitudes and actions that lead others to trust in and follow a person.

Learn2Lead

Supervise · Influence · Motivate

LEADERSHIP

UNPROFESSIONAL BEHAVIORS

What does it look like when someone is being unprofessional?

Learn2Lead
Supervise · Influence · Motivate

LEADERSHIP

VALUES

The standards, social norms, or objectives held or accepted by an individual, class, society, group, culture, etc.

LEADERSHIP

MORALS

Relating to, dealing with, or capable of making the distinction between right or wrong conduct.

- principles
- standards
- beliefs with respect to right or wrong behavior

LEADERSHIP

RIGHT

In accordance with fact, reason, justice, law, and morality.

WRONG

Contrary to fact or reason, unlawful, crooked, twisted, immoral, improper.

LEADERSHIP

CODE OF CONDUCT

A set of conventional principles and expectations that are considered binding on any person who is a member of a particular group.

LEADERSHIP

PSYCHOLOGICAL CONTRACT

Expectations from the employee on how they will be treated and from the employer on how the employee will perform their work.

LEADERSHIP

CHARACTERISTICS OF A PROFESSIONAL

- Honest
- Service Oriented
- Skilled
- Courteous
- Team Player
- Reliable
- Considerate
- Dependable
- Cooperative
- Committed

LEADERSHIP

PROFESSIONALISM IS JUDGED BY:

- Unwritten rules
- Code of conduct
- Culture
- Expectations and standards
- One's personal values
- BEHAVIORS

LEADERSHIP

HOW ARE YOU JUDGED AS A PROFESSIONAL?

Your Communication
Your Image
Your Competence
Your Demeanor
Your Appearance
Your Behavior
Your Attitude

LEADERSHIP

UNPROFESSIONAL BEHAVIOR

- Conduct that could be characterized as harassment or discrimination.
- Verbal threats of violence, retribution, or revenge.
- Verbal outbursts.
- Inappropriate physical touching or contact.

LEADERSHIP

UNPROFESSIONAL BEHAVIOR

- Arguing in front of customers, coworkers and families.
- Physical actions that threaten others such as throwing or knocking down objects.
- Insults, verbal comments, or criticism intended to belittle or berate others.

Learn2Lead

Supervise · Influence · Motivate

LEADERSHIP

YOU ARE IN CONTROL OF YOU!

YOU CONTROL YOUR...

Thoughts

Actions

Emotions

Words

LEADERSHIP

GREAT COACHES...

- Think about a time that you had a great coach in your life. It could have been in sports or academics or any other activity where someone worked to bring out the best in you.
- What was it that made them great?

LEADERSHIP

Title
Expertise
Relationship
Contract

What are the types of authority?

LEADERSHIP

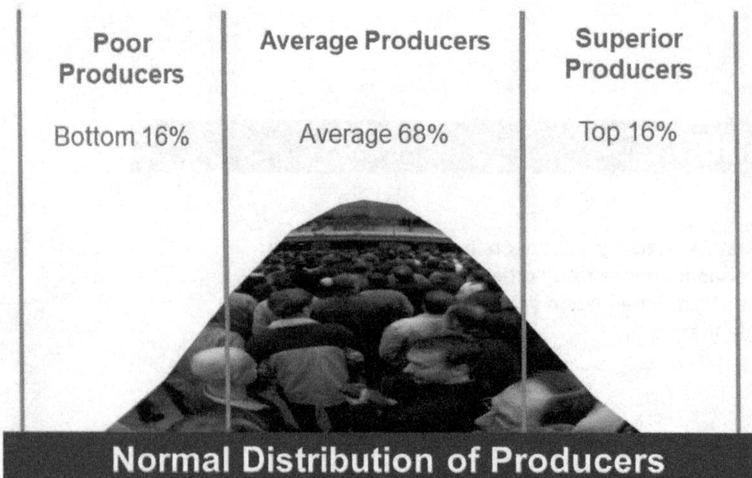

Learn2Lead

LEADERSHIP

WHY THIS MATTERS

Unskilled / Semi-skilled
Average is 19% higher than Poor
Superior is 38% higher than Poor

Skilled
Average is 32% higher than Poor
Superior is 64% higher than Poor

Management / Professional
Average is 48% higher than Poor
Superior is 96% higher than Poor

LEADERSHIP

LET'S MOVE FORWARD

- Many organizations operate worse than these figures.
- The potential losses are great for allowing sustained poor performance.
- Every time you move performance from one level to the next, you have a positive financial impact on the organization.

LEADERSHIP

CHARACTERISTICS OF A GREAT COACH

- Listens
- Cares
- Positive
- Clear in Expectations
- Goal-oriented
- Respectful
- Focused
- Always Growing Personally

LEADERSHIP

WHY POOR PERFORMANCE EXISTS

- Bad technology creates bad performance.
- What is technology? A body of specialized knowledge, or a set of principles and procedures, which, when applied, produces certain predictable outcomes.

LEADERSHIP

WHY THEY DON'T PERFORM

Lack of…

- Awareness
- Ability
- Resources
- Motivation
- Resourcefulness

LEADERSHIP

WHAT MODEL SHOULD WE FOLLOW?

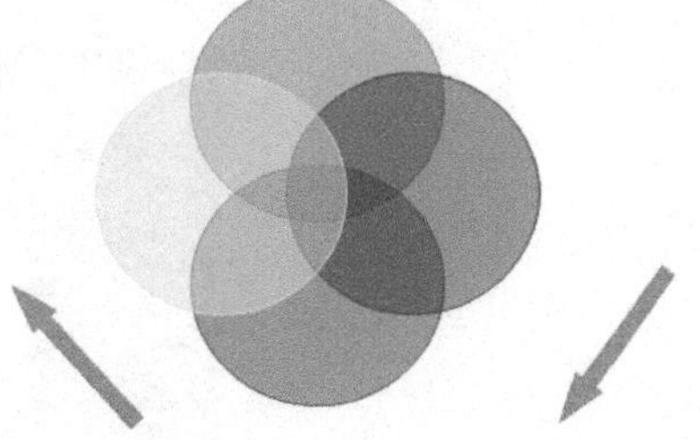

LEADERSHIP

CREATE BETTER TECHNOLOGY

- Define the desired performance —— Create Awareness
- Teach to the desired performance —— Build Ability
- Equip for the desired performance —— Provide Resources
- Create the right environment for the desired performance —— Motivate through culture

Learn2Lead
Supervise · Influence · Motivate

LEADERSHIP

7 LAWS OF COACHING

1. Expectation / Accountability
2. Relationships
3. Consistency
4. Vision
5. Growth
6. Patience
7. FUNN

LEADERSHIP

EXPECTATION / ACCOUNTABILITY

We create self-fulfilling prophecies every day. When you expect greatness, people tend to live into that. When you expect failure, people tend to live into that.

LEADERSHIP

THE LAW OF RELATIONSHIPS

- People don't care how much you know until they know how much you care.
- People work for people, not for companies.

LEADERSHIP

THE LAW OF CONSISTENCY

- Make sure that others know who you are, and what they can expect from you.
- Be Positive

LEADERSHIP

THE LAW OF VISION

- Purpose
- Values & Beliefs
- A Picture Of The Future Now

LEADERSHIP

THE LAW OF UNENDING GROWTH

- Laurence J. Peters…
- People can only operate at the level that they have been trained to operate at.
- You can only develop them to one step below where you are.

LEADERSHIP

THE LAW OF PATIENCE

- How long would you help your child learn to walk?
- Every person has the ability to succeed, as long as you work with them toward that end.

LEADERSHIP

THE LAW OF FUNN

- Functional
- Understanding
- Not
- Necessary

- Why Not Make Work FUN!?

LEADERSHIP

WHAT IS COACHING?

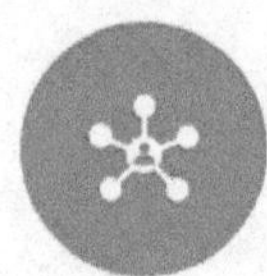

Coaching is a powerful process of communication and problem-solving between an employee and his or her supervisor.

Coaching assumes that the employee is naturally creative and resourceful. A coach guides an employee to their own solution.

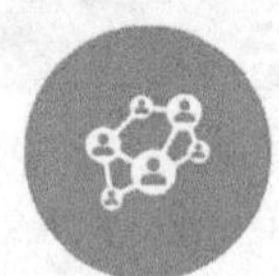

It is a mutually respectful relationship that is focused entirely on the employee's professional needs, interests, challenges, and goals.

Coaching is based on asking key questions, inviting shifts in thinking, developing realistic action plans & measuring progress.

LEADERSHIP

WHAT IS COACHING?

Learning

Understanding

New Actions

New Outcomes

LEADERSHIP

The Objective Is A Change In Self-Belief

B.T.A.R.

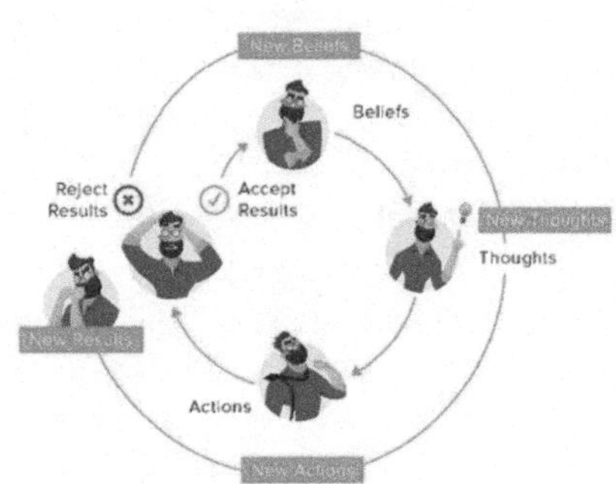

LEADERSHIP

COACHING DEFINED…

Coaching is the day-to-day, hands-on, never-ending process of helping employees recognize both strengths and opportunities to improve their work performance.

Coaching is done by the manager, supervisor, and/or experienced employees.

LEADERSHIP

HIGH PERFORMANCE COACHING

It focuses on…

- Individuals
- Performance
- Achievement
- And unlocking a person's potential

By having…

- Clearly defined goals
- Measured performance
- Frequent feedback

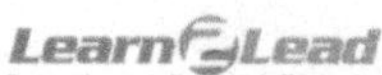

LEADERSHIP

WHERE CAN YOU COACH?

- Face To Face
- Over The Phone
- In A Small Group
- In An Email (be careful)
- Via Video Conference
- Sometimes even via text

LEADERSHIP

WHY COACH?

- According to a study by Bersin & Associates…
    - 130% more likely to achieve greater business results
    - 39% stronger employee engagement and productivity
    - Nearly a 40% increase in customer satisfaction
    - 21% higher profits

THE S.O.F.T. MODEL

Set clear expectations

Observe behaviors

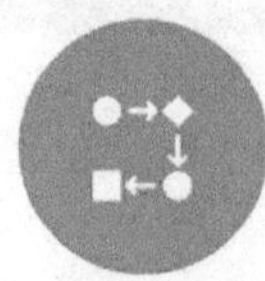

Follow the process

Teach them to self-lead

LEADERSHIP

WHAT DO YOU WANT DONE?

What do you want done?

When do you want it done by?

How will you measure success?

LEADERSHIP

OBSERVE BEHAVIORS

Behaviors Reflect Beliefs
Look For Abnormalities
Address **Behaviors** And **Outcomes** When You Coach

LEADERSHIP

SET THE STAGE

1. Set The Stage
2. Stepped WALK-THRU OF WHAT HAPPENED
3. Seek A point of attribution
4. Set Up Their Ownership For The Future

LEADERSHIP

SET THE STAGE

- Build Rapport
- Establish Your Purpose
- Determine Your Desired Outcome

LEADERSHIP

STEPPED WALK-THRU OF WHAT HAPPENED

- Look at each step that they followed
- Remain non-judgmental during this process
- Seek To Understand

LEADERSHIP

SEEK A POINT OF ATTRIBUTION

- At what point could you have done something different?
- Look for their perspective on when and what they could have changed.
- This establishes internal locus of control.

LEADERSHIP

SET UP THEIR OWNERSHIP FOR THE FUTURE

- Change only happens when they believe that they are in control of themselves.
- When they choose their path, it is more likely to stick.

LEADERSHIP

TEACH THEM TO SELF-LEAD

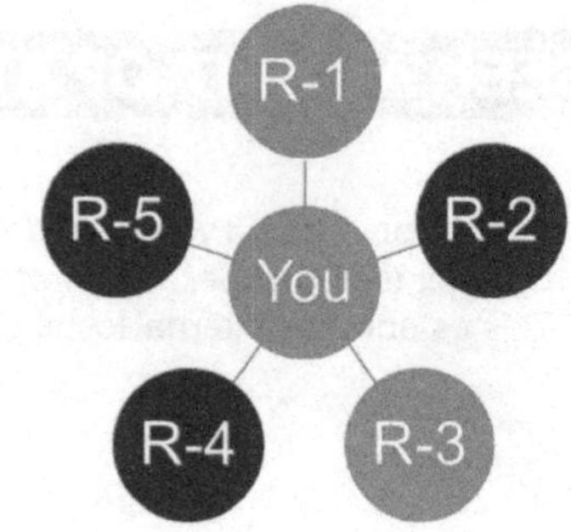

Look at each of your key relationships and identify something that you can do to improve that relationship.

Write down something that is good about each of those key people.

Find ways to serve!

How To Share Ideas That Will Improve But May Not Be Well Received…

CONSTRUCTIVE CRITICISM

LEADERSHIP

THIS IS ALWAYS THEIR CHOICE

- Each person is in charge of themselves.
- You cannot MAKE someone change.
- Your power is in your desire to help… your relationship.
- Say, "I am not here to make you change. You get to choose."

LEADERSHIP

TIPS TO CONSTRUCTIVE FEEDBACK

- Identify the problem clearly and behaviorally.
- Set the time and place for the discussion.
- Follow the S.O.F.T. Model
- Deal with behaviors. Don't make it personal.
- Make your case.

LEADERSHIP

TIPS TO CONSTRUCTIVE FEEDBACK

- Stand your ground
- Listen & Explore the issue fully
- Positive Consequences
- Negative Consequences
- Outline the change that you agreed to

LEADERSHIP

CLEAR FEEDBACK RULES

- Only describe the behaviors that you see.
- Tell the person within a 48 hour window… no later
- Be proactive on coaching... Before things mess up
- Be specific and clear
- Describe your desired outcomes

LEADERSHIP

WE COACH IN ORDER TO...

Help others meet expectations

Achieve results through others

Address...

- Behaviors and attitudes as they relate to productivity
- Progress and accomplishments in achieving goals
- Gaps in skills critical to work success
- Any other matter linked to job performance or work expectations

LEADERSHIP

TUNE IN TO W.I.I.F.M.

- Know your people
- Seize the feedback opportunities
- Select the best time, place, medium, and approach
- When in doubt... give feedback, observe, and adjust

Learn2Lead
Supervise • Influence • Motivate

6 CONFLICT RESOLUTION

Conflict is a natural part of our lives. In fact, conflict is necessary for any story to be great! Conflict is used to draw us into the storyline of a movie or TV series or book. It is used to force us to choose sides at times. Conflict is necessary to create a better decision-making model. It is something that each of us deals with on almost a daily basis. And yet, it is one of those things that people regularly avoid. It isn't that you should go out and try to create conflict at work in order to make things more interesting. The research shows that you won't have to do that. Conflict will already be there. It is just that you need to think about the way in which you frame, or label, conflict. The label that you give it is the meaning that it will hold for you. Negative labels create negative internal responses. Positive labels create proactive internal responses. A positive label is one that focuses on the potential good that rests with dealing with the conflict. A positive label focuses on improving a relationship, solving a problem, moving work forward, and building a great culture. In order to get to this positive point, however, you have to be honest about what labels exist in your mind right now.

When you think about the word conflict, what comes to mind?

____

____

Look at the words or manner in which you describe conflict. If you are like most people, those are not a list of positive words that you just put down in the book. If you are like most, they are some scary words that really don't make you think… "I can't wait to deal with this."

As you go through this chapter, I want you to think about conflict as an opportunity to create deeper understanding. It is a way for you to reconcile varying patterns of thought from one person to another. It is a way for you to understand another person's perspective and connect the dots for people when they are not lining up. Conflict, just like life, is whatever you make of it. You can make it into something that makes your relationships better. Or, you can make it into something that makes your relationships suffer.

In this chapter, you will learn each of the following…

1. How does conflict impact our work lives?
2. What are the fundamental issues of conflict?
3. What are the two types of conflict?
4. What are the phases of conflict?
5. What is the best approach to resolving conflict?
6. What is the best model for ensuring that resolution is achieved?

How conflict impacts our work lives

As supervisors, managers, and leaders, we spend a great deal of time dealing with the challenges that are created by conflict. Supervisors spend a great deal of time stepping into the middle of conflict and trying to solve challenges for other people. Not only do people stress about conflict when they are in the middle of it, many people take that stress home with them and let it impact their personal lives as well. Knowing that conflict impacts us regularly, it only makes sense to develop a strong skillset in resolving it. During a typical year, a supervisor or manager will spend around 20% of their time dealing with conflict. Assuming you work 40 hours per week and take two weeks per year off, you would be working 2000 hours per year. That means that you are spending around 400 hours, or 10 weeks full-time, dealing with conflict… every year. That is 500% more time spent in conflict than on vacation. So why is it that a supervisor has to spend so much time dealing with conflict?

Conflict is a part of our everyday lives. At work, we are dependent on one another and yet we don't see the same world as each other. Think about how you grew up, what your parents were like, and what the world around you was like. Now, think about how your siblings, if you have them, still see the world differently than you do. They grew up in the same house, with the same basic experiences, but they see a world that doesn't exist for you at times. The same is true going the other direction as well. Because we give meaning to the experiences that we have based on our current perception in combination with our past experiences, our meaning is uniquely ours. When the meaning that we assign is in conflict with the meaning that someone else has assigned, and we overlap on our dependence on one another, conflict often arises. When conflict exists, the way that we perceive reality can shift as well. We begin to create new labels. Some of them are negative and create a stress response in our lives. That stress response sets off a chain of reactions in our mind and consequently in our bodies.

When we have prolonged negative stress and it is not dealt with, the results are that we suffer from the equivalent of jet-lag. Social jet-lag, based off of stress, can create all of the same symptoms that one would receive if they took a flight to another part of the world, with a drastically different time zone. That person could become sluggish, suffer from gastro-intestinal issues, lose interest in things that have been good for them (such as exercise), lose sleep, get headaches, and a whole lot more. We are impacted by our interpretation of the meaning of conflict. It is our view of what is going on and the subsequent labels that we give the events that create both meaning and biological responses in our lives. Therefore, learning about conflict resolution isn't just a good idea to make our working lives better. It is a good idea to make our physical and mental health better as well. But what is it that we are labeling that is creating the potential negative response in our bodies?

Direct personality clashes constitute a large portion of the conflict that is dealt with at work. The Bureau of Labor Statistics indicated that personality clashes are among the top reasons that people lose their jobs, or are fired from their jobs. This clash between employee and supervisor is also listed as the top reason that people leave their jobs. When an employee dislikes their supervisor, they tend to leave the organization. In fact, 80% of the reason that employees quit their jobs can be traced directly back to not getting along with their direct supervisor. 10% of why employees quit their jobs can be traced back to clashes with their coworkers. This means that relationships, at least negative ones, cause 90% of turnover in the workplace. Conversely, when the skills are in place and relationships are good, this could constitute 90% of why a person would stay and be engaged at work. Think about some of the people that you know or have known that simply "rubbed you the wrong way." Their personality, or their personal style, clashed with yours. When this goes unresolved, the conflict simply festers and gets worse. As a supervisor, much of the conflict that you deal with is two or more of your employees not getting along with one another. Not dealing with the issue will simply make it worse in the end.

Unresolved conflict, or not confronting another person about the issue(s) is often seen as you condoning that behavior. For example, if you have an employee that has consistently not turned their work in on time and you have not addressed the situation, then it is virtually the same as saying, "I don't expect your work on time and it is perfectly ok to turn it in on your own schedule." In the mind of the employee, when things are not addressed, that is the same as saying that those things are acceptable. If several employees are allowed to show up late for work and you don't address the situation, it will be seen as acceptable to be late, and then often even later by the employees. Others will observe the behavior and lack of consequences and soon begin thinking that they too can show up late to work and everything will be fine. It is incredibly difficult for you to reverse this behavior in one person if you don't address it in others. When you choose not to deal with conflict, you are choosing to make things tougher on yourself. You are choosing to accept the negative behavior or attitude as acceptable. People do what they do because it meets their needs. If you need or want someone to change in your employees, they will only do so if you address what is going on.

Unaddressed conflict festers in your mind and in your attitude. When you are disturbed by something and don't address it, you begin to think about it more and more. You get more upset with the person for not knowing that they should change. You begin noticing more and more of the negative things that they do. In fact, most people will begin looking for the bad in another person instead of looking for the good in them because of the unresolved conflict. Our minds are fantastic at filtering reality to make it mean what we want it to mean. This is why it is so important to deal with things as soon as possible. Once you begin thinking that a person is bad because they have done something that needs to be addressed, but you have not addressed it, then you lose sight of the good that they do. Dealing with conflict helps to stabilize those relationships. It helps to make all the difference in the world. It helps to connect you with your employees and them with you. When you care enough to deal with conflict in the right manner, it indicates that you care about their success as well as the success of the department.

The Fundamental Issues of Conflict

There are four key areas that surround the conflict that we deal with. We focus on the facts, our goals, the methods used, and the values that the person demonstrates through their behaviors. When we begin to think of conflict in these terms, we are better prepared to stay objective in the process. The only challenge that we really face is that facts in one person's mind are opinions in another person's mind. Truth, then, is relative and is based on interpreted reality.

"Everything that you invent is true. You can be sure of that."
--Julian Barnes in *Flaubert's Parrot*

Facts, or more accurately, the interpretation of facts, are often the subject of conflicts between people. The human tendency is to look at the world through our own lens and not to trade out lenses even when it would improve our situation. The need to trade out lenses, however, is often exactly what is needed. The act of trading out interpretive lenses is known as empathy. It doesn't mean that you are adopting the other person's view. It simply means that you are trying to put yourself in their position and see what they see. By doing this, you can often see how their "facts" and your "facts" are misaligned. Take time with each conflict to put yourself into the other person's frame. Think about what they see and why they see it. Think about their experience of reality and why they might believe as they do. Facts are the labels that we believe and can prove in our own minds. Some facts can be given up and replaced with new truths. In order for this to happen for a person, however, they must trust you and want to see from your perspective. This means that you have to desire to see the world from their perspective first. Facts are not always absolute, but they are always absolutely believed by their creator.

The goals that a person has for their job, or a task, or a process can be in conflict with the goals of a supervisor as well. Think through your life to different times when you were working hard towards a goal and someone got in your way. When the path of one person's goals crashes into the path of another person's goal, then they both feel that their goals are threatened. At times, a person will simply see that there could be a crash and will feel conflicted. If a person feels that their goal is threatened, or if their goal actually is threatened by the behaviors of another person, or by their values, then conflict will exist.

At other times, it is the methods that a person uses in doing their job, pursuing a goal, or relating to others that creates the conflict. One's style, or methodology, is often at odds with another person's style or methodology. Think about the way in which you interact with others and then think about someone that seems to work the opposite of you. In fact, think about a time when you accomplished a task in a manner that was different than the manner that another person accomplished the same task. When your method is different, your tendency will be to think that your method is right. After all, you did accomplish what you set out to accomplish. Often times, there is more than one way to accomplish what you wish to accomplish. Your method and their method are different, but neither may be wrong: or, both may be wrong, or both may be right. The tendency of most people, however, is to assume that the way that they are doing something is the right way and the way that another person is doing it is the wrong way.

The most challenging thing to deal with is when the conflict centers around the values that one person holds that are in contrast with the values that another person holds. In the words John Farr, "Never talk politics or religion because both of you are right and both of you are wrong." A person's values are uniquely theirs and yet they were ingrained into the person's subconscious when they were young by someone else. Values are the beliefs that a person has accepted as true that guide the decisions that they feel are right. Values are as varied as thought patterns. Values include the music that a person likes, the work ethic that a person holds, the religious beliefs that a person has, and virtually every aspect of the way a person makes their decisions. When conflict is based on values, it is incredibly difficult to quantify the cost of the other person's behavior and therefore virtually impossible to make the conflict legitimate in the other person's mind. When you are in conflict with another person based on their values, it is best to be prepared to embrace your ability to see the world through their eyes/lens and embrace the truth that reality itself is subjective.

Two Types Of Conflict

There are really only two types of conflict that exist in this world. Even though people tend to disagree over what the truth is, what goals are correct, or even how something may impact their personal or professional lives, we are still just disagreeing on one of two things. Either we have a conflict of needs or we have a conflict of values. These are the only two things that truly create conflict.

The wars that we have fought and the lives that have been lost are often based just on conflicting values. Differences of opinion on religion, political viewpoints, taste in music, dress and appearance and the like are all based on varying values that a person holds. What is so difficult about the disagreements that we have regarding which values are correct is that it is virtually impossible to explain how the other person's values have impacted us. Say for example that you have a tattoo and you love it. Despite the fact that your shirt covers your tattoo at work, you believe that your tattoo is a symbol of who you are and what you are all about. Another person has no tattoos and believes that having them is bad. You look at that person and think, "Man, you are missing out on the chance to express who you really are." They look at you, knowing that you have a tattoo, and think, "Man, you are not a professional because of that tattoo." Which one of you is right? Which one of you is wrong?

Unfortunately, there really isn't any way to know because one person having a tattoo and the other not having one doesn't cost either of you anything. When there is a collision of values, the impact is impossible to quantify. This is how you would know that the conflict is related to values instead of being related to needs. When you can measure, or quantify, the results of the conflict, then it is a collision of needs, not values. Both can be solved, but one is much easier than the other.

When you are analyzing the conflict itself, ask yourself for the following information…
What is the specific (non-judgmental) behavior that is being exhibited?
How do I feel about that behavior related to the way it is impacting me and/or the workplace?
What is the measurable effect, or impact, of that behavior?

In your analysis of the situation, be very clear with yourself about what is going on before you confront another person about their behaviors. The way that you know if you are confronting over needs is that the third question, the one about the measurable impact, can be clearly answered. If you are confronting about values differences, you will likely come up with things like "because it bothers me" or "because I don't like it" or "because it isn't supposed to be that way." Those are all value reflections and not need reflections. Needs are much easier to resolve than values are. Both can be dealt with, but there is less emotion with a collision of needs.

The Main Causes of Conflict

There are three main causes of conflict. In each of our interactions with others, we are dealing with our interpretation of what is real. We are in conflict over what we believe the facts to be, what our unresolved emotions are, and how the conflict might impact us. When you take the time to understand the viewpoints of others, you are best prepared to deal with each of these things.

Stan Freberg, in his parody of the show "Dragnet," made the catchphrase "Just the facts ma'am" popular. So often, we look at others in the same manner. We, like Sgt. Joe Friday, want just the facts. However, as you learned earlier in this chapter, facts can be subjective. Facts are the interpreted truth based on both our current perceptions and our past experiences. We filter the world that we live in and give meaning to events and experiences. Without our labels, the "truth" doesn't actually exist. The perspective that is necessary is for you to look at the truth from every angle. The facts, as we see them, may not be the facts, as someone else sees them. Facts, therefore, require multiple vantage points to be fully understood. The unfortunate reality that we live in is that people will often attribute negative meaning to another person's behaviors based on what they think the intent was behind the behavior. They will then see that interpretation as truth, as fact, instead of as the label that it is. So, step back and try to see the world from another person's viewpoint before you make the truth absolute.

The second cause of conflict that is common in the workplace, as well as in people's personal lives, is the act of ignoring emotions. When you are interacting with your team, they are continuously displaying their emotions in their non-verbal communication. Their facial expressions, their body language, their reactions to what you say or do, will unlock the secret of what they are really thinking. In the book, Authentic Communication, I outline in depth how to read another person. You learn how to tell what is good, what is bad, what is frustrating, and what is not the truth. You learn to get past the false reality that is often displayed by people and understand the authentic side of who they really are. When you are in conflict with another person, never ignore the emotions that they are displaying. If they open up and talk about their emotions, then embrace the fact that they are truly experiencing that emotional state. One of the best things that you can do is to acknowledge that a person is experiencing emotions and that it is legitimate to do so. Most people just want to know that you see, and/or feel, what is going on with them. A simple acknowledgment such as, "It seems that you are upset about…" or "I can tell that you were hurt by…" will open the door for the conversation. You would then follow that up with, "If I had experienced this the same as you, I would likely feel the same way." In validating their emotions, you help the person to let go of some of their hurt and focus on interacting with you to heal the relationship.

The third most common cause of conflict is concern over the impact that the other person's behavior has had, or could potentially have on them. When a person doesn't turn in the information that another person needs to do their work in a timely manner, it could cause the other person to not be able to complete their work on time. This could potentially get the person needing the information in trouble with their boss. When a person doesn't do a good job and they were recommended by another person for the job, it could potentially impact the reputation of the person who recommended them and damage the trust that superiors have in them. It is very common for people to think, and often worry, about the impact or potential impact that another person's actions could have on them. When another person is upset with you, ask yourself if your actions could have any kind of a negative impact on the other person. Then try to see the world from their perspective. How would you feel if the roles were reversed? Taking the time to understand the other person's perspective will open the doors to better communication and will create a deeper relationship between you and that person. Always remember that your objective is to make the relationship better. It isn't to win, or put them in their place.

The Five Phases of Conflict

There are five phases to conflict that our minds take us through. In each of these phases, we have the opportunity to resolve the conflict and make things better. With each subsequent phase, it does get a little more difficult to resolve it though. This is why it makes the most sense to act as soon as you realize that a conflict exists. By taking action as soon as you can, you head off many of the issues that would otherwise arise from the conflict. Let's dive into the five phases. They are represented in the following graphic. Please notice that the graphic is a pyramid. If you have the top phase, you have already gone through the other phases.

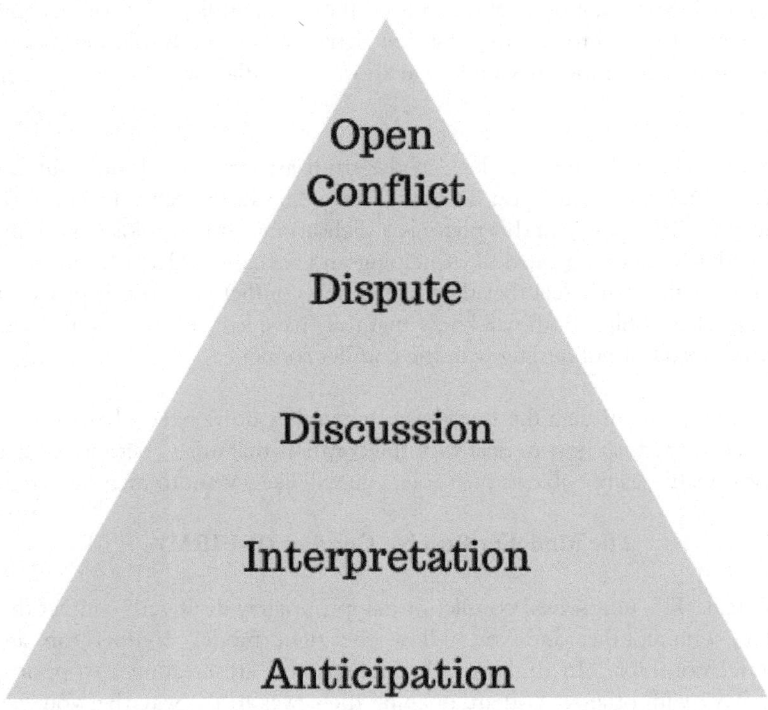

The anticipation phase is the the foundation of where conflict arises. There is a sense of something going wrong that most people get as the conflict first happens. As you are observing others, you begin to notice a change in their behaviors and in the mood of the interactions that you have with them. You begin to think that something is wrong. Many people try to ignore it or just brush it off as if nothing is really wrong. They make say things like, "they are just in a bad mood." If you address what is going on as early as possible, it makes the conversation much easier. If things are not dealt with early on, then the conflict moves into the next phase.

The interpretation phase is where people begin to assign labels, or meaning, to what is going on. They begin to look at the behaviors of those that they have anticipated conflict with and create meaning. This meaning is often negative and will intensify the emotions of both sides. Although the two might not be truly at odds with one another, they begin to think that the other is at odds with them. This belief that the other person is "out to get them" is what leads them very quickly into the third phase of conflict.

Once the discussions of what "that person" is doing becomes open, those in the middle of the conflict will try to recruit. They will recruit others to believe their side of the story and will begin to build negative beliefs about the other person. During this phase, the individuals involved are intensifying their emotions and charging the emotions of others. Once conflict is to this stage, it often takes a catalyst or outside pressure for others to have a discussion. Many times, you as a supervisor, will witness two of your employees move into this phase and begin getting others on their side. It is often up to you to step in and initiate the resolution of the conflict. Always be ready to be the calm voice of reason that is there to help others build their relationships instead of tearing them down. If there isn't an outside force, or a catalyst, that intervenes, then it is extremely likely that the conflict will escalate to phase four, which is dispute.

Once the conflict moves into the dispute phase, the two or more people involved are truly at odds with one another. They have solicited help in believing that the other person is bad. They are now building their case, like a criminal prosecutor would, to discredit the other person and to win. The relationship is now truly adversarial. It is no longer about finding a win-win solution in the minds of those in conflict. It is often more about proving the other person wrong instead of even proving that you are right. Without a resolution model and outside forces acting to move to resolution, it is almost inevitable that those in conflict will move to the fifth and final phase, which is open conflict.

In this phase, we often look through the lens of the truth assumption. I am right, which means you are wrong. I have the facts, which means that you do not. I am going in the right direction, which means you are going in the wrong direction. Everything in this phase is a dichotomy. It is win-lose in the minds of each person. The unfortunate truth is that it takes a great deal of helping and focus in order to keep the situation from being lose-lose. Very seldom will either party feel that they won when conflict gets to this phase. Both will know that they have lost trust in the relationship. Both will know that they have lost hope in the relationship. Both will feel that they have suffered as a result of not dealing with the conflict sooner.

Because people move rapidly through the five phases when they don't have a basis for resolving conflict, it is critical that a model be established for how to deal with the conflicts that arise. Because you, as an up and coming leader, will want to be as effective as possible in your role, you will likely want to memorize the following model.

The Model to Resolve Conflict (B-FIRM)

Conflict itself isn't bad. It is unresolved conflict or inappropriately dealt with conflict that is bad. When you are proactive in dealing with conflict and you follow the right model, conflict can and often does yield improvements in your relationships. In dealing with conflict, you are creating an opportunity to deepen the understanding that you have with others. You are opening their eyes to the way that you see the world and they are opening yours to their perspective. You are improving your empathetic response and demonstrating the qualities of a great leader in dealing with challenges up front.

The components of the model are **b**ehavior, **f**eeling, **i**mpact, **r**eflective listening, and **m**y expectations. Too often, in conflict with others, people will outline the fact that they are upset and even describe what the other person has done, but will not listen to them after the confrontation, nor will they set clear expectations going forward. Following this model will open up the possibilities and lower the emotional temperature in the interaction.

The **behavior** that the other person has exhibited must be described in non-judgmental terms. There is a clear difference between being descriptive and being judgmental. If a person is late to work by 15 minutes and they have been three times in three weeks, each time on a Monday, and you begin your Mondays with a staff meeting, then describe only the behaviors and not a judgment about the behavior. For example, "You have been late the last three Mondays in a row by about 15 minutes each time." That is descriptive without being judgmental. Judgmental would be to assign meaning to that behavior. An example of assigning judgment to a behavior would be, "You have been disrespectful the last three Mondays in a row by being late 15 minutes each time." It is in assigning judgment that we throw up a roadblock to resolution in the mind of the other person. Be clear about the behavior, but leave your judgment out of the description. Don't assign meaning to the behavior. After all, we don't know what the person was thinking or what they intended by the behavior.

The second component of an effective confrontation is to describe your **feeling** or emotion that you experienced. You do NOT describe how EVERYONE feels about the behavior. You don't and can't know how EVERYONE feels. You can only know for sure how you feel about it. Additionally, the person that you are confronting can't disagree with you describing your own feelings. They can, however, disagree that EVERYONE feels a certain way. They are, after all, a part of the definition of everyone. Do your best to go beneath the emotion of anger and identify the "catalyst emotion." There is always an emotion that precedes anger. Anger is the tip of the iceberg, the part that is above water, but it only represents 10% of the iceberg itself. The other 90% is beneath the surface and houses all of the precursor emotions that lead to a person being angry. Embarrassment, fear, disappointment, frustration, and a whole host of other emotions happen before a person becomes angry. The more clearly you can analyze your own thoughts and feelings, the easier it will be for the other person to accept them as true and real.

The **impact** of that person's behavior(s) needs to be clearly explained as well. You are looking for the measurable effect of their actions. Did their actions cause the meeting to start late or did they cause you to use up your additional time to catch them up for not being at the meeting on time? In the case of what was explained for this scenario, let's assume that you did not start the meeting on time because you were waiting on them. This means that you kept your entire staff from starting their work fifteen minutes sooner on three occasions. You waited on them to start the meeting and therefore lost fifteen minutes of time for you and the staff.

Once you have explained the behavior, the feeling or emotion, and the measurable impact, it is time to shift gears. Think of yourself as moving forward, like you are in "drive" in your car, as you confront the other person and outline what you observed, felt, and lost. It is now time to put the car in reverse and **reflectively** listen to their side of the story. As you learned in the communication chapter, you must use your active or reflective listening skills. When you listen to the other person and reflect back what you heard them say and feel, but put it in your own words, then you are allowing their emotions be expressed and for them to calm down. Let's face it, even if you do a great confrontation, it can still upset the person. When you listen, you are calming the situation down. Each person has their side of what happened. You don't know what was going on with them that made them late. If you take the time to listen, you will get some insight into their thoughts and feelings as well as learning what choices or circumstances resulted in them being late three Mondays in a row. Good reflective listening requires that you suspend your judgment about the person and simply try to understand their perspective. When you are willing to do this, it is much easier for the person to open up. Always remember that your objective is to resolve the conflict <u>and</u> improve the relationship.

Once you have taken the time to listen, it is now time to set your expectations going forward. Ideally, the other person will want to change to meet your needs without you having to do much here. If you are the supervisor, and they don't see the need to change, you still have the authority to set clear expectations and hold them to those expectations. It is significantly more effective to indicate your expectations than it is to indicate your desires. "I want you to…" is less impactful than "I expect you to…" do something specific. The wording that has proven very effective with other organizations is…

In the future, I expect you to be on time every time. What is it that you can put into place to ensure that you achieve that?

It is important to keep the responsibility for the change with the other person. Don't say things like, "What do I need to do for you to make that happen." By taking on the responsibility for their change, they will not own the new behavior. By asking them what they can do to achieve the desired results, they will have to describe their intended actions and will have to own that path.

Ultimately, good conflict resolution is about taking the right approach, with the right attitude, and allowing the other person to own their future behaviors. When you are seeking a resolution that improves the relationship instead of putting the other person in their place, everything works out better. The following fill-in-the-blank model can be used as you prepare for confronting an employee, coworker, or even a supervisor.

Practice Table for Developing Your Conflict Statement

What is a non-judgmental description of the other person's behavior?	
What is the precursor emotion(s) that I feel related to that behavior?	
What is the measurable impact that I have personally experienced?	
What are the expectations that I have for this person related to this behavior?	

LEADERSHIP

LEARNING OBJECTIVES

- How conflict impacts our work lives
- The fundamental issues of conflict
- The types and phases of conflict
- The best approach to resolving conflict
- The best model for ensuring that you achieve resolution

LEADERSHIP

IS CONFLICT ALL BAD?

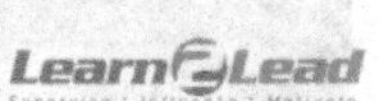

LEADERSHIP

- Every great movie is only great because there is conflict.
- The best decisions are the result of a conflict being worked out.
- Conflict prompts us to create new products and new solutions.

LEADERSHIP

HOW OUR LIVES ARE IMPACTED BY CONFLICT

- Managers spend almost 5 weeks out of the year dealing with conflict.
- Many of these conflicts are between employees and not even with the manager.
- Personality, Values, Behaviors, Assumed Intentions, and more lead to issues.

HOW SHOULD WE SEE CONFLICT?

- Conflict is not a bad thing. In fact, it is a necessary thing.
- Conflict is essential for making good decisions.
- The absence of conflict is not harmony. It's apathy.

Learn2Lead

FRAMING CONFLICT

Every time you enter into conflict with another person, you have the choice to frame it as…

- Something that will damage the relationship.
- Something that is unlocking what was missing in the relationship.

A CRITICAL POINT TO REMEMBER

There is nothing that I can teach you about how to handle the other person in conflict. It is always about how you handle yourself in conflict.

Manage your thoughts and emotions and you manage the conflict itself.

LEADERSHIP

CONFLICT IS NOT THE PROBLEM

- Conflict is natural, normal, and inevitable.
- The problem isn't the presence of conflict.
- The problem is the thought that there should never be conflict.

LEADERSHIP

WE ARE IMPACTED

"I've had thousands of problems in my life. A few of them were even real."
--Mark Twain

Consider that we are more impacted by our thoughts related to conflict than our experience of conflict.

LEADERSHIP

YOUR END GAME

You end game needs to be…

- Build the team
- Enhance the effectiveness of your communication
- Make better decisions
- Build trust
- Move forward

Your end game in conflict cannot be to…

- Assign blame
- Prove a point
- Release your negative emotions onto another person
- Put them in their place
- Intimidate them

LEADERSHIP

SUCCESS BEGINS WITH…

Success in conflict begins with defining your purpose in conflict.

Whether you are in personal or professional conflict, take a step back.

What is the end result for the relationship that you desire?

LEADERSHIP

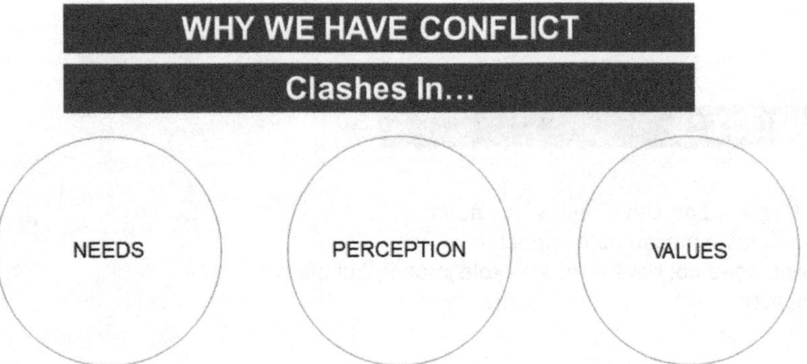

LEADERSHIP

3 MAIN CAUSES OF CONFLICT

- Our Version of The Truth
- Ignoring The Displayed Emotions of Others
- Concern Over Impact

LEADERSHIP

DIAGNOSE CONFLICT

- A conflict can be based on either needs or values.
- A needs collision has a measurable impact.
- A values collision does not have a measurable impact, but often has strong emotions.

LEADERSHIP

THE TRICKY PART

Conflict is opposition or incompatibility between two or more people or groups.

Our emotions cloud our ability to objectively deal with conflict.

Our definition of the intent of another person often determines our approach.

What conflict do you see in this world and why do you think it exists?

LEADERSHIP

CONFLICT HAPPENS AT EVERY LEVEL

- Do not confuse leadership with:
  - Status
  - Power
  - Authority
- Don't assume that you are always right just because you are in charge. When we become unapproachable, conflict grows.

LEADERSHIP

OUR MINDS ARE POWERFUL

"Everything that you invent is true. You can be sure of that."

--Julian Barnes in *Flaubert's Parrot*

LEADERSHIP

ISSUES WITHIN CONFLICT

- Facts according to self
- Goals
- Methods or Processes
- Values and Beliefs

LEADERSHIP

5 PHASES OF CONFLICT

Anticipation – You think that it is coming but nothing has happened yet.

Conscious Awareness – You now know that it is coming, and word has leaked about the conflict.

Discussion – People are talking and looking for information

Open Dispute – People begin to argue and pick sides.

Open Conflict – Now we are in a positional struggle (win/lose

THE OPPORTUNITY TO HANDLE CONFLICT SMOOTHLY AND WITHOUT INCIDENT DECREASES AT EACH STAGE.

LEADERSHIP

What Are Our Options?

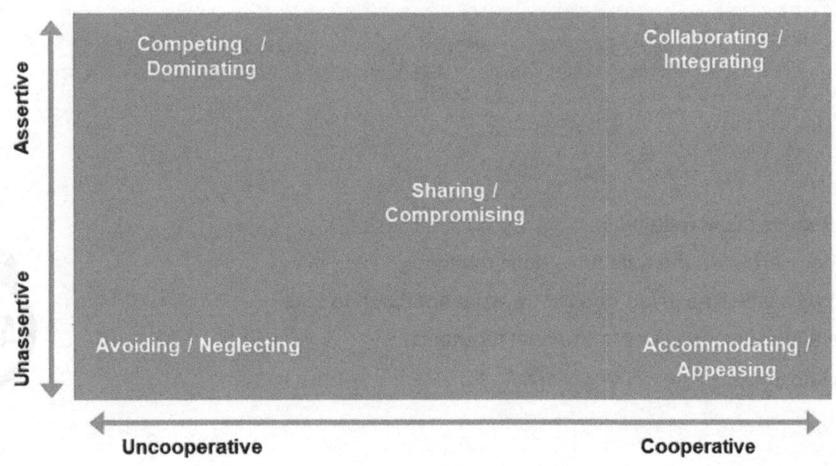

Learn2Lead

LEADERSHIP

DEALING WITH CONFLICT

- Competing – High assertiveness and low cooperativeness. The result is win/lose.
- Avoiding – Low assertiveness and low cooperativeness. The result is lose/lose.
- Accommodating – Low assertiveness and high cooperativeness. The result is lose/win on important issues and win/win on unimportant ones.
- Compromising – Moderate assertiveness and moderate cooperativeness. The result is either win/win or win/lose.
- Collaborating – High assertiveness and high cooperativeness. The result is win/win. This is the ideal approach to take!

Learn2Lead

LEADERSHIP

AVOIDING

- Low Results / Low Relationship
- Can be used when the outcomes don't matter
- May buy a little time if you don't know what approach to take
- Generally damages your professional reputation
- Generally wastes time / energy / effort

LEADERSHIP

COMPETING

- High Results / Low Relationship
- Can be used when you have to get it done your way
- Can be used when safety or survival are at stake
- Accomplishes significantly more than avoiding or accommodating
- Generally deteriorates trust

LEADERSHIP

ACCOMMODATING

- High Relationship / Low Results
- Can be used when it is more important to put the other person first than to get your way
- Generally a good idea when dealing with your superiors
- Generally causes internal frustration for you
- Not recommended when outcome is important

LEADERSHIP

COMPROMISING

- Medium Results / Medium Relationship
- Can be used when you need to preserve the relationship and accomplish some of what you need.
- Achieves better long-term results than competing or forcing your way

LEADERSHIP

COLLABORATING

- High Results and High Relationship
- Can be used when your team has been developed beyond group think and equipped with the right conflict resolution models
- Outcomes have the highest chance of implementation
- Demonstrates respect and creativity

LEADERSHIP

THE MODEL
B-FIRM

It is important to have a specific model to follow in order to create predictable results, reduce your stress, and resolve conflicts.

LEADERSHIP

B-FIRM

- B – Behavior
- F – Feeling
- I – Impact
- R – Reflective Listening
- M – My Expectations

LEADERSHIP

BEHAVIOR

The behavior must be described in terms of only what is observable and not what is implied from an observation.

Remove all judgment from the description of the behavior.

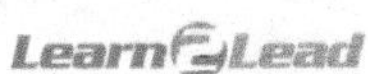

LEADERSHIP

FEELING

The feeling that you are looking for is the precursor emotion or initial emotion that is associated with both the behavior and the outcome of the behavior.

Anger is the tip of the iceberg. We need to look for what is beneath the surface.

LEADERSHIP

IMPACT

The impact is the measurable result of the behavior that was exhibited. If, for example, a person is 15 minutes late to a meeting, the measurable result can be that you delayed everyone for 15 minutes as you waited for the person.

IMPACT IS MEASURABLE!

LEADERSHIP

REFLECTIVE LISTENING

The process of reflective listening requires that you let the other person explain their point of view and you reflect what you heard, but in your own words.

Reflective listening seeks to understand their perspective.

LEADERSHIP

MY EXPECTATIONS

As you redirect the other person, you will take the time to be clear about what your "expectations" are moving forward. They are not your desires or wants. They are expectations.

People meet expectations.

They do not meet hopes.

LEADERSHIP

- What is a non-judgmental description of the other person's behavior?
- What is the precursor emotion(s) that I feel related to that behavior?
- What is the measurable impact that I have personally experienced?
- What are the expectations that I have for this person related to this behavior?

Conflict Exercise...

LEADERSHIP

THE TRUTH ASSUMPTION

If I am right, then…	You are wrong.
If I know the facts, then…	You are mistaken.
If I understand, then…	You are confused.
If I did it right, then…	You did it wrong.

LEADERSHIP

WE GENERALLY LOOK EXTERNALLY

Our natural tendency is to focus on what the other person has done and assume their intentions from their actions.

We look at ourselves and judge ourselves based on our best intentions, often without regard to outcomes.

IT IS NOT US, IT'S THEM!

LEADERSHIP

WHY DO WE SEE THINGS DIFFERENTLY?

- We live in the same world as the rest of humanity, yet we interpret it from our own perspective.
- The meaning that any event has is based on the labels that we have given to that event and not to the event itself.

Learn 2 Lead

Supervise • Influence • Motivate

LEADERSHIP

THE RETICULAR ACTIVATING SYSTEM

- The mind can filter, sort, delete, and more all in the blink of an eye.
- Your RAS is the sorting component of the brain that helps you pay attention to certain things and ignore others.
- You filter your world and give it meaning.

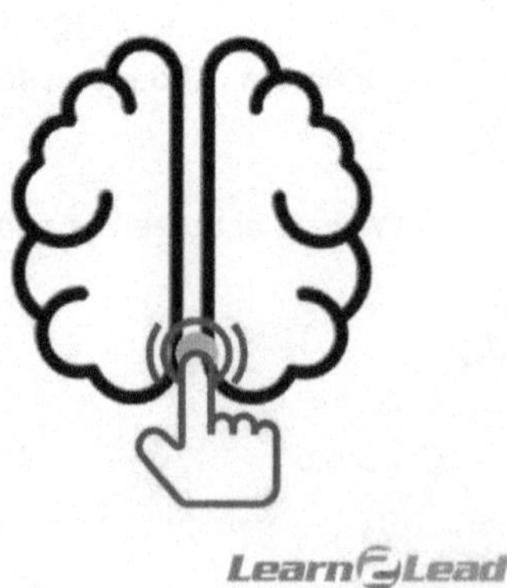

Learn 2 Lead

Supervise • Influence • Motivate

LEADERSHIP

YOU CONTROL YOUR CHOICES

The truth assumption is fixed by…

- Admitting when you are wrong
- Verifying your information
- Listening to their side of the story
- Looking for the good in others
- Being intentional about believing in others
- Knowing your own biases and beliefs

LEADERSHIP

MAJOR ISSUES WITH ASSUMING INTENTIONS

- We are not and cannot be in their head.
- Assuming the worst leads to labeling that person as bad instead of the behavior as bad.
- Selective perception takes over once our made is set on who a person is.
- Impact and Intentions don't always match up.

LEADERSHIP

CHALLENGING CONVERSATIONS HAPPEN!

MOST UPSET PEOPLE WANT…

- To be heard
- To vent their frustrations
- To know that someone cares
- To feel that there is a chance to resolve the conflict
- To be valued as a member of the team.

LEADERSHIP

WHEN A PERSON IS UPSET

- Take the time to listen
- Validate their emotions
- Focus on seeing the world from their perspective
- Move them from opposition to collaboration
- Ask if they would be willing to work with you to solve the challenge

LEADERSHIP

AND THEN…

- You must always value the relationship and want to resolve the conflict.
- When people focus on needing to be right and become petty, we take a trip back to Jr. High School instead of staying in the professional world.

Learn2Lead

Supervise * Influence * Motivate

LEADERSHIP

B-FIRM AND DEAL WITH CONFLICT

Sample B-FIRM Statement

"Angie, when you were late to today's staff meeting I was embarrassed because you had the report information that was to be presented first and I was not prepared to handle it. I delayed the meeting until you arrived causing each person there to delay their day."

(Listen)

My expectations for future meetings is that you will be on time, ready to present your part.

LEADERSHIP

THE CENTRAL FOCUS – M.O.S.T.

The central focus is on…

- Me – I will speak for myself and not for others.
- Observable – I will discuss what is observable behavior without judgment added.
- Setting Expectations – I will be clear about what is expected next time.
- The Responsibility – The responsibility for change rests with them.

LEADERSHIP

YOUR PERSONAL POWER

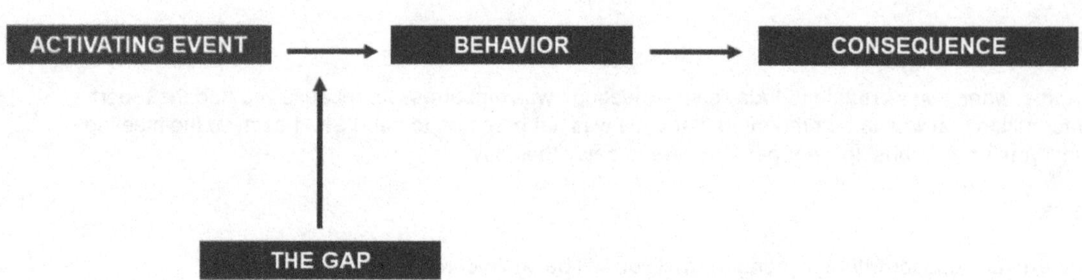

LEADERSHIP

YOU GET TO CHOOSE

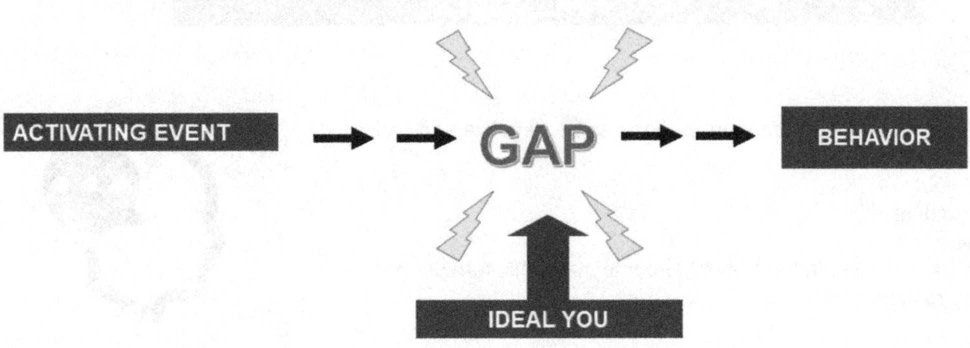

Learn2Lead

LEADERSHIP

NOBODY CAN...

- Make you mad, you choose anger
- Make you happy, you choose joy
- Make you depressed, you choose sadness
- Offend you, you choose to be offended
- Hurt your feelings, you choose to be damaged

Learn2Lead

LEADERSHIP

CALM THE VOICES

Often times our intrapersonal communication can be negative and cause us to look for the bad.

- Stop and think
- Gain perspective
- Ask, “what do I need to believe right now to make this turn out good?”
- Own my responsibility

LEADERSHIP

WHEN THE CONFLICT WILL BE TENSE...

Follow a model that will allow you to maintain control.
Keep your emotions in check.
Focus on the B-FIRM process
Follow these steps!

LEADERSHIP

THINK THROUGH WHAT HAPPENED

- Take a 30,000-foot view of the situation and remove yourself and your emotions from what happened.
- Map out the thought patterns and judgments that you have made.
- What part did you play in this?
- What can you do right now to make it better?

LEADERSHIP

KNOW YOUR PURPOSE

Your purpose must be to improve the relationship through better communication and connection.

It cannot be to…

- Assign blame
- Prove a point
- Make them feel bad
- Prove superiority

LEADERSHIP

SET IT UP FOR A WIN

- Go in with an open mind
- Be ready to listen to their perspective
- Let them know that you value them being in the workplace
- Clear your mind of the negative
- Visualize a positive outcome

LEADERSHIP

FOCUS ON THEM FIRST

- Ask for their perspective and their story
- Use empathy to try and see things from their vantage point
- Listen fully without thinking of your response while they are speaking
- Focus on wanting good for them while they are speaking

LEADERSHIP

SHARE YOUR PERSPECTIVE

- Be honest, confident, and direct
- Connect the dots between their story and yours
- Be clear, even toned, and specific
- Set a clear expectation moving forward
- Garner their support through inviting reflective listening

LEADERSHIP

COME TO AGREEMENT

- Agree on a clear picture of where the relationship is
- Agree on a clear picture of what has happened behaviorally
- Agree on what needs to happen to move forward with the relationship as well as with the new behaviors

LEADERSHIP

PROBLEM-SOLVE TOGETHER

- Once you are in agreement to move forward, the goal is to find a solution that eliminates the problem.
- Seek a win/win solution together
- Be open to a brand new path for both of you
- Stay focused on wanting good for the other person

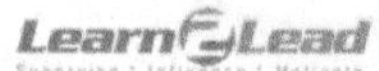

LEADERSHIP

MOVING FORWARD

- State that you want to be able to address conflict sooner in the future
- Ensure that you have built stronger trust by following the SOFT model for coaching
- Focus on the good of the relationship for the future

LEADERSHIP

DO'S AND DON'TS

- Do ask open-ended questions
- Do focus on the good of the other person
- Do follow the process you have learned

- Don't try to put them in their place
- Don't look for the bad in the other person
- Don't skip over the process

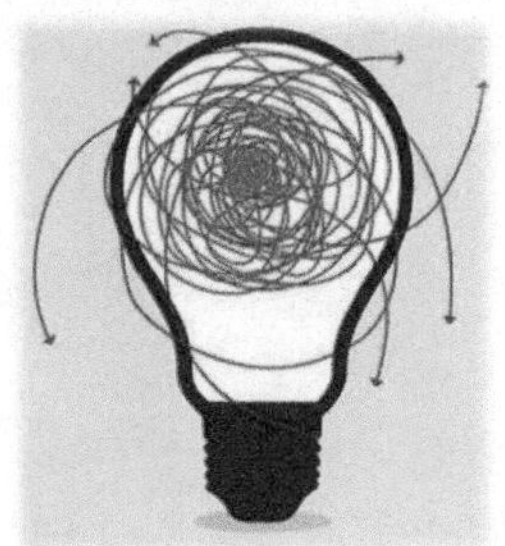

LEADERSHIP

A FEW QUESTIONS TO KEEP THINGS MOVING

- Can you help me to understand your perspective?
- Can you help me understand the process that you followed that got you and I to this point?
- Can you help me understand your intentions?
- Can you help me figure out a way to make this a win/win resolution?
- Can you help me come up with some options that would be good for both of us?
- Can you walk me through what you would like to see happen next time?
- Would you be willing to work with me to solve this problem?

LEADERSHIP

STAY FOCUSED ON SUCCESS

LEADERSHIP

FOCUS ON UNDERLYING ISSUES

- What happened?
  - Difference in expectations:
    - What did I expect to happen?; What actually happened? Who did what?
  - Intention inventory (Who meant what?)
- Feelings
  - Don't ignore or fail to acknowledge
  - Feelings make relationships enjoyable and difficult conversations difficult (can't have one without the other!)
- Identity
  - Must face ourselves as well as other person
  - Am I competent?; Am I a good person?; Am I worthy of respect?

LEADERSHIP

STEPS TO SUCCESS

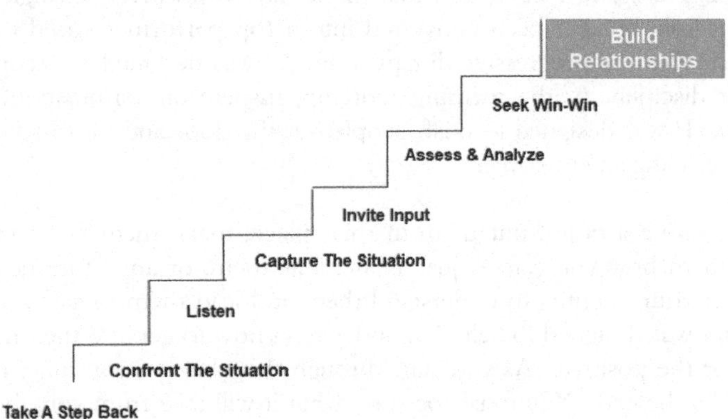

Learn2Lead

Thank You For Your Attention

Check Out www.jodyholland.com

7 CORRECTIVE COUNSELING

Time and again, I have seen supervisors jump straight to writing employees up in order to set an example of how things should run. Time and again, I have seen that model fail to positively change behavior. Not once in my experience has a chronic rule breaker been converted into a top performer based on the progressive discipline model. In fact, that isn't what the progressive discipline model was designed to accomplish from a psychological perspective. Progressive discipline (verbal warning, write up, suspension, termination) was designed to get people to stop working for you. It was designed to push people out the door and on to some other job. So, I ask you, what is your point in counseling an employee?

If your point is to prove a point, put them in their place, make them feel bad, push them out the door, embarrass them, show them how you can be just as awful as them, or any other negative intent, you will NOT change their behavior. If your intent is to understand them and lead them to a new behavior, then you will love this chapter. This chapter was designed to help you understand how to get into their head and help them decide to change their behavior for the positive. As you start through this chapter, you must remember to focus on what you hope to accomplish in the end. You must focus on what it will take from you, the supervisor, in order to get others to want to move forward, to change their behaviors, and to be your next top performer. In any situation, take the time to think about life from the other person's perspective.

Why do employees fail to perform?

There are obviously a number of reasons that a person could fail at work. However, when you sift through all of the reasons/excuses, you find that it really comes down to three basic things that we, as supervisors, are dealing with. As you learn to address these three things, you learn to lead your people to higher levels of performance and more consistently positive behaviors.

1. Lack of knowledge – People will fail when they don't have the knowledge that is necessary to succeed at that particular position. Imagine asking someone to do the books for the company when they have never balanced their own checkbook. Imagine asking them to design the electrical map for a new building when they have never messed with electricity before. With things at that level, most of us could never imagine doing that to an employee. However, we hire new people and then just throw them into the fire and tell them to figure it out. Employees fail because they were not taught how to do the job that they were placed in. In the past, mentoring happened in a very natural way. Previous generations found new employees and "took them under their wing." They found ways to develop skills in the "newbie" even if they were not necessarily their supervisor. In today's world, that doesn't seem to happen as often. That is why is it so important to have a process mapped out to learn the necessary information for any job in your organization. It is ideal to outline the required knowledge to be successful in a job and then map out how the person will learn that information. Ideally, you should have a 30-day on-boarding plan where the employee is learning new skills every day of the first month. Have ways to verify that they have learned the information necessary for the position (tests/observation/conversation) and give them the opportunity to ask questions about the job.
2. Lack of ability – Sometimes, even when the person has been exposed to the right information, been given the chance to ask questions and master the required knowledge, they still aren't succeeding. This statement isn't a negative one towards a person, but there are simply some things that some people cannot learn. As an example, I will not be teaching any of you Calculus. I didn't do poorly at math, but try as I may, Calculus was beyond my mental scope. It is critically important that we place the right people in the right positions. When we put a person in a job that they simply cannot do, we are doing

them a disservice as well as hurting our company. Supervisors often hire people that they like instead of hiring people that can and will do the job. Take a look at a person's past experience and determine if they actually CAN do the job. As you begin observing the person on the job, which you should be doing intently in their first 30 days, verify that they CAN do the job. When you are proactive about training and investing in your people, whether new or simply new to a position, you are helping to ensure that they enjoy as much success as possible in their careers.

3. Lack of engagement – There are a variety of reasons that one could use as justification as to why a person isn't engaged. The most common, however, is that they have not developed the right emotional energy to be engaged. In other words, they don't see a reason to be engaged. Engagement is an emotional response that produces physical results. The culture that exists for a company will determine, to a large degree, whether or not a person is going to be engaged. When you have developed a culture that is accountable, fair, caring, and celebratory of success, then engagement is very likely. When you have developed a culture that is aggressive, unfair, uncaring, and doesn't celebrate success but focuses on failure instead, you are likely to create highly disengaged employees. When you see a large percentage of your people disengaged at work, ask yourself about the culture that you have created. In all fairness, there are some people who are actively disengaged either because of past experience or simply because they have chosen to be a non-performer. Those are the folks that will need to be presented with an opportunity to excel in another company. When a person has chosen to be a non-performer, to do just enough to get by, they have chosen a work lifestyle. Through the use of the counseling process, you will want to give them ownership of that choice and make sure that they understand that they can either make a new choice to perform, or they can make a choice to work elsewhere. By addressing the non-performer, we let the average and top performers know that we value what they are doing. By allowing a non-performer to just keep their job without accountability, we are indicating that performance doesn't matter to us.

In Charles Duhigg's book, The Power of Habit, (Buy Here: http://bit.ly/habitduhigg) we learn that people often do the things that they do because that is the habit that they have formed. If we wish for them to move in a new direction, we have to understand the fundamentals of the work habits that they have developed.

The Queue

The queue, or the trigger that initiates a response is important to understand. For any learned response pattern, there is a queue that happens. Most of the time, the employee doesn't have any idea what that queue is. They simply know how they do what they do. As you observe the employee, you are focused on what their routine is, what processes they follow, what is happening in their day, and when they perform versus when they act in the wrong manner. Almost every person that acts in the wrong manner is following a pattern that they have created on how to respond. This activating event, or queue, is what sets everything in motion. When you can understand what the trigger is, you can understand why the pattern exists.

The Response Pattern

Once the trigger has occurred, then the pattern sets itself into motion. People create neuro-pathways for behaviors which allow them to think less, or with less conscious effort. Over the years and years of our brains developing, adapting, and adjusting, this response model has created a much more effective way for us take predictable action while conserving brain-power for other needs. Robert Cialdini would refer to this as a "Click-Whir" response. Duhigg says that these neuro-pathways, or response patterns, are how we would explain why an employee makes the same mistake over and over again. It also explains the need for a cigarette when a stressful event happens, or why some people only smoke when they drink. It is a conditioned response.

This component of the 3-part habit loop is the part that we, as supervisors, will seek to change. You will need to know exactly what you want the response to be in order to begin inserting a new response pattern after the queue and before the reward. The two components that will need to remain the same are the first and the third. There will always be an activating event. There should always be a reward for behaviors. In cognitive behavioral therapy (CBT), the reward is called "the consequence." Whatever you wish to call it, there is a result for every action taken. When a response pattern is activated, the resulting feeling is what is sought after.

The Reward

People are conditioned throughout their lives to look for specific feelings. They associate those good feelings with the completion of a task, a job well done, the opportunity to move on to the next thing, etc. The reward isn't always the same for everyone. There is, however, a reward that each person looks for. In one of the habit experiments, Duhigg demonstrates that response patterns can be trained through the initiation of a queue and subsequent delivery of rewards. After the response pattern becomes a habit, the rewards can be removed and the response pattern will remain in tact as long as the queue is present.

This is important to remember, particularly when conditioning an employee to change their behaviors in a specific manner. If you don't have the queue and the reward in the beginning, you will not change the response pattern. However, when you introduce a reward, even a compliment of a job well done for showing up on time, for example, you begin to re-route the neuro-pathways of the person. The objective is to create new neuro-pathways, or thought patterns, for the person in order to overwrite the old ones. It isn't until we create a new path from queue to reward that the old path will be overridden.

Tim was an executive that was chronically late turning in his reports. His supervisor had scolded him, pushed him, thrown fits at him, and still not gotten him to change. Tim's conditioned response was to operate in crisis mode. He would consistently take assignments that were given to him and push them back until the last minute. He said on several occasions, "I operate best under pressure." His response pattern was that he got a thrill out of the crisis and out of being able to deliver what seemed impossible to others. Even though he was getting in trouble for it, at some point he had been the guy that his boss went to in a clutch. He had rescued people on multiple occasions that would not and could not have completed a task. The queue was the crisis and the virtually impossible deadline. The developed response pattern was to work like crazy to the detriment of everything and everyone around him, and to deliver. The reward was the praise and gratefulness that he had gotten for saving the day from his boss. Fast forward to him moving up into a management role. He was still following the same habit loop. In order to get Tim to change, he needed an adjustment to the response pattern. He didn't need to be a different person or give up who he was. He simply needed to condition himself in a new direction.

In working with Tim, I helped him to identify the queue of getting the assignment, and then to reformat the response of procrastinating and then saving the day to one of immediately scheduling out what it would take to do the job and starting that day. I made sure that I arranged for lots of praise for Tim when he demonstrated the new habit. I even recruited his supervisor and his supervisor's supervisor. I had them praise him every time it appeared that he was on top of things and praise him even more when the assignment was done early. It took about 10 times of praising his new response pattern to make it stick. He now created a new craving in his own mind. He craved praise for doing a proactively good job. Even in the absence of praise, he still continued to use the new response pattern once it was conditioned.

Keep in mind that in order to get a new behavior, we have to condition that behavior into the mind of the individual. People do what they do because it meets their needs in some way. If we want them to do something new, we have to condition something new into who they are. It still has to meet their needs, just with a new pathway.

Cognitive Behavioral Therapy and REBT at Work

People are not disturbed by events. They are disturbed by the label that they have given to those events.

Understand a person's thoughts on their choices and you begin to understand the person. Most supervisors don't take the time to understand the people that are working for them, though. They simply assume that everyone should be just like them. You can be different. You can begin to look at the people that work for you and seek to understand who they are, why they are, and what you can do about it. CBT at work functions very closely to the same manner as the habit loop.

The A,B,C's of who a person is are ingrained in CBT. With each of us, there is an activating event (A). This event is the trigger for the response pattern that is generated. In other words, our behavior (B) will flow out of our conditioning related to the triggering event(A). Every behavior that a person exhibits is the result of a choice, and conditioning, within that person. Behaviors always lead to consequences (C).

In order to learn a new way of doing things, we must first unlearn what we already knew. Creating a new neuro-pathway for success means overwriting the old one.
The ABC's of Rational Emotive Behavior Therapy (Nouveau) are consistent with both the habit loop and CBT. An integral component of this approach is the reality that each person is free to choose their own emotions, their own actions, and their own results. In counseling an employee, it is critical to explain to them that they are in charge of themselves. They get to choose the behaviors that they exhibit. They get to choose the pathway that they follow. They get to choose whether they ultimately stay in the position that they are in or pursue a different position. People don't get moved into progressive discipline and get fired. They move themselves based on the choices that they make. It is critical to explain to an employee who is being counseled that what happens next is up to them. You, as the counselor, need to clearly outline what you are expecting, when you are expecting it by, and how you will measure its success or failure.

This understanding of how we process events and utilize our conditioned responses is very good and very important. It only leaves out a couple of components, however, that are critical to understanding the pattern or habit loop. The diagram below helps to explain the two components that complete the loop. The two components that are not explained in the ABC's are the choice that exists and the belief that is either reinforced or modified.

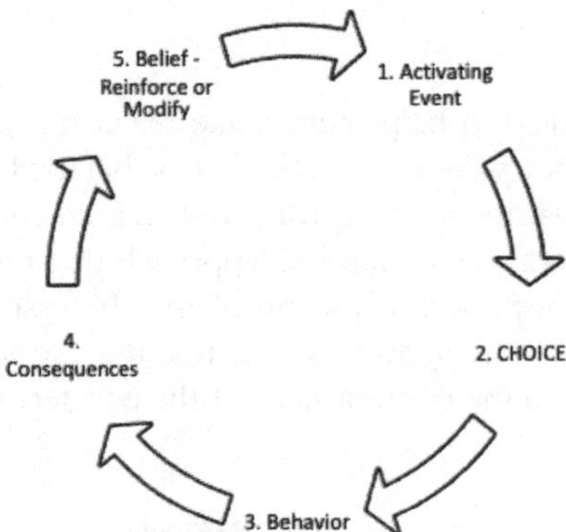

When an event happens that triggers a response, it takes conditioning to create new neuro-pathways to overwrite old behaviors, but it can be done. One of the challenges, however, is that the person is pulling from past reinforcements of a belief, which is why they do what they do right now. Until we can change the response pattern, or behavior, we can't have the opportunity to provide the same or better consequences/rewards. When a person keeps the triggering event and the reward, but changes the behavior, they begin to see that the new pattern is worthwhile. Changing behaviors in a person is ultimately about changing beliefs about behaviors. When the belief is modified, the new behavior becomes the norm.

The Greek Philosopher, Epictetus, observed that people are not disturbed by things that happen but by the view they take of things that happen. Your objective should be to understand what their view is, or how they are labeling the reward that they receive. Once you can understand who a person is and how they seek rewards, you can modify your approach to fit their needs. Adaptation to an employee is not weakness. In fact, adaptation is strength. It demonstrates that you are the type of supervisor that has the capacity to take care of people where they are, just as they are. Label your leadership and interactions with your employees as an opportunity to increase performance through understanding your people and inspiring them to create better behavior patterns. You are not here to change people. You are here to facilitate people changing themselves for the better.

Like you learned in the chapter on conflict resolution, once you have dealt with the behavior, you must move into setting clear expectations. One of the struggles that I have found to be more and more common is that of employees not knowing what their boss is looking for. They can tell that the boss is upset. They know that what they did wasn't what the boss wanted. The problem comes in when the boss/supervisor doesn't explain three critical components of what has to happen next.

1. What are you expecting? What were the specific behaviors and outcomes that you expected and expect for the future?
2. When you are expecting it by? What is a specific time and date that you expect to see the new results?
3. How you will measure its success? What are the measurable effects of the new behavior that should be evident? The more clearly that you can describe this, the more likely you are to get it.

Once you, the supervisor, have set up a clear set of expectations moving forward, you have to make sure that you have buy-in and accountability from the employee. Accountability comes in the form of monitoring results by you as well as by the employee. Self-monitoring is a way of conditioning their mind to look for what you will be looking for. By setting up the right systems, you are laying the groundwork for their success.

Setting up self-monitoring requires that the individual who is being coached have the trust in their supervisor to be comfortable sharing when they mess up. If they are yelled at, belittled, or made to feel worthless when they make a mistake, they will shut down. Your role as a counselor is to facilitate their decision to change their behavior.

With one of my clients, I was asked to help them make fewer mistakes in their financial firm. The history was that when a mistake was made, they were either yelled at or belittled, often in front of others. The partners were very frustrated with the results that they were getting and wanted changes as soon as possible. In looking at what was going on, I identified that it was the counseling approach that they were using (aggressive tones and acts towards mistakes) that was actually perpetuating the problem. It wasn't that the employees wanted to make mistakes, but the pressure that they were under, and the way that the partners were dealing with things that actually made the mistakes more likely. I secured the commitment of the partners to back off and allow me to follow a 30-day process.

The Process

Each time an employee made a mistake and the mistake was identified, I would interact with them and let them know of the mistake. I would ask them to fill in the information on three questions. In the beginning, I would bring up the mistakes and have them interact with me to uncover the answers. By the end of two weeks, they were identifying their own mistakes and following the process. This moved them from being monitored into the process of self-monitoring.

1. Walk me through each of the steps along this path that lead to what happened?
2. At what point on that path, or at which step, could you have done something differently that would have gotten us the result that we wanted instead of the result that we currently have?

3. What will you put into place to ensure that this particular mistake doesn't happen again in the future?

By following this model, we reduced the number of mistakes from more than 10 per day down to less than 10 per month by the second month. One of the critical components of this was that there was no yelling involved. Everything was done with a calm and even tone with the best of intentions for each staff member. Additionally, the employees were actually rewarded for finding the mistake, for correcting the mistake, and even more so for not making the mistake again. We initiated a new loop into their minds for what was supposed to happen when a mistake was made. By doing this, we created new neuro-pathways for the employees and new results for the employer.

People do what they do because it is what meets their needs. In order to get a new result from a person, you have to get them to accept ownership of what has happened. By using this model of understanding the steps, and the point at which change could have happened, and what comes next, you are creating positive accountability. One theory that really helps to explain why this is so important is the Attribution Theory.

A synonym for attribution is explanation. When you think about anything that a person does, break it down in terms of whether or not they were in control of their behaviors and therefore their outcomes. The attribution theory states that people have a need to understand "why" something happens. The explanation of why something happens will always be either internal or external. If the explanation is internal, then the person accepts that they were in control and can, and likely will, change their behavior in the future. If the explanation is that it is external, then the person is saying that they were not in control and likely cannot and will not change.

Change happens when the person accepts responsibility for their actions and their results, and they desire a new result. When a manager yells at an employee, it pushes their thoughts to external explanation. The focus becomes the supervisor being a jerk and not understanding instead of what the person did. When you ask "why did you do that" instead of following the three-step process of questioning, you lose their buy-in. You also usually get only a shoulder shrug or an "I don't know" instead of a legitimate answer. If you ask the wrong questions, you get the wrong answers. If you ask the right questions, you get the right answers. The Attribution Theory is the basis for knowing how to ask the right questions.

Think back to the last time that you asked an employee, "Why did you do that?" What was the response that you received? If you are like virtually every other supervisor that I have spoken to in the last couple of decades, you got some version "I don't know" or a blank stare. The reason that you need to learn the processes and principles in this chapter is to set the right path for others to own their actions and own their results. I would encourage you to use this model with anyone that has not responded to your coaching. This is the next logical step in creating lasting behavior change in another person. It opens the door for them to choose the new behaviors that are necessary. It gets people behaving in the right manner and moving towards success.

What if it doesn't work?

One of the more common questions that I am asked at my live events is, "What if it doesn't work?" There are people in this world, that despite doing everything just right, will still choose to take the wrong path. Going back to how this chapter started, each person is responsible for themselves. Each person controls their own choices. Not everyone will be willing to own their choices and consequently make better choices as a result. It has been my experience, as well as that of Adeco, that around 20% of the average workforce is made up of non-performers. People who are non-performers are who they are because they have chosen that as the definition of who they are. They don't see themselves working hard (by your definition), nor do they believe that they should. They typically do enough work to not get fired, but not a lot more than that, if any.

Knowing that not everyone is going to be willing to be what you need them to be, some people won't make it. Some people will simply choose not to perform. That is their choice. Ultimately, you can't make them be a performer if they want to be a non-performer. If this is the case, an ideal response to them would be…

I know that you are in control of yourself and your choices. I have been very clear about what I expect from you and what helps you do well in this organization. I have also explained to you that you can choose to perform in the right manner, or you can choose not to do so. Either choice has a consequence. Performing has the consequence of being appreciated, possibly promoted, and being a contributing member of this workforce. If you choose not to do what is expected of you, that is also your choice. The consequence of that choice is that you are choosing to no longer be an employee in this organization. It isn't my choice, though. It is yours. Please take the next 24 hours and think about which path you will choose. I will require an answer from you tomorrow at this same time to know whether you will be staying and changing your behaviors or whether you will choose to move on.

By presenting it as a choice, they will have to consciously accept one path or the other. This means that you also cut off the non-performance more quickly by forcing the choice. Whatever they decide, accept their choice and hold them accountable. If they choose to stay and perform, make sure that you receive the behaviors that you described and the results that you described as necessary. If you don't, then move through your company's progressive discipline process towards termination of that employee.

Changing employee behaviors isn't about "making them" do what you want them to do. It is about clearly delineating the choice that they must make. They will either choose to perform for you or they will choose not to perform for you. The choice has always been theirs and it will remain theirs. Allow them to choose. Even if they choose to leave, you at least know where you stand. You know for sure that they never would have performed for you. Find a new employee who will, recruit them, and invest in their future and the future of your team.

LEADERSHIP

LEARNING OBJECTIVES

- Understand what employees want and what they will respond to
- Learn how to establish internal control in the mind of an employee
- Learn the right questions to ask that lead to employees being personally responsible
- Learn the process to follow with corrective counseling
- Learn the process that the mind goes through to determine internal or external control

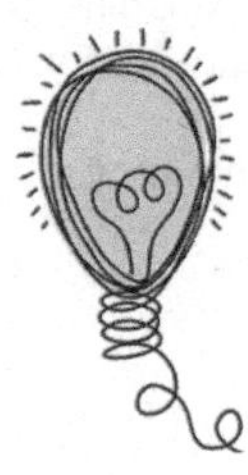

Learn2Lead
Supervise · Influence · Motivate

LEADERSHIP

WHY EMPLOYEES FAIL TO PERFORM

- Lack of Knowledge
- Lack of Clear Expectations
- Lack of Ability
- **Lack of Engagement**

LEADERSHIP

THE MODEL FOR BEHAVIOR CHANGE

The job of a supervisor is to inspire the right behaviors, to accomplish work through others, and to build a fully engaged workforce.
This is less of a push and more of a pull.

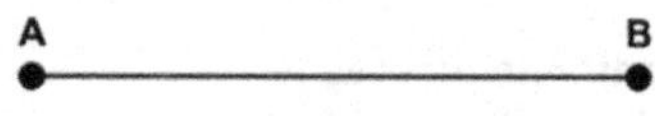

LEADERSHIP

WHAT DO EMPLOYEES WANT?

- They want to work for a purpose beyond money.
- They want to work for someone who cares about them as a person.
- They want to work with other people that they like, know, and trust.
- They want to have the necessary resources to do their job.

LEADERSHIP

THE BALANCING ACT

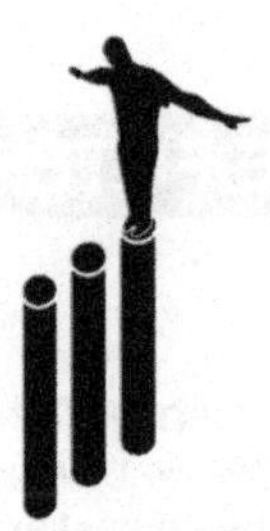

- You are continuously balancing the needs of employees with the needs of the organization.
- You are balancing how hard to push employees to work with how to inspire them to want to work.
- You are balancing culture and strategy.

LEADERSHIP

A SENSE OF REALITY

"That which I perceive is my reality."
--William James

Reality is simply a set of labels that one has for their experiences.

LEADERSHIP

THE FILTERING PROCESS

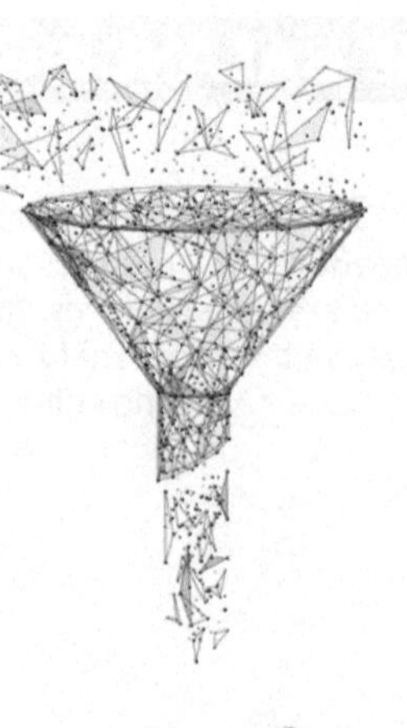

- Perceptual filters are housed in the apperception mass in the brain.
- How we label a current experience begins with how we have labeled past experiences.
- It is the label, not the experience, that matters most.

Learn2Lead
Supervise · Influence · Motivate

LEADERSHIP

OUR LABELS HAVE CHALLENGES

DELETE
We delete information that goes against our beliefs.

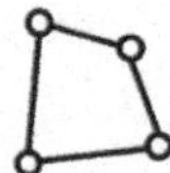

DISTORT
We modify the meaning of results in order to make it fit with our beliefs.

GENERALIZE
We lump behaviors and intentions together in order to validate our beliefs.

MISALIGNED ATTRIBUTION

We often assume by another person's actions or outcomes that we know the intent behind those actions or outcomes.

When we intend something good, we give ourselves the benefit of the doubt. When others produce a bad outcome, we assume their intentions were bad as well.

LEADERSHIP

BUT WHY?

We have a need to understand why things happen, why others do what they do, and why we have the results that we have.

When something happens, we want to know...
BUT WHY?!

LEADERSHIP

LOCUS OF CONTROL

Internal Locus of Control

- I am in control of my choices.
- I am in control of my thoughts.
- I am in control of my emotions.

External Locus of Control

- My circumstances control my choices.
- My circumstances control my thoughts.
- My circumstances control my emotions.

LEADERSHIP

WELL THAT EXPLAINS IT…

What we want is an explanation.

Change Happens

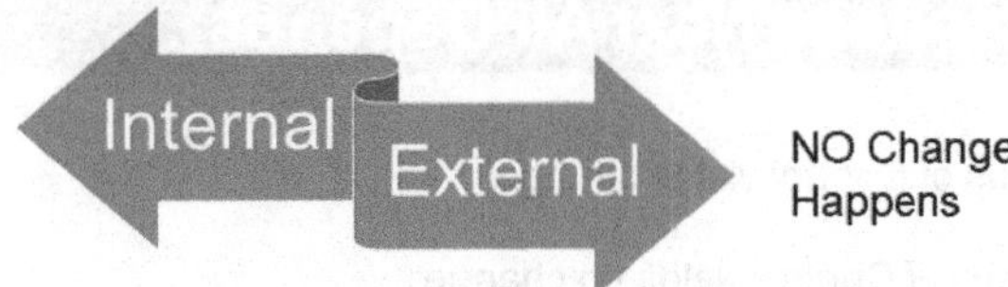

NO Change Happens

Learn2Lead
Supervise · Influence · Motivate

LEADERSHIP

OUR NORMAL IS…

When something good happens, it is internal.

When something bad happens, it is external.

THINK PERFORMANCE REVIEWS!

LEADERSHIP

What Happens Next All Depends...

Internal Locus of Control yields change.

External Locus of Control yields no change.

We only change that which we believe we can change, and that is limited to what we can control.

Learn2Lead
Supervise · Influence · Motivate

LEADERSHIP

GENERATING INTERNAL CONTROL

Planting The Seeds of Thought: The supervisor would say to the employee:

"I believe that you know how to do X and can do it well if you want to."

"You appear to have the capability to do X well."

"I believe that you are working hard to be good at X, don't you?"

LEADERSHIP

GENERATING INTERNAL CONTROL

Anchoring The New Idea. The supervisor would say to the employee:

"When you do X(behavior), I really appreciate it (feeling) because it makes my job easier (effect)."

"When I see you doing X(behavior), I am inspired(feeling) because I see that you are progressing (effect)."

LEADERSHIP

GENERATING INTERNAL CONTROL

Reinforcing The Behavior.

It will take at least 21 correct repetitions with reinforcement to solidify the new behavior set as normal, natural, and a part of who they are.

LEADERSHIP

IT WORKS IF…

- The steps of what happened are discussed without judgment
- A point of attribution is identified and accepted by the person
- A plan is formulated by the person for how they will do it better and different the next time.
- In other words, ALL ownership remains with them.

LEADERSHIP

CONDITIONS FOR SUCCESS

- Address the situation within a 48 hour window whenever possible
- Follow the right process for success
- The counseling has to be done when the person is thinking about "why" things turned out the way they did
- Internal control must be established

LEADERSHIP

WHY WE DO WHAT WE DO

Charles Duhigg's Book The Power Of Habit

We have a trigger, then "click-whir" response, then a reward (real or perceived)

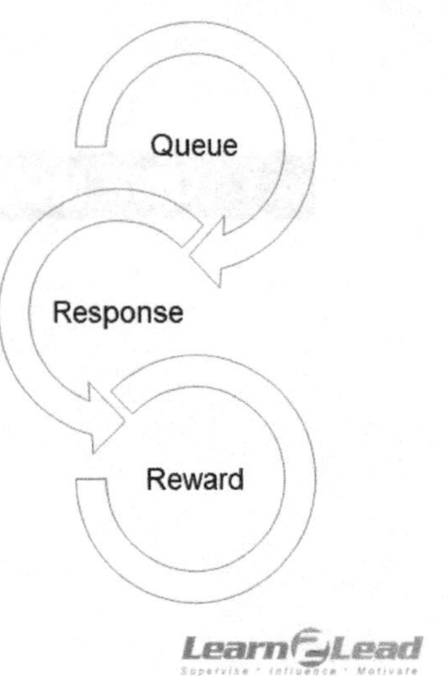

LEADERSHIP

WHAT'S MY FOCUS?

- We are here to generate a better response.
- The response a person implements determines the outcomes that the person achieves.
- You can't control the triggers!

ONE MORE TIME – ATTRIBUTION THEORY

The world asks "why"

We either explain internally or externally.

The explanation leads to the future behavior.

RATIONAL EMOTIONAL BEHAVIOR THERAPY

A – Activating Event

B – Belief / Label about what it should mean

C – Consequence of the action we take related to our belief.

Your power is always in the belief!

LEADERSHIP

FRAMING OUR WORLD

How a person frames, or labels, their world demonstrates the world that they live in.

New frame = New world

LEADERSHIP

FULL LOOP FOR BEHAVIORS

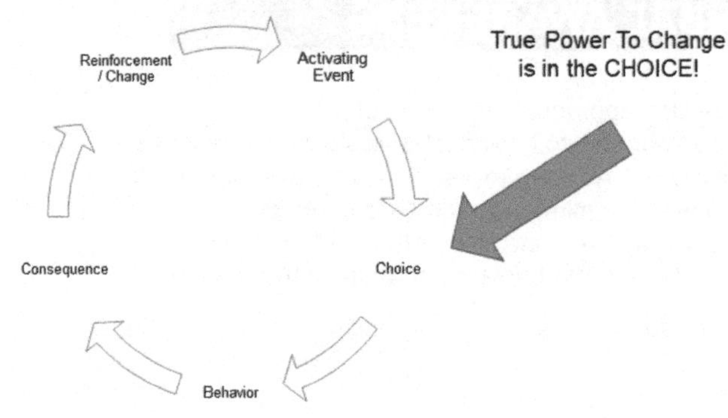

LEADERSHIP

CHOICE

- C – Conscious evaluation of what you believe and why
- H – Honest and tactful conversations
- O – Options are the key to creating a better direction
- I – I-Statements keep the emotions under control
- C – Change is always internal
- E – Emotions cloud logic

LEADERSHIP

NON-VERBAL AWARENESS

- Eye Contact – Use appropriate eye contact
- Silence – Take your time to think but be aware of their reactions
- Facial Expressions – An open expression is always more inviting
- Body Language – Use mirroring in order to connect
- Tone of Voice – Stay even and calm with your tones
- Spatial Positioning – Avoid barriers and respect the bubble

LEADERSHIP

CLARIFY THE MESSAGE

- Feed back what you heard but in your own words
- Check for understanding
  - If I understand you correctly, you are saying…
  - To summarize what I heard…
  - I want to make sure that I am connecting all the dots…
  - So what you are saying is…
  - Your primary concerns are…
  - Can you help me understand that better? I think you are saying…

KNOW YOUR END GAME!

LEADERSHIP

COUNSELING IS DIFFERENT

THE FUNDAMENTALS OF THE SESSION

- It will generally go the best if it is face-to-face
- Avoid using technology when you can be with the person instead
- Don't create panic before the session (tell them why you want to meet and do it quickly)
- Keep your focus on the right purpose
- Make it relevant to their success

THE PURPOSE

- The purpose of counseling is to help an employee embrace where they are, what they have done, and to own their actions moving forward as well as from the past.
- It is designed to enhance the performance of the employee, not to "put them in their place."

LEADERSHIP

WHAT COUNSELING ACCOMPLISHES

- It communicates concerns
- It creates ownership of behaviors
- It generates trust and respect
- It generates a plan for the future
- It inspires employees to want to perform better in the future

LEADERSHIP

WHAT HAPPENS WHEN WE DON'T COUNSEL?

- The negative behavior or outcome is affirmed
- The supervisor has an increased workload
- The employee is not developed to higher levels of potential
- Morale is hurt
- Turnover increases
- Profit potential is limited

LEADERSHIP

WHEN SHOULD YOU COUNSEL?

- If you have already coached and it didn't take
- If you have inherited an employee that has traditionally caused problems
- When it is time to re-establish expectations
- When you want to avoid the progressive discipline process

LEADERSHIP

PROGRESSIVE DISCIPLINE

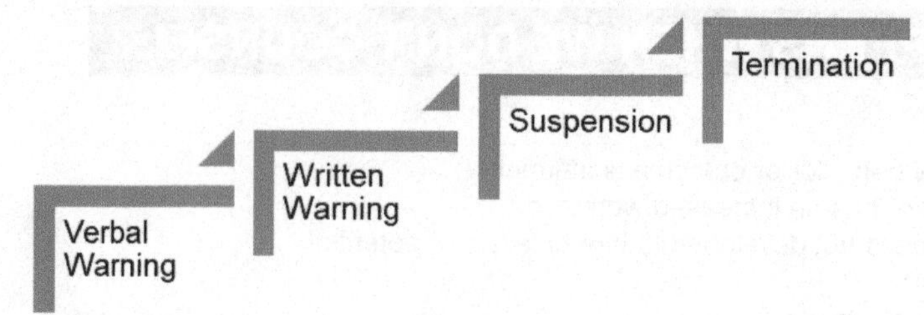

Progressive discipline has never turned a chronic rule breaker into a top performer, but there is a place for it.

LEADERSHIP

GET YOURSELF READY

- Define your objectives for the session
- Get your documentation ready and be clear on what generated the need for the session
- Create an outline
- Control your emotions
- Arrange for privacy
- Inform the employee in person

LEADERSHIP

DURING THE COUNSELING

- Start by setting a positive tone
- State the situation from your perspective
- Seek an explanation for the current results
- Search for solutions together
- Set an expectations moving forward
- Don't forget your listening skills!
- Recap what has been established!
- Conclude the session.

LEADERSHIP

Position Yourself For Success

- Focus on the relationship AND the outcomes
- Be honest AND tactful
- Be consistent AND understanding
- Be trustworthy AND trusting
- Focus on the outcome AND be completely honest (don't ever manipulate)

LEADERSHIP

THERE IS A DIFFERENCE

Constructive Feedback

- Focuses on behaviors and/or outcomes
- Focuses on what is right
- Attempts to lift others up and help them find success
- Looks toward the interest of the organization and the success of the employee… over self-interests

LEADERSHIP

THERE IS A DIFFERENCE

Destructive Feedback
- Focuses on the person
- Focuses on why you, the leader are right
- Attempts to put others "in their place"
- Looks toward self-interest over company interest

LEADERSHIP

KNOW WHAT BEHAVIORS YOU ARE LOOKING FOR

Top Performers…
- Come to work on time and ready to work
- Have a good attitude and improve the attitude of the team
- Solve problems proactively in order to contribute
- Look for solutions, NOT excuses
- Go out of their way to mentor and develop peers
- Enable you to relax when they are on the job
- Compete with who they were yesterday

LEADERSHIP

WHAT IS AVERAGE?

Average Performers…

- Generally come to work on time
- Play off the attitudes of the rest of the team (react)
- Are willing participants in solving a problem as long as the leader initiates the process
- Will help mentor when asked
- Often times, they work for the "what & how" but not the "why" of the organization
- May need more training or more attention

LEADERSHIP

WHAT IS A LOW PERFORMER?

Low Performers…

- Knows how far they can push before they get fired
- Reacts to the attitudes of others and doesn't feel that they can control their own emotions
- Look for problems and point them out in a negative way
- Often see work as punishment
- Say things like "I was here when that leader was hired and I will be here when they are gone… they can't touch me."

LEADERSHIP

TRAINING MOVES THE TOP HIGHER

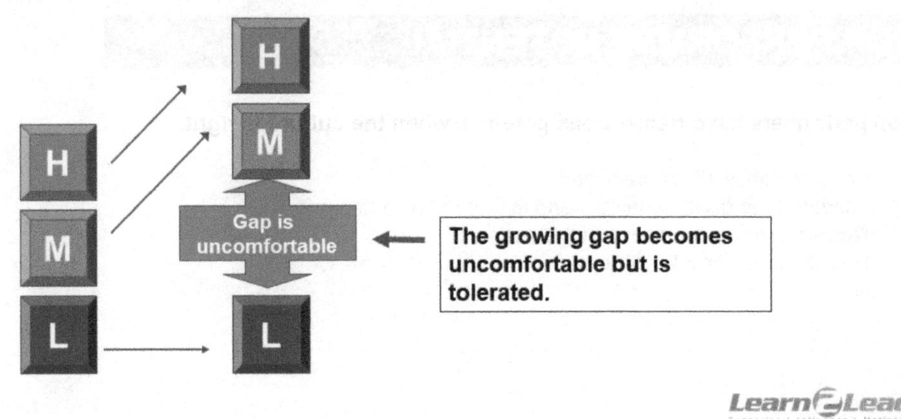

Learn2Lead
Supervise · Influence · Motivate

LEADERSHIP

TRAINING & COACHING KEEP MOVING THE BAR

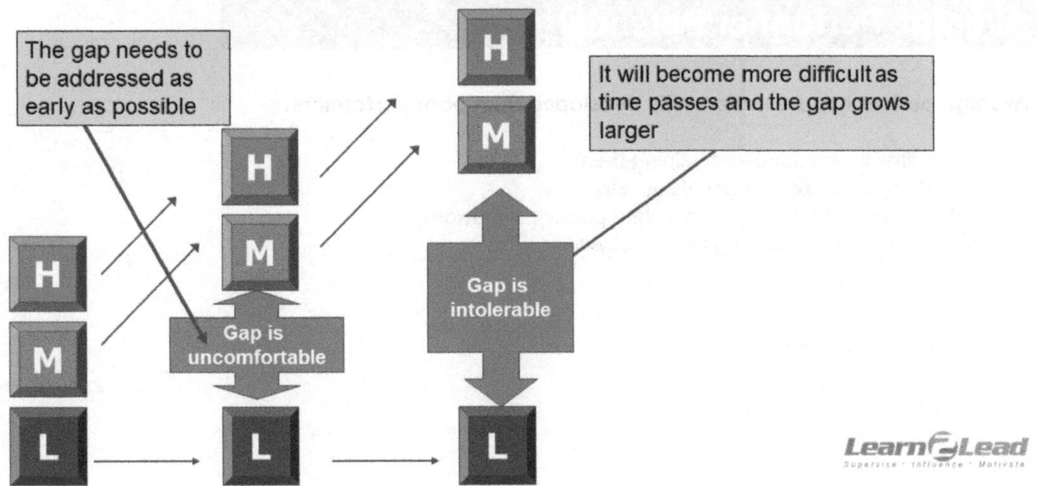

Learn2Lead
Supervise · Influence · Motivate

LEADERSHIP

TOP PERFORMER POTENTIAL

Top performers have tremendous potential when the culture is right.

- Focus on showing appreciation
- Validate their good behaviors and their positive outcomes
- Reward them in the soul and the wallet.
- Praise them in front of others!

LEADERSHIP

Average Performer Potential

Average performers are more easily developed than poor performers.

- Invest time in coaching and training them.
- Help them visualize a target of success.
- Consistently reinforce and appreciate positive behaviors.
- Find them a top performing mentor at work.

LEADERSHIP

POOR PERFORMER POTENTIAL

Poor performers have to change their framework in order to find their potential.

- Build a framework for them to accept responsibility for themselves.
- Use great conflict resolution strategies.
- Find little behaviors that are desired and reinforce those.
- Plant, Anchor, Reinforce, Repeat

LEADERSHIP

4-S Model

- State the situation as you see it
- Seek attribution
- Search for solutions
- Set a performance expectation

LEADERSHIP

STATE THE SITUATION

State the situation as you perceive/interpret it

- Speak for yourself
- Don't exaggerate
- Outline the outcome or behavioral problem
- Stay focused on the measurables
- Outline the costs to you and/or the organization
- State your expectations
- B-FIRM about those expectations being met

LEADERSHIP

SEEK ATTRIBUTION

Seek out a point of attribution

- Walk me through the steps of what happened that got us to this outcome.
- At what point could you have done something different that would have gotten us the desired outcome?
- What can you put in place to ensure a better outcome next time?
- Note: You must remain calm and non-judgmental in the process

LEADERSHIP

SEARCH FOR SOLUTIONS

- Look for ways to facilitate them solving the problem.
- Define the need and the expectations for the future.
- Help them brainstorm for options
- Help them evaluate their options for the good and the bad
- Get them to choose which option they will choose.

LEADERSHIP

SET A CLEAR PERFORMANCE EXPECTATION

- Focus on setting expectations…
    - Not setting desires or wants or hopes – Hope is not a strategy!
- Be clear about the outcomes that you expect moving forward.

- If they don't agree…
    - Explain that it is not a request but rather an expectation (be respectful and tactful)
    - Reiterate that they have the option to choose, but…
        - Every choice yields a result!

LEADERSHIP

WHAT HAS BEEN ACCOMPLISHED...

THIS MODEL WILL:

- Value and appreciate top performers
- Coach and develop average performers
- Create accountability with low performers
- Ensure that employees feel valued and appreciated
- Create role models out of leadership
- Ensure that people know that performance is important

LEADERSHIP

DISCIPLINE VERSUS COUNSELING

DISCIPLINE
- Generally Needs a Witness
- Lead by HR
- Focused on Shortcomings
- Increases Turnover
- Last Resort
- Creates External Locus of Control

COUNSELING
- Generally One on One
- Lead by the Supervisor
- Focused on Potential
- Increases Retention
- 1st Form of Action
- Creates Internal Locus of Control

LEADERSHIP

AN OUNCE OF PREVENTION

AN OUNCE OF PREVENTION IS WORTH A POUND OF CURE.

- Doing things right the first time involves creating a culture of success.
- It involves creating accountability.
- It involves using a model that creates predictable results.

LEADERSHIP

THE RIGHT-UP CULTURE VERSUS THE WRITE-UP CULTURE

WRITE UP

- Reactive
- Seeks to punish behavior
- Builds a fear-based culture
- Reveals favoritism
- Ignores and Devalues good behaviors

RIGHT UP

- Proactive
- Seeks to correct behavior
- Builds a success-based culture
- Avoids favoritism
- Affirms and Appreciates good behaviors

LEADERSHIP

CORRECTIVE COUNSELING DO'S

- Encourage people to monitor their own behaviors
- Teach people to own their behaviors and their choices
- Create a model for supervisors to give appropriate feedback
- Motivate and Engage employees

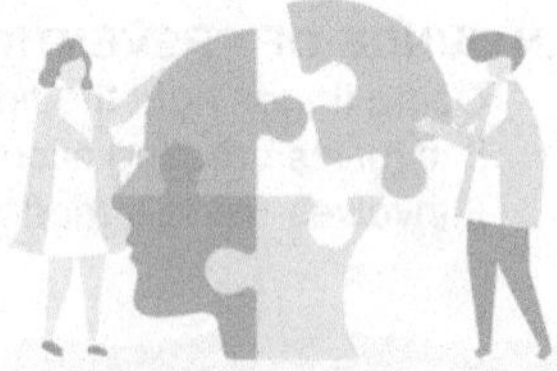

LEADERSHIP

A FEW THINGS TO REMEMBER

- You control your emotions. Don't ~~lose~~ give up control of your temper
- Hit things head-on
- Don't play therapist… focus on work
- Create behavior ownership within the mind of the employee

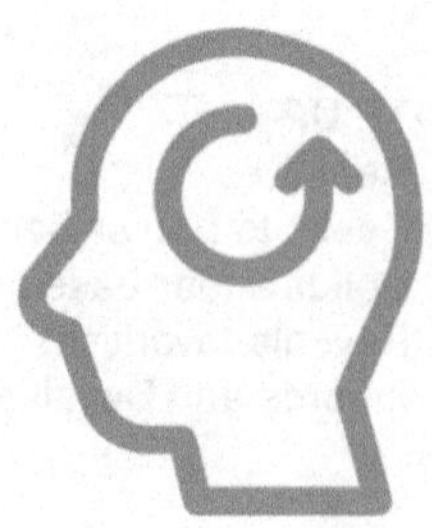

LEADERSHIP

DEFENSIVENESS VERSUS COOPERATION

DEFENSIVENESS

- It is about the person and proving a point
- It is about being right
- It is aggressive
- The boss tells
- The symptom is dealt with
- External attribution

COOPERATION

- It is about behaviors and outcomes
- It is about getting it right
- It is assertive
- The leader guides
- The problem is solved
- Internal attribution

LEADERSHIP

DEFENSIVE TACTICS

DEFENSIVE TACTICS	SPEAKER	EXAMPLE
POWER PLAY	BOSS	"Finish this report by month's end or lose your promotion."
PUT DOWN	BOSS	"A capable manager would already be done with this report."
LABELING (NEGATIVE ATRIBUTION)	BOSS	"You must be a slow learner. Your report is still not done?"
RAISING DOUBTS	BOSS	"How can I trust you, Chris, if you can't finish an easy report?"

LEADERSHIP

MORE DEFENSIVE TACTICS

Defensive Tactic	Speaker	Example
Misleading Information	Employee	"Morgan has not reviewed with me the information I need for the report." [Morgan left Chris with a copy of the report.]
Scapegoating	Employee	"Morgan did not give me input until just today."
Hostile Jokes	Employee	"You can't be serious! The report isn't that important."
Deception	Employee	"I gave it to the secretary. Did she lose it?"

LEADERSHIP

REMAINING COOPERATIVE / NON-DEFENSIVE

- The speaker is centered, calm, and focused on positive outcomes
- Speaker keeps control of their emotions and their non-verbals
- Listener feels accepted rather than rejected
- The goal is success AND relationship

LEADERSHIP

RULES OF ENGAGEMENT

- Define the situation
- Ask the 3 questions
- Listen to understand
- Redirect
- Set ownership for any outcome with the employee
- Low tones, calm voice, controlled non-verbal expression, non-emotional

Questions or Comments...

JODY HOLLAND

8 GOAL SETTING FOR SUCCESS

Most supervisors have struggled with how to set effective goals for themselves, their departments, and with their people. The science of setting and tracking goals isn't elusive. In fact, it is pretty straight-forward. It does, however, require self-discipline for the goals to mean anything. It also requires the establishing of the right habit-loops in order to make success automatic.

The premise of success in goal-setting is to effectively THINK about what you are doing and what goal you wish to achieve. By utilizing the right model of success and managing both the thoughts and the behaviors with goal-setting, it is significantly easier to achieve your end-game. Far too many people never set themselves up for success. They simply snatch a goal from the air and then lay it down somewhere. Towards the end of the year or as the original deadline gets close, they sort through all of the thoughts and notes they had taken and find the goal, unattended, with virtually no progress towards its attainment. Then, they work like crazy for a week or two in order to eliminate their guilt about not working on it all year. After a short push, they give up on the goal and say… Well, I tried but there just wasn't enough time.

The number 1 killer of goals is procrastination. For a great video on this, check out Tim Urban at: http://bit.ly/urbantnow. People put things off until later, whenever that is, in hopes that the goal will magically begin working on itself. It doesn't happen though. Goals don't accomplish themselves. Goals also don't magically happen at the end of the timeframe that had been set for them. Goals happen because of consistent daily effort towards their attainment. Procrastination is the false belief that waiting until later will somehow be more effective than acting right now. Procrastinate, as a word, came about in the 1580's from the Latin procrastinatus. It literally means to put off until tomorrow. The challenge is that we never reach tomorrow. We live only in today, in this moment. There is no future. There is no past. There is only now. So, the question that I would have you ask yourself is…

When would NOW be a good time to take action on my goals?

Before we start discussing goal-setting, however, it is important to know what setting a goal does for you versus reacting to the world around you. Goal-setting helps to shape your thoughts. When you have a goal for your future, you begin to filter your present actions through the lens of that goal. For example, if you are trying to add 12 new clients this year, you will think about playing around on social media for an hour differently. You will think about the fact that you need to spend time connecting with people in order to get them to want to do business with you. You will realize that playing on social media is NOT going to do that for you. So, you will pick up the phone and begin calling your contacts instead of messing around. When there is a goal in front of you, you think about what you are doing right now and how that will impact your ability to make it to the goal. This act of self-regulating is one of the most critical factors that distinguishes people who are successful from people who are not.

Success in life, in business, in relationships, in any endeavor is based on understanding how to map and monitor your day. The ability to win in life requires you to operate with a goal mind-set. The following components of goal-setting will help you to stay on TARGET.

Think

T – Think from the end to the beginning. This allows you to map out an exact timeframe and account for the amount of time that will be required. It also enables you to schedule out that time in the proper increments. This component of goal-setting is known as reverse planning and it is the first critical step to you being successful.

Let's say, for example, that you have 50 customers that you serve. You want to grow your business by 20% this year, or end the year with a net 10 new customers. You lose an average of 10% of your customers on a yearly basis, or this year, an estimated 5 customers. This means that you will need to add 15 new customers and only lose 5. You will need to think about how many presentations it takes to bring on a new customer and how long the average customer acquisition cycle is. Let's say that it takes 5 presentations to bring on 1 new customer (national average) and it takes an average of 60 days to close a new customer. This means that all of your sales will need to be initiated on or before October 31st of the year. You will then need to think about how many contacts (phone or in person) it takes to move a potential customer into the category of prospect and into the sales pipeline. Let's say that it takes 10 contacts to get one presentation. This means that you will need to make 50 contacts for every 1 new client that you bring on. If the goal is 15 new clients, then you will need to make 750 contacts to achieve your goal and you will need to do that in the first 10 months of the year. Now that we have our number related to mapping out our daily behaviors, we go backwards. We need to make 75 contacts per month, or 18.75 per week, or 4.69 per day at 4 days per week of contacting people. For the ease of implementation, and since you probably only know whole people, let's say 5 contacts per day, 4 days per week, and 2 to 3 presentations per week. Following this simple daily formula, you are able to think from the end (15 new clients) to the beginning (daily behaviors).

For most people, the tough part is thinking in abstract terms of business growth. Once you are able to break it down to what you need to do on a daily basis, you are able to eliminate the guesswork. You then have a solid plan for what needs to happen in order to achieve the success you are looking for. You can work any goal in this same manner. Whether you are looking to reduce turnover, improve morale, cut expenses, increase revenues, or any other goal, starting with the end in mind and then breaking it down will create a roadmap of what needs to happen quarterly, then monthly, then weekly, then daily. When we manage our daily behaviors, we are prepared to find success.

Assess

A – Assess you skills and skill-gaps related to achieving the goal. You can only do what you can do. You will need to be honest about what you abilities are and what you are missing. If you are missing a skill, can you learn it? If you can't learn it, can you recruit it? Regardless of whether it is you or another person that will be implementing the skills, it is critical to have a realistic view of who you are and where you are.

The first step in the process is to map out the skills that are required for the specific goal that you are trying to accomplish. For example, if the objective is to reduce turnover, you will need to know what people who have successfully reduced turnover know. You will need to map out the skills that they possess in order to understand what has been done. You will want to be as thorough as possible on listing out the skills. Talk with folks who have accomplished the same goal in the past. Ask them what they had to learn along the way in order to accomplish the goal. Write out everything that they had to learn and the skills that they believe they already had that are relevant as well.

The second step in the process is to compare the skills that you have mastered to the skills on the list. You are looking for places where your skills are missing compared to the skills of an already successful person in that area. If you have a familiarity with a skill, then mark that you are at a level 1 out of 5 on that skill. If you have completely mastered the skill, then mark that you are at a 5 out of 5 on that skill. It is critically important that you be honest about your actual skill level. If you are not that great at seeing your own short-comings, then recruit a very honest friend to help evaluate where you are at. You have to be very honest on this though. If you are not honest in your self-reflection, the likelihood of you finding your success is greatly diminished.

The third step in the process is to map out three places that you can learn each of the missing skills. These can be learning from mentors, reading books and learning, going to seminars, searching the web, etc. The key is to accurately identify the places that you can learn those skills. If there is a cost associated with any of the places, map out the cost. If there are restrictions to you accessing the information, map that out as well. When you create a clear path to the knowledge, the obstacles tend to fall out of your way.

The fourth step is to go after the skills and information that are missing. You identified what was missing, where it could be found, and who could help you get there, now act on it! Each step is critical, but the first three are pointless without this step. You must take action to fill in the gaps in your knowledge and abilities. Without action, everything else was a waste.

Recruit

R – Recruit the talent that is needed to achieve the goal. People generally don't succeed in a vacuum. They have help from coworkers, friends, and even from the collective wisdom of books, seminars, training, etc. Whatever is missing from your tool belt, or whatever you need assistance with, recruit it early! One of the greatest mistakes that I see made in business is to hire the "cheapest person" that you can find. In hiring, when the focus is on hiring a person for as little money as possible, they are often worth less to you in the end. Hiring should be done with the idea of hiring a superstar. When a NBA team is recruiting a new top performing player, they don't go out and look for the player that costs them the least. They go out and find the player that will bring them the most and then pay them as well as they can. In business, when you recruit talent and pay them as much as you can, you can expect more from them.

When you hire a new person, you want to identify whether or not they actually fit within your organization. Fit is all about the person aligning with the belief structure of the organization and their behavioral makeup meshing with that of your other team members. For clarification here, behavioral makeup refers to the way in which a person portrays themselves based on their personality. A person may have developed their personality at a very early age and they may find it very difficult to change it, but they can control the way in which they portray that personality. If you are recruiting someone to help you, or to work for you and/or the team, you have to make sure that they fit with the team and believe in going in the direction of your goals. If they don't, there is no point in having them on the team, even if they are a "good person."

The success or failure of the team is dependent on the people that make up the team. Be very protective of your team. It only takes one bad person on a good team to destroy the integrity of the team. Be very slow to hire and quick to fire. Your team is the lifeblood of your ability to accomplish your goals and objectives. Over the years, I have seen quite a few brilliant ideas fail because the team was wrong. If you are like most supervisors, you have either hired or worked side by side with one of those "wrong people" as well. The cost to the team, the cost to your ability to achieve your goals, and the cost to the entire organization can be astronomical.

On the other side of that, the benefit of hiring the right person and allowing them to take you to the next level is incredible. This is the component of goal setting where "the whole is greater than the sum of the parts." In other words, when your team clicks, it can accomplish more together than you could have ever imagined accomplishing with each individual doing their very best. You build each other up. You encourage each other. You hold each other accountable. You function as an incredible team.

Give It Emotions

G – Give it emotions. Human beings are very interesting creatures. According to research conducted by Daniel Pink, in his book Drive, humans are driven by emotions more than logic. William James, considered the Father of American Psychology, said that we pursue pleasurable experiences and we avoid painful ones. All human motivation flows out of an understanding of how we make decisions related to the actions that we take. Many of us believe that we are very logical, highly evolved creatures. The reality, however, is that we are bundles of emotions that act out of either the pursuit of what we deem pleasurable or the avoidance of what we deem painful. It is the label that we give it, the meaning that we assign to it that makes the difference. When we determine that something is to be avoided, then all the logic in the world will not likely move us to action. It is taking charge of your labels, your perceptions, that allows you to modify your actions in the end.

There are essentially two sides of emotions that we will need to infuse into our goals. The first side is that of understanding what we, or our team, or our company, will gain if the goal is attained. You will want to make a list of all of the positive benefits of succeeding at your goal. You will want to describe, in as much detail as possible, how you will feel when you achieve your goal. It is in the building up of positive energy toward your goal that you get your team revved up for success. Once you have built up that positive energy, you will need to back-fill your emotions with reasons why you cannot stay where you are as a team. You will accomplish this by creating a list of all of the drawbacks of staying the same, what you will lose, and what it will cost. You want to describe, in as much detail as possible, how awful you will feel if you do NOT hit your goals. The stacking of emotions on top of one another helps to ensure that you stay focused on the end game. Keep both the positive emotions towards the attainment of your goal and the negative emotions towards remaining the same in front of you.

Never forget "why" you are pursuing your goals. Far too many executives spend their time talking about the goal itself, or how the goal will be achieved, and too little time talking about why the goal is important. People work for the emotional charge that they get from being a part of something incredible. You have the opportunity to provide that for them in the form of accomplishing something that truly matters.

Eyes Wide Open

E – Eyes wide open – A great number of people will enter into the goal attainment process without a real picture of what is happening around them. They will often overlook the measurables that exist in the process. They will think only of what the end goal is and not of what the subset of goals are. Imagine playing a sport at a professional level and getting your team pumped up before the start of the game. You have the energy, the drive, the passion to win the game and achieve another victory. Then, you head out to do battle and realize very quickly that the scoreboards have been removed. You ask the official why there isn't a score and they tell you, "Don't worry about it. I will tell you who won in the end." You play your best, but never know if you have scored, if the other team has scored, or what the heck is going on. You desperately want to succeed, as does the other team. You make it to half-time and head to the locker room. You don't know if you are supposed to inspire them to do better or praise them for being ahead. So, you do nothing. You head back out for the second half of play and do your very best. Once the game is over, the official comes over to you and says, "Sorry, you guys lost." You want to know by how much, at what point you were behind, and how you could have won, but they offer nothing more. All you know is that it didn't work out the way that you had hoped.

That is exactly what it is like for far too many people in business. They see at the end of the year whether they won or not. However, they don't have any idea at the end of the first quarter, at half-time for the business year, or at any other time what is going on. They would have changed strategies at various points throughout the year if they had known things weren't going well. They would have reinforced strategies at other times if they had known what was working. Just like any other incredible game, business is won or lost by being fully aware of where you are in the moment related to where you want to be for your end game. Keep your team fully informed and you stay fully informed of where you are in relationship to your objectives. The more informed you are, the better decisions you and the team will be able to make. Make sure that everyone is aware of who is supposed to do what, by when and with what outcomes.

Map out the incremental steps along the pathway to success. Assign components of accomplishment to each player on your team and equip them with the tools and resources to get the job done. In the very beginning, and a few times throughout the year, conduct a "pre-mortum" on your goals. Sit down with the team and role play as if the goal was not met and identify why the goal wasn't met. Look at every reason that could prevent you and the team from achieving your objectives. By doing this, you can open up the discussion and create contingency plans to overcome any challenge. This model of contingency thinking will help prepare you and the team for any obstacle that might come your way. Don't skip this step. It is critical that you are brutally honest about what could possibly go wrong and aggressive as a team about coming up with strategies to make sure that those challenges can be overcome.

Talk About Your Goal

T – Talk about the goal in front of others. There is little that is more influential in achieving a goal than knowing that you will have to "eat crow" in front of your respected peers, colleagues and mentors if you miss the mark. When you know that you will have to answer for what happened, for why you chose not to do what was necessary to achieve your goal, you build up significantly more momentum towards the attainment of the goal. Talk about your goal in front of your coworkers. Talk about your goal in front of your mentors. Talk about your goal in front of your family. Talk about your goal and how incredible it will be to achieve it as often as you can.

Talking about it and owning the responsibility to achieve it creates personal accountability for the goal. It makes it where you can't simply back down or walk away when things get tough. It builds your personal resolve and your team resolve to hit your targets. It keeps the discussion of where you are in comparison to the goal in front of you at all times.

With your team, dream about how incredible it will be to attain the goal. Talk about it in present tense, as if it has already been achieved. Talk about the way that you and the team will feel upon succeeding at the goal. Talk about why the goal is important. Talk about where you are, what is missing, and what is up next for achieving the goal. When you talk about it regularly, you cannot forget the goal or the process for achieving it. Stay on target by keeping your goal(s) forever in front of you.

Let's practice for a moment on mapping out a goal. Your mission, should you choose to accept it, is to identify one specific goal that you have and follow the steps in the process to outline the goal. You can use the following worksheet to accomplish this.

Goal Statement	
Description of Goal	
Positive Emotional Reasons for Goal	
Negative Emotional Consequences for Staying The Same	
Daily Behaviors That Will Help Me Achieve The Goal	
Measurement Points For Goal	
Things To Watch Out For And Overcome	

Give a person a bow and arrow and tell them to shoot. They will always want to know... At what?

Learn2Lead
Supervise · Influence · Motivate

LEADERSHIP

LEARNING OBJECTIVES

Develop the right attitude that is required for setting and achieving goals

How to find your "why" for success

Building the right TARGET for success

How to create SMART goal statements

How to create balance in your goal setting

What can keep you from achieving your goals

LEADERSHIP

GOAL SETTING FOR SUCCESS

Success is the ability to go from one failure to another with no loss of enthusiasm.

Winston Churchill

LEADERSHIP

ALL SUCCESS BEGINS WITH THE END

Success is about creating the right image of the end in one's mind and then working from the end to the beginning.

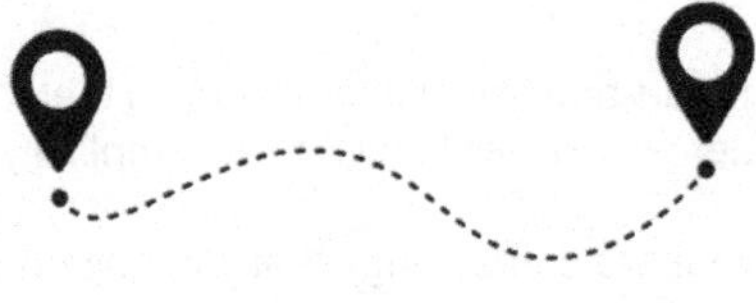

LEADERSHIP

ACHIEVING SIGNIFICANCE

To achieve anything of significance, we must work for purpose and with purpose. It is action backed by emotion and supported with daily behaviors that leads to ultimate success.

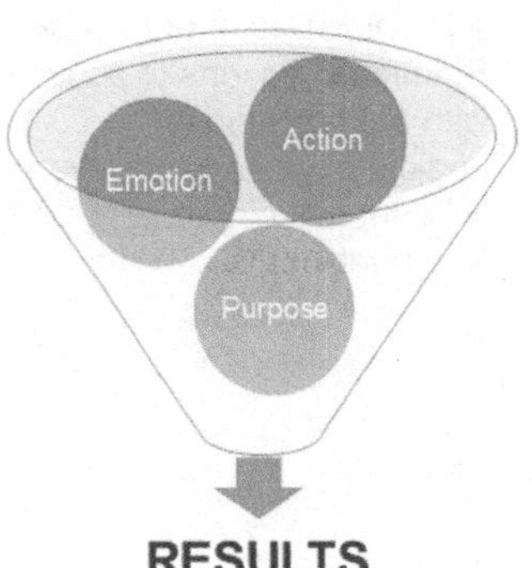

LEADERSHIP

THE BIGGEST GOAL KILLER IS...

PROCRASTINATION...

The art and science of assuming that there will be plenty of time later (whenever that is) to accomplish your goals.

What are some things that you have procrastinated on?

LEADERSHIP

WHAT ELEMENTS DRIVE US?

- A Burning Desire or Focused Obsession
- Emotional reasons to achieve the goal and the pain associated with not reaching it.
- Logical reasons to achieve the goal and the pain associated with not reaching it.
- The right inputs...

LEADERSHIP

THINK & GROW RICH

If you think you're beaten, you are.
If you think you dare not, you don't.
If you like to win, but you think you can't
it's almost certain you won't.
If you think you will lose, you lost.
It's all in the state of mind.
You have to be sure of yourself
before you ever win a prize.

The man who wins is the man who thinks he can.

Learn2Lead
Supervise · Influence · Motivate

LEADERSHIP

SUCCESS IS THE BYPRODUCT

Happiness, wealth, and success are the byproducts of goal setting. They cannot be the goal themselves.

--Dennis Waitley

Learn2Lead
Supervise · Influence · Motivate

LEADERSHIP

SETTING GOALS FOR SUCCESS

"Setting goals is the first step in turning the invisible into the visible."

--Tony Robbins

Learn2Lead
Supervise · Influence · Motivate

LEADERSHIP

WHO'S DRIVING YOUR CAR?

Learn2Lead
Supervise · Influence · Motivate

LEADERSHIP

T.A.R.G.E.T.

LEADERSHIP

T – THINK FROM THE END

Think from the end to the beginning.

End Goal
Steps To Get There
Time Required
Scheduled out time
Start Date

LEADERSHIP

PICTURE THE PRESENT

Picture what the business is like when you get everything right!

Write out what you have already accomplished one year from today as if it is already done.

Draw a picture of what your world now looks like.

LEADERSHIP

GOAL TIMEFRAMES

Short Term	–	Quarterly
Annual	–	Each Fiscal Year
Mid Range	–	1 to 5 Years
Long Range	–	5 to 10 Years
Future Cast	–	Beyond 10 Years

LEADERSHIP

A – ASSESS YOUR SKILLS AND SKILL GAPS

LEADERSHIP

R – RECRUIT THE TALENT/INSIGHT NEEDED

LEADERSHIP

G – GIVE IT EMOTIONS

Learn 2 Lead
Supervise · Influence · Motivate

LEADERSHIP

E – EYES WIDE OPEN

Learn 2 Lead
Supervise · Influence · Motivate

LEADERSHIP

T – TALK ABOUT YOUR GOAL

LEADERSHIP

GOAL STATEMENT

✓ Short Term	Quarterly
✓ Annual	Each Fiscal Year
✓ Mid Range	1 to 5 Years
✓ Long Range	5 to 10 Years
✓ Future Cast	Beyond 10 Years

LEADERSHIP

SPECIFIC

Fuzzy is… I want to be more successful.

Specific is… I want to increase revenues by 22%.

LEADERSHIP

MEASURABLE

Fuzzy… I want to make more money by bringing in new clients.

Specific is… I want to increase revenues by 22% by adding 4 new clients.

Learn2Lead

LEADERSHIP

ACTION-DRIVEN

Fuzzy… I want to make more money by bringing in new clients through outreach.

Specific… I want to increase revenues by 22% by brining in 4 new clients. This will take 16 face to face presentations and 48 outreach calls.

Learn2Lead
Supervise · Influence · Motivate

LEADERSHIP

REALISTIC

Unrealistic… I will make 100 connected calls on Monday and will close 4 new deals by Friday.

Realistic… I will make 2 to 3 connected calls per day for 20 business days and will present to 4 potential customers per week.

LEADERSHIP

TIME-DEFINED

Wrong… I want to bring in new clients as soon as possible.

Right… I will bring in 1 new client per week for 4 weeks by following my daily plan.

LEADERSHIP

The Goal Statement

The goal statement must be clear and concise. It must outline what will be done, by when, by whom, and with what measurable outcome. It cannot leave any room for doubt.

LEADERSHIP

HOW DO YOU EAT AN ELEPHANT?

LEADERSHIP

OBSTACLES

"Obstacles are those frightful things that you see when you take your eyes off the prize."

--Henry Ford

LEADERSHIP

THE WRITTEN WORD

There is power in the written word. When we write out our goals and share them with others, we commit at a subconscious level.

The written word develops certainty. Certainty initiates action!

GOAL SETTING EXERCISE

FOUR QUADRANTS

LIFE	YEAR
MONTH	WEEK

TODAY:

____

____

____

____

____

____

____

____

____

Learn2Lead

LEADERSHIP

QUESTIONS TO ANSWER

- Do you know where you will be in the future and what point in the future that is?
- Have you identified what your most important daily behaviors are?
- Are you spending your time today in a way that will most likely get you where you wish to be in the future?
- Have you accepted control of your life and your choices?

LEADERSHIP

TAKE ACTION NOW

"In any moment of decision, the best thing you can do is the right thing. The next best thing you can do is the wrong thing. The worst think you can do is nothing."

LEADERSHIP

ACHIEVING GOALS

- Know your starting point and desired end point
- Identify your resources, skills, and skill-gaps
- Identify your partners and recruit more if needed
- Use Positive and Negative emotions as anchors
- Make a plan
  - Plan for the obstacles
  - Make a timeline
- Measure progress
- Talk about your drive to keep more pressure on yourself
- Celebrate success at each level

LEADERSHIP

Hitting Homeruns With Goals

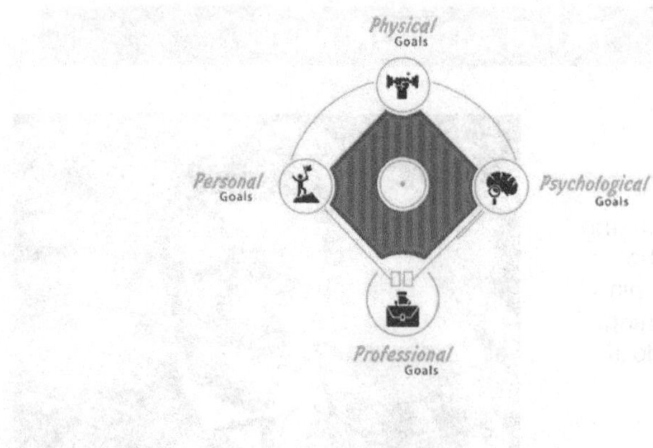

REASONS THAT PEOPLE FAIL AT ACHIEVING THEIR GOALS

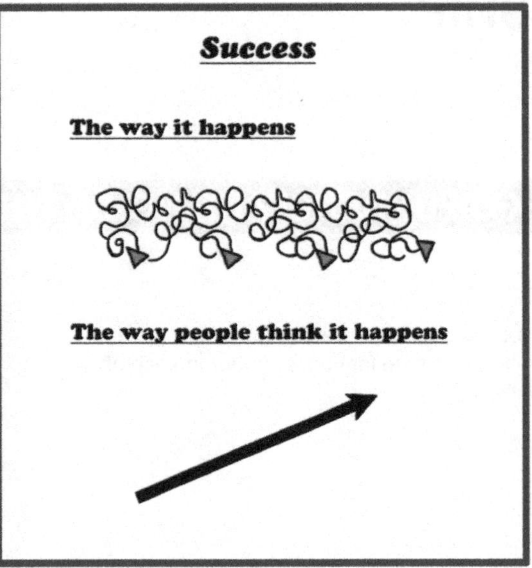

LEADERSHIP

FEAR OF SUCCESS OR FAILURE

We can either have our excuses or our actions.
People often fail because they are afraid of what it would mean if they tried.
Success means being different.
Failure means being inadequate.

Or does it?

LEADERSHIP

LACK OF UNDERSTANDING OF THE PROCESS

Goals are not a one-time thing. Setting goals is a process of creating a continuous plan for improvement in each of the domains of life.

LEADERSHIP

LACK OF COMMITMENT

Wanting to achieve a goal and being fully committed to achieving a goal are not the same thing.
Commitment is both logical and emotional. It is a sense of certainty that supersedes logic.

LEADERSHIP

INACTIVITY

Most people will write out a goal, go through the exercise, and then back away from action.
Action and action alone moves a person toward their goal.
Setting a goal simply starts the engine.
Put your life in Overdrive with action.

Learn2Lead
Supervise · Influence · Motivate

LEADERSHIP

PARALYSIS BY ANALYSIS

People will often spend so much time trying to research all of the possibilities that they paralyze themselves. They look for all the reasons that things might not work and that keeps them from trying in the first place.

Learn2Lead
Supervise · Influence · Motivate

LEADERSHIP

LACK OF A REAL DESTINATION

A real destination is about who you wish to become, not what you wish to have.
To achieve anything of real significance, you have to become the success that you wish to achieve and then behave as if.

LEADERSHIP

NO ACTION PLAN

People will often create a desired end result without reverse planning to determine the amount of time and the specific behaviors required of them.
It is in planned action that we find success, not in simply having a plan.

LEADERSHIP

TOO MANY PLANS / GOALS

If we do not narrow our focus, we will be overwhelmed and will stop working because we are too distracted, too misguided, and too confused.
Pick your primary end game.
Be the best at one thing!

LEADERSHIP

INSECURITY

Until we become the success that we seek, our minds will find a way to destroy the progress.
People fail more often because of self-sabotage than any other reason!

LEADERSHIP

LACK OF MOTIVATION TO CHANGE

Have you ever thought, this is my lot in life; it's not a lot but it is my life. When good enough becomes truly good enough, we stop attempting to grow, develop, and succeed at the next level.

BE AGILE – BE SUCCESSFUL

LEADERSHIP

THE WORLD IS CONSTANTLY SHIFTING

- Your approach to achieving success will necessarily have to change.
- Your goal plans are a living document.
- Stay focused on the end game, not the short game.
- Change deadlines if you have to, or approaches if you have to, but stay focused on achieving success.

LEADERSHIP

A SUCCESSFUL LIFE

My Wage by Jessie Rittenhouse

I bargained with Life for a penny,
And Life would pay no more,
However I begged at evening
When I counted my scanty store;

For Life is a just employer,
He gives you what you ask,
But once you have set the wages,
Why, you must bear the task.

I worked for a menial's hire,
Only to learn, dismayed,
That any wage I had asked of Life,
Life would have gladly paid!

9 PROBLEM SOLVING

Problem solving is not about being good at finding problems. It isn't about being good at seeing other people's mistakes. It isn't about being a perfectionist. It really isn't even just about solving problems. Problem solving is really about being good at fulfilling needs. It is about being able to see what is missing. We only know that a problem exists when we have a need that is not being met. It is that need that isn't being met that triggers the response in us that says, "Hey, this is a problem and I need to fix it."

We have to keep in mind that what is a problem for one person may not be a problem for another person. Think back to the chapter on conflict resolution. In that chapter, you learned that you confront someone because your needs are not being met. You don't confront them because their needs are out of alignment. Instead, it is about you. As an organization, as a department, even as just you, the supervisor, you must clearly figure out what you need. This means outlining what you actually should be pursuing, and then identifying what is missing. This positons you to be successful in solving problems. For any goal that is not being met, there is a problem that needs to be solved. For any challenge that is preventing success, there is a problem that needs to be solved.

3 Basic Responses

There are three basic responses that come up when problems arise at work. Some supervisors will immediately blame others. Some will accept the situation and either attempt to fix it or try to learn to simply deal with it. Others will measure what is going on in order to make a more informed decision. The BAM (Blame Accept Measure) mentality is what drives problem-solving in most companies. Taking a look at each of these areas, only one of them serves very little value and we will deal with that one first.

Blaming others for what has happened without searching for a solution is pointless. This seems happen with the largest portion of supervisors, however. As young employees, many of us witnessed our supervisors and bosses looking around feverishly for someone, besides themselves, to blame when something went wrong. They point a finger at the HR director when someone is hired who doesn't fit, even though they demanded a hire be made within 24 hours, no matter what. They blame department managers for not meeting their budgets and demand an immediate reduction, even though they were often following what they were directed to do. At times, this demand is made despite the fact that quality standards cannot be met on the lowered amount of money. On a "ropes course," also known as an outdoor adventure course, there is an ugly monster that shows up when something goes wrong. This monster chants Boo Loo Ah Moo Eee and it destroys the integrity of the team. It takes away from performance and it diminishes trust. Essentially, the BLAME monster is better at destroying the performance of a team and stopping problem-solving than any other monster out there.

Other supervisors will **Accept** the problem as it is and either solve it or try to exist in the midst of it. No forward progress happens unless the reality of the situation is first accepted. This means that you look at the problem for what it is. It is the unsuccessful execution of duties on the job. It is doing your job but not achieving the results because some component of the job is missing. On the first side of this response sits the supervisor that says, "We are in a mess, and now it is time to fix it." The other side of this response is accepting without changing. It is looking at the situation and saying things like, "Well, we are no worse than industry norms." This is one that is often said in relationship to turnover as well as to customer satisfaction. Accepting the reality that there is a problem and that a need exists because of that is the first step. The second step in a good response is to choose to be a person of action. In Andy Andrew's book The Traveler's Gift, (http://bit.ly/travgiftaa) he tells the story of Joshua Chamberlain. This is a lesser know figure from the American Civil War who turned the tide of the war by living under one simple principle. The principle, according to Andrews, is that "I will be a person of action." I may not know the right answer. I may not be the most prepared. But, I will do something. I will not sit around and hope for things to change because hope alone is not a strategy.

The third common response to a problem is to **measure** the problem. The component of measurement has advanced by incredible leaps and bounds since the year 2000. The advancement of big data and the application of that data for decision-making has changed the playing field when it comes to solving problems. In the past, it was common for organizations to have a little information and then take action to solve a problem. Often times, they would end up solving the wrong problem on the first, and often on the second try. They would have limited information and then act upon that incomplete information. The use of data and data analysis has turned the tides on understanding trends, habits, processes, and ultimately on understanding the nature and cause of problems. Charles Duhigg, in his book The Power of Habit, discusses the use of data to predict shopper trends, gambling habits, decision-making, and virtually everything else that drives us. Measuring what is going on and creating a true and measurable picture of the situation enables a supervisor, or an organization, to solve the right problem armed with the right information.

Types of Data

There are really only two types of data that we gather. Regardless of whether you are conducting surveys, interviews, or measuring numerically categorized output, the two types of data cover them all. Very seldom do small and medium sized companies ever make it to the category of a large and successful organization until they master the art of data. Data must be collected. It must be cleaned up to ensure that it is accurate. It must be categorized and organized to ensure that it is properly mapped. And, it must be challenged or tested. The right process of data collection must be followed in order to ensure that the data is fit for the problem-solving process. When done right, the predictability of the data is truly explosive.

The first type of data is qualitative in nature. Qualitative refers to subjective opinion, conversation, or any other format of information gathered that cannot be tied to a numeric value. This type of data can be extremely useful, particularly for identifying causes to relational challenges. One way to add a quantitative aspect to qualitative data is through the use of word clouds. A word cloud, sometimes called a "wordle", is a measure of how many times a particular word or phrase is used. It helps to quickly identify themes in the responses of those that are sharing the information. Qualitative data is used most commonly when it comes to solving problems related to both people and systems, when data streams have not been tracked.

The second type of data that exists is quantitative data. This is the data that often excites the statisticians of the world. It is concrete, numeric, measurable, and more easily proven to be accurate or inaccurate. This type of data is the measurement of performance output. It is the measurement of turnover in the workplace. It is the measurement of virtually anything that can be calculated, tracked, organized, and processed. Quantitative data is used for most aspects of decision making. It is used for statistical analysis and it is used to prove points. Often times, quantitative data is considered more accurate. However, I have found that the qualitative data leads to an understanding that is more driven by the group, rather than by the person doing the research.

Data Analysis Versus Data Interpretation

Data analysis is the collection and summarizing of the data that has been collected. During this component of problem solving, you are gathering the information and trying to determine the direction that the data is taking you. When you listen to the data and allow some of your preconceived notions to take a back seat, you will find that there are themes that emerge. In order to be successful at this, you will need to follow three easy steps. To remember it, it is outlined in a simple acronym. BET – You will want to hedge your bets in solving problems in order to have the greatest advantage.

B – Become familiar with the data. You accomplish this by reading through the data (particularly qualitative) and making notes or memos about what you are seeing emerge. The more familiar you are with the data, the easier it will be to see the patterns.

E – Examine the data and ensure that you have a clear understanding of the setting, the participants, and the activities that were going on with and around the person. This examination helps to put findings into context and ensure greater understanding.

T – Themes unlock the patterns. When you categorize and code the data, you will begin to see various themes arise in the data. These themes reveal the truth about your findings and help you to understand where the data wanted you to go in the first place.

The data interpretation portion is what comes next. In this portion of discovery, you are looking for the messages that are in the data. In order to do this, you will need to answer four (4) questions.

1. What is important in the data? When you have been able to unlock the themes in the data, you will begin to draw conclusions, see what is missing, and uncover the information that has always been there, but has been buried under layers of pointless information and hidden from your view.
2. Why is that important? In order to know that there will be a direction that emerges from the data, you will need to understand why the themes are important in the data. You take the areas that are important and you relate them to your goals and objectives at work. This creates a stronger "why" and gives the process a solid direction.
3. What can be learned from it? This is the component where you have to keep your mind open. You have to be open to learning things that may go against the "accepted norm" for behaviors. Keep in mind that at one point, the American Dental Association recommended that you eat a spoon full of sugar every day to keep your teeth healthy. It wasn't until the effects of sugar were studied that they realized that they were giving advice contrary to the truth.

What is the data prompting me to do? The idea behind researching problems is to discover needs. Once you have discovered the need, you will be better prepared to take direct action. It is only in acting that we make a difference. Use what you learn from the data in order to make a new decision and move forward.

Albert Einstein once defined insanity as doing the same thing over and over again and expecting a different result. Data provides you with the opportunity to do something new, to find a new result, and to have the justification to act in this new direction. Newton said that an object in motion tends to stay in motion unless acted upon by an outside force. This is true of our businesses as well. When we develop momentum in a specific direction, we will tend to continue down that path until we have new information and a new direction that results in new actions. Data helps provide the guidance system to move us in that right direction.

If you always do what you've always done, you will always get what you've always gotten. So, if you want to have what you have never had, you will have to do what you've never done. Calculated change is what propels our businesses towards greater heights of success. Now that you understand what you are gathering and what to do with it, the next step is to follow the process. By operating inside of a problem-solving process, you create greater levels of objectivity.

The Problem Solving Process

The problem solving process, itself, has five (5) steps that must be followed. When the focus is on the process, the outcomes are more predictable. When the focus is on the outcomes, the process isn't followed and, consequently, the outcomes are no longer predictable. Complex problems will always have simple, easy to understand, wrong answers. To avoid those wrong answers, the process must be in place and followed. Each step along the path requires you to be honest and to let down your guard. Dealing with reality instead of the illusion of perfection positions you and your organization for success. Never forget that the objective is to meet a need. It is not to protect your former decisions. When you made that decision, you made it with all of the information that you had at the time. Armed with new information, and with valid data, you are best prepared to make the right new decision now. Use what you have… now!

Step 1: State The Need As You See It

S – State the need as you see it. In this first step in the problem solving process, you are identifying the reality of the situation. It is incredibly important to get past the discussion of the symptoms of the problem and focus on what it is that you need now. When the focus is on the need instead of the problem, you will focus on the pathway to the fulfillment of that need. When the focus is on the problem, you will only splinter off into more problems. The objective isn't to blame anyone for where you are or defend how you got there once you begin the process. You have already gathered your data. You have already looked at the situation and know the path that was followed to get where you are. The objective now is to get to a better place. When you state the need, be as specific as possible. Identify what the end result is that you are looking for, by what time, and with what measurable result. You are looking at where you are now, or what you have been, versus where you intend to be, or what you want. Make sure that you clearly define the need. As an example…

You are a top level executive with the Holland Marker Company and we have been struggling to stay afloat the last couple of years. We have one person that is in charge of monitoring and filling the ink reservoirs used for placing the ink inside of the markers before they are sealed. Our ink specialist did not pay attention for an entire week and we produced 1 million markers with no ink in them. They are metal markers and are crimped closed. This makes it too costly to take them apart and add ink back in. We can't throw them away because we would go out of business from that extra waste. Our need is to find a way to make at least $1 per marker off of the 1 million markers that were produced without ink and to do so within 60 days.

When you look at your situation and identify what you need moving forward, you are ready for step 2 in the process. Note that, in that example, we cannot go back and add in ink. We cannot throw the markers away. Those ideas represent a jump straight to conclusions. What we defined as the need is that we need to make at least $1 per marker off of the 1 million markers without ink.

Step 2: Open Up Discussions And Brainstorming

O – Open up discussions and brainstorming. This can be the most engaging step in the process, as well as the most irritating step. When done right, you will get a large quantity of ideas. Some of them will be good and some of them will be… well, very bad. Do not judge ideas in this stage, simply keep an open mind to all ideas. Your objective is to get as many ideas as possible in a specified amount of time. One of the tactics that makes the creative process work more effectively is to ensure that the group knows that there cannot be any judgment of any of the ideas presented. You will want to have a recording secretary, or someone to write down all of the ideas. Once you are ready to generate ideas you will need to agree to the following…

The ground rules for the brainstorming… Make sure that everyone is on board with not judging the ideas. Make sure that everyone participates in the generation of ideas. Encourage people to share all of their ideas, especially their bad ones (in their mind). It is often the bad ideas and the crazy ideas that spark the greatest creativity. Make sure you set a large goal for as many ideas as possible. For example, shoot for a new idea every 10 seconds for the entire time allotted for brain storming. 5 minutes should yield 30 ideas. 10 minutes should yield 60 ideas. Finally, you the supervisor should go first. It is ideal that you share the worst idea you can think of because this makes every other idea sound better in the minds of your employees.

The objective is to get everyone participating in the process of thinking of ideas to meet the need that has been presented. Lots of people have been conditioned to keep their ideas to themselves. They were called on in school and then told that their idea was bad. Or, they were called on at work and then told that they didn't have good enough ideas. You are working with them to overcome that mistrust of supervision that let them down in the past and drove home the message that they shouldn't think creatively. We want, no we need them to be creative. The better we are at this, the more we practice being creative, the easier problem solving becomes. Once you have finished your brainstorming, regardless of how many ideas you end up with, you move to step 3.

Step 3: Let Go Of What Doesn't Work

L – Let go of the things that are not moral, ethical, legal, or possible. This will leave you with a realistic set of solutions to choose from. The process of reviewing each of the ideas is fairly quick. You will have the person who recorded the ideas read the first one and then you will ask… "Based on the criteria of it having to be moral, ethical, legal, and possible, do we keep it or get rid of it?" You will likely end up with between 5 and 10 ideas that fit all four of those criteria.

Is it moral? With this question, you will want to evaluate the likelihood of you being comfortable with someone using the idea with your favorite person, your kid, your parent, or someone that you would protect at all costs. If you would not want the idea used with you or with your favorite person in the world, then it probably wouldn't pass the test.

Is it ethical? You are looking at the credibility of the company with this question. You want to evaluate whether or not you would have to bend, or even break, the truth in order to carry out the idea. If you would have to do something that "your mother wouldn't be proud of" then it isn't a good idea. For example, if you said that you were going to put one bad marker in every 5 pack of markers and just see if anyone complained, that would not be ethical. You would be sending out a bad marker without being honest about what you were doing.

Is it legal? You will now want to look at the ideas from the perspective of the law. You cannot intentionally misrepresent a product. You cannot cheat people. You cannot falsely advertise, for example, that you are selling markers with invisible or magic ink. There is no ink in them. If you have a legal department, their input in the process can be helpful. Most of the time, if it isn't ethical, it also isn't legal. On the other hand, sometimes it can be legal and not be moral or ethical. Those cases are fairly rare. Most of the laws that we have were enacted because something bad first happened and someone tried to be unethical in their business dealings.

Is it possible? Over the years, I have heard some fantastic ideas that just weren't possible with the resources that were available. You will want to closely evaluate each of the ideas to ensure that you and your team would actually be able to implement the ideas. If they are not possible with the people and/or resources that you have, then move on to the next idea. If you find that you have no ideas, move back to step 2 and try again. You should have several ideas, usually between 5 and 10 to move into step 4 of the process.

Step 4: Vet The Remaining Ideas And Implement

V – Vet the remaining ideas and choose one or a combination of them, then implement. You may choose to run your own "A-B Test" with a couple of the ideas. An A-B test is where you implement two of the ideas simultaneously and then move your attention to the idea that is working the best. Or, you may choose to take your three best ideas that compliment each other and implement them in harmony with one another. Or, you may just choose one idea and put all of your focus into that one.

Whatever you choose to do, the objective is to trim down the remaining ideas into something that you can implement and can track. When you have narrowed it down through discussion and chosen the idea or set of ideas to implement, you will need to outline the following…

1. Who will be responsible for each aspect of idea implementation?
2. How will we measure the success of the implementation?
3. What could possibly go wrong with the idea and with each step of the implementation?
4. What are our contingency plans for each part that could go wrong?
5. What is the timeframe for the implementation?

6. When will we get back together?
7. Can we all agree to be open and honest about how it is working and how we did on the implementation? In other words, we will not make any excuses.

This component of the process is the most time consuming because you are in the actual process of implementing. This could be one week, or one month, or one year, or whatever you agree on as a team. Whatever the timeframe is, make sure that you have your checkpoints set up along the way. Make sure that you know what the steps to success are and how to measure them for each person on the team. Once you have implemented and measured your progress along the way, you are ready to move to the final step… evaluation.

Step 5: Evaluate The Results And Adjust Accordingly

E – Evaluate the results and adjust accordingly. If you have built a strong team and worked on trusting one another, this step isn't that tough. If, however, you don't trust the people that you work with or they don't trust you as their supervisor, this can be a very tough thing to do. Earlier in the process, you outlined the criteria that you would use to measure the success of the implantation. It is now time to put that measurement into practice.

One of the greatest struggles that I see in businesses is the component of leaders trusting their team enough to be vulnerable. The same could be said for teammates trusting one another. Vulnerability is about being willing to admit your mistakes or shortcomings and ask for assistance from others. This only happens when you know that your team wants the very best for you and when they are not out to judge you. When you know that they are there to work with you in order to make the organization successful, then, and only then, will you open up and be vulnerable. If you have followed the process the right way, you will have already discussed what could possibly go wrong in the process and what the contingency plans would be if one of the wrong turns should occur. If, however, you have something happen that you did not anticipate, you need to be open about what it was. If each member of the team is on the same page and the objective is the success of the organization instead of just the success of one individual, then you will be able to have a solid conversation about what went wrong, establish the point where something different could have been done, and establish what you will do in the future. This process of analysis without negative blame sets the team in motion to be wildly successful.

The post-mortum evaluation needs to involve the following…

1. What were the specific steps that we actually implemented? How did these steps differ from what we outlined before the implementation process began?
2. Did we achieve the intended result in the specified timeframe? If not, at what step did things seem to go awry? Who made what decisions that changed the course of our actions or kept us from succeeding?
3. Is there anything that we could have done that would have made it more effective? If so, what would have helped, at what point in the process, and with whose involvement?
4. What can we do next time in order to be more effective?

The problem solving process requires that the team really trust one another in order to make good decisions in the right timeframe. The next two chapters will really help with ensuring that you stay on track in the process. Group Decision making (Chapter 10) will outline the process that groups follow during implementation and what typically goes well and what does not. High Performance Teams (Chapter 11) will outline the stages that teams go through in order to develop trust in one another and set their course for top performance as a team and as a company.

We can't solve our problems using the same thinking we used when we created them.
--Albert Einstein

Learn 2 Lead

LEADERSHIP

LEARNING OBJECTIVES

- What are problems and how do we define them?
- What are the advantages of addressing problems proactively?
- What are the aspects that enhance problem solving? And, what hinders it?
- How do you properly research the root causes of a problem?
- Define the Steps to Effective Problem Resolution.
- What helps us succeed or holds us back from succeeding?

Learn2Lead
Supervise · Influence · Motivate

LEADERSHIP

SO WHAT'S THE PROBLEM?

The problem with problems is that we focus on the problem and not on the solution.

Our objective is to find a solution, not to hash and rehash the problem.

We are simply identifying what is missing so we can build a bridge to success.

LEADERSHIP

WHY WOULD WE SOLVE THE PROBLEM?

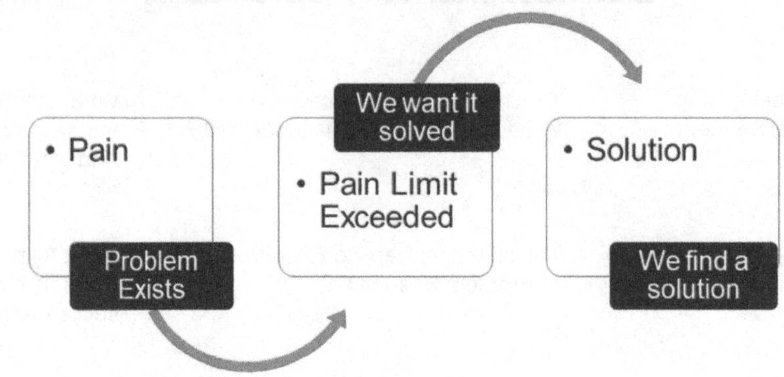

LEADERSHIP

3 RESPONSES TO PROBLEMS

- Blame – Blame someone or someone else for the existence of the problem
- Accept – Accept the problem as a fact of life and try to move on
- Measure and Act – Measure what is going on and take action

Learn2Lead

LEADERSHIP

COMPLEX PROBLEMS

COMPLEX PROBLEMS HAVE SIMPLE, EASY TO UNDERSTAND

WRONG ANSWERS!

Learn 2 Lead
Supervise · Influence · Motivate

LEADERSHIP

WHOSE OPINION DO YOU HOLD IN HIGHEST REGARD?

Learn 2 Lead
Supervise · Influence · Motivate

LEADERSHIP

OUR FOCUS

We are continuously faced with great opportunities that are brilliantly disguised as unsolvable problems.

It is not the presence of the problem that is the problem. It is where we are focusing that is the problem.

LEADERSHIP

INTERNAL VERSUS EXTERNAL

Internal Problems

- Policies and Procedures
- Leadership
- Staffing
- Retention and Engagement
- Employee Development
- Systems

External Problems

- Customer Relationships
- Product Quality
- Reputation of the Organization
- Supply and Demand
- Marketing Message
- Customer Communication

LEADERSHIP

PROBLEMS ARE A FACT OF LIFE

- Problems happen all the time.
- When they are left unattended, they can generate conflict and reduce efficiency.
- When they are not faced, they continue to grow and become more difficult.
- Given a long enough time unresolved, problems become larger than life!

LEADERSHIP

SOMETHING TO CONSIDER...

- Problems can be "gold nuggets" of opportunity.
- They are valuable pieces of information pointing us to how we can become better.
- Being a great problem-solver simplifies your life, helps your organization, and increases your circle of influence and power.

LEADERSHIP

WHAT YOU SEE IS WHAT YOU LOOK FOR

- Things go wrong… so that they can go better
- Bosses and coworkers are not perfect… so that we will grow
- Things get lost… so that we will have a better system to organize
- Customers complain… so that we will innovate
- We have turnover… so that we will hire and train better

LEADERSHIP

ARE YOU MINING FOR GOLD?

- Each problem you solve is like finding a treasure leading to greater success.
- Each problem that you identify represents a major opportunity.
- We continue to pick away at the surface in order to ensure that problems are continuously dealt with.
- Shift your perspective and you shift your experience.

LEADERSHIP

THINGS THAT HINDER PROBLEM SOLVING

- Closed-minded attitudes
- Complacency
- Preconceived ideas
- Focus on the urgent without regard for the important
- Crisis management and firefighting
- Silo-thinking
- Short-sighted focus
- Groupthink

LEADERSHIP

FIXATED ON THE PAST

We often become fixated on using the same solutions that we have used before… even when they have not worked.

We often become fixated on doing what we have always done… even when we have never measured the success of our past efforts.

LEADERSHIP

THINK ABOUT YOUR THINKING

- Metacognition is the process of thinking about what you are thinking about.
- How problems are stated and/or presented will impact the resolution of that problem.
- Problems must be explored from every angle while keeping the focus on the need instead of the problem.

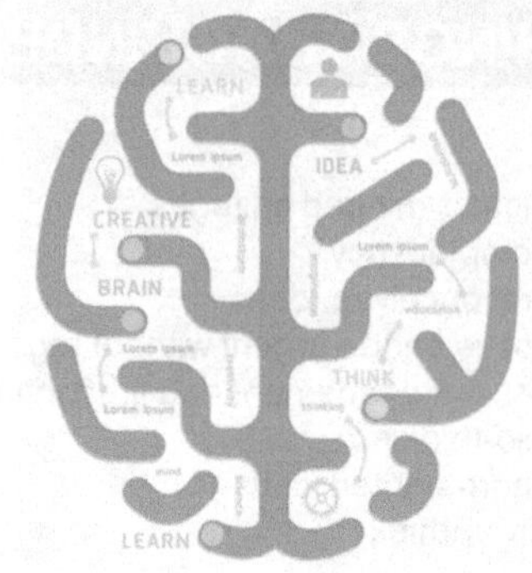

What process will help us move from problem to resolution?

WHAT IS PROBLEM SOLVING?

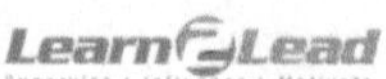

LEADERSHIP

PROBLEM SOLVING IS...

Any method by which fitting solutions are determined within a reasonable time-frame, with an acceptable expenditure of resources.

Learn2Lead
Supervise · Influence · Motivate

LEADERSHIP

WHAT IS PROBLEM SOLVING?

- Problem solving is the mental process that occurs when people work toward determining the solution to a problem.
- Problem solving is the shift in focus from the problem to what is needed.
- Problem solving helps us to discover what has been missing.

Learn2Lead
Supervise · Influence · Motivate

LEADERSHIP

DEFINITIONS MATTER

- **Well-Defined Problems**
  We know exactly what is wrong and exactly what we need as an answer.
- **Ill-Defined Problems**
  We know things are wrong and stuff needs to happen, we just don't know what on either one.

LEADERSHIP

PROBLEM STATEMENTS

The First Key Is To Clearly Define Where We Are
- What is wrong?
- How do we know?
- Where is the problem occurring?
- How long has this been going on?
- What is the measured impact?
- What is the gap?

LEADERSHIP

WHAT PROBLEM STATEMENTS ARE NOT...

- They are not phrased as questions, such as "Why are we having this problem?"
- They are not "lack of" statements, such as, "We are struggling because we lack the resources to get on track."
- They are not abstract statements, such as "the problem is that morale is low."

LEADERSHIP

THE GOOD AND THE BAD

Correct Statements

- Our staff productivity has decreased by 25% over the last 6 months.
- The productivity struggles have been specifically with our new hires.
- The problem we are facing is in training our new hires to perform at the same or greater level as our existing team.

Incorrect Statements

- We haven't had enough staff to meet our productivity goals this year.
- Our on-boarding process isn't working.

LEADERSHIP

A FEW TIPS TO HELP...

- Keep your cool.
- Ask good clarifying questions in a calm manner.
- Check with multiple sources after the conversation.
- Do your research!
- Hypothesize but don't assume.

Learn2Lead
Supervise · Influence · Motivate

LEADERSHIP

PROBLEM DEFINITION AND PERCEPTION

- How a person represents a problem has a significant impact on the problem itself.
- To solve a problem, one must reorganize or restructure the representation of the problem.

Different kinds of problems require different approaches.

TYPES OF PROBLEMS

LEADERSHIP

INSIGHT PROBLEMS

- This type of problem requires an "AHA!" moment in order to solve it.
- Solutions come in a flash, or even in a dream.
- Re-organization representations are required to gain insights.

LEADERSHIP

MAKE THE TRIANGLE CHANGE

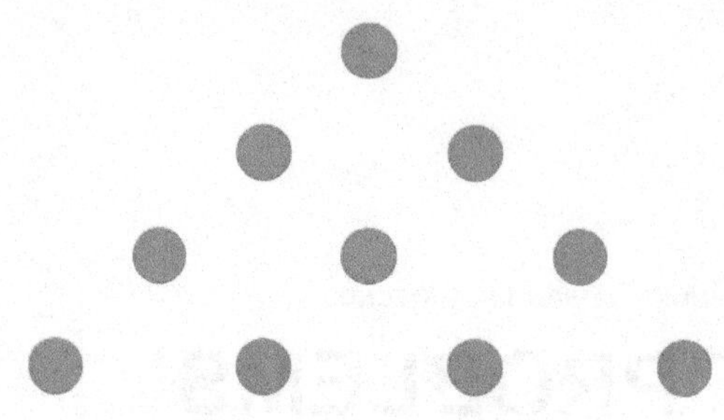

Triangle problem: show how you can move three of the circles (dots) to get the triangle to point to the bottom of the page.

LEADERSHIP

WHY DIDN'T THAT WORK… AGAIN?

Becoming fixated on the old familiar, or what we have always done, restricts our options for finding a solution.

Without research, we naturally stay focused on what we know. Research unlocks more of what we could know.

Learn2Lead
Supervise · Influence · Motivate

LEADERSHIP

MAKE THE TRIANGLE CHANGE

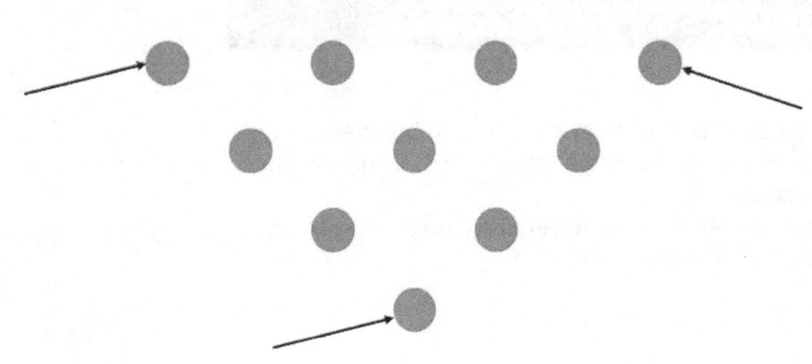

LEADERSHIP

NON-INSIGHT PROBLEMS

- There is a progression of thoughts that come together.
- Each of the thoughts and experiences builds another piece of the puzzle.
- At some point, the rest of the puzzle comes into view.

LEADERSHIP

COMMON BUSINESS PROBLEMS

There are two primary types of problems that we face in business.

- People Problems – Problems that are related to HR, Management, Leadership, and Relationship
- Systems Problems – Problems that are related Capital, Revenue, Resources, Distribution, Marketing, Etc

THE PROBLEM-SOLVING PROCESS

LEADERSHIP

S: STATE THE NEED AS YOU SEE IT

- When a problem exists, there is a gap between what exists now and what is desired.
- It is the gap that must be resolved.
- Identify what needs to happen to eliminate the gap.

LEADERSHIP

O: OPEN UP DISCUSSION & BRAINSTORMING

- Brainstorming is the process of generating as many ideas as possible within a given amount of time.
- Remember that it is about quantity more than quality.
- New ideas often can be combined to produce additional new ideas.

Learn 2 Lead
Supervise · Influence · Motivate

LEADERSHIP

L: LET GO OF WHAT DOESN'T WORK

Go through the ideas that were generated and eliminate the ones that don't pass all of the following…

1. Is it legal?
2. Is it moral?
3. Is it ethical?
4. Is it possible?

LEADERSHIP

V: VET THE REMAINING IDEAS

- Go through the remaining ideas and determine how to generate the final idea.
- Use one idea or a combination of ideas in order to solve the problem.

LEADERSHIP

ALLOCATE AND IMPLEMENT

- Allocate who will be in charge of what.
- Determine when each of the items will be completed.
- Outline the measurement that will be used for implementation.
- Determine the timeline for follow up

LEADERSHIP

E: EVALUATE THE RESULTS AND ADJUST ACCORDINGLY

- It is critical follow up on the implementation.
- It is more critical to have an atmosphere of trust where each person will accept responsibility for their results.
- Review the results and start over as necessary.

LEADERSHIP

THE RESULTS

- Evaluate the process that was followed in the implementation.
- Evaluate the work that was contributed by each person.
- Evaluate what went well and what could have gone better.

LEADERSHIP

PLAN FOR FAILURE – PRE-MORTUM

- Utilize a contingency map in order to plan for what can go wrong.
- Each contingency branch should have a detailed plan for overcoming the challenge.
- The goal is to learn to think in resolution models.

CREATIVITY AND PROBLEM SOLVING

LEADERSHIP

CREATIVITY

- Little c Creativity – An idea that is original to the individual
- Big C Creativity – An idea that is original, useful, and novel to the world
- Business Creativity is about changing the outcomes for good.

LEADERSHIP

8 STAGES TO CREATIVITY

1. Ask – Research continuously to uncover the next path to a great resolution.
2. Learn – You are never done learning. Live in a growth mindset.
3. Look – Look and really see what is happening. Let go of your ego and look for discovery.
4. Play – Try new things, new processes for the sheer joy of discovery.
5. Think – Your mind is a muscle. Exercise it regularly and it will produce more.
6. Fuse – Bounce ideas off of others. Blend and fuse ideas together.
7. Choose – Your focus is yours. Stay balanced between the possible and the probable.
8. Make – Ideas are only worthwhile when implemented.

LEADERSHIP

YOUR FRAMEWORK

- There are a number of different models for solving a problem. They range from the simple to the complex.
- The key is to follow a predictable model.
- Models generate success.

The qualities of each model are:

- A sequence of steps that usually require collaborative effort
- Identifying and defining the problem through a series of questions and study
- Use of data based analysis to find underlying causes of the problem
- Development of solutions to mitigate the problem
- Implementation and monitoring phase to evaluate the outcome.

LEADERSHIP

DIMINISHING PROBLEM SOLVING

- Allowing personal bias to determine which information is used
- Jumping to conclusions without data
- Taking shortcuts in data collection and analysis
- Researching only to prove your theories, not to find the truth

LEADERSHIP

ADVANCING PROBLEM SOLVING

- Positive attitude
- Concern for accuracy
- Breaking the problem into parts
- Avoiding guessing
- Using a model or a system
- Encouraging collaboration

RESEARCH

LEADERSHIP

TYPES OF INFORMATION GATHERING

Qualitative

- Ask open ended questions
- Interview multiple people
- Identify themes
- Use this information as a basis to create a quantifiable model
- Let the information guide you

Quantitative

- Ask measurable questions (multiple choice, forced choice, multi-option)
- Survey multiple people or…
- Case Studies of specific people
- Let the information tell a story
- Let your hypothesis be proven or disproven

LEADERSHIP

TYPES OF RESEARCH

- Archival Research
- Case Study
- Simulation or Modeling
- Content Analysis
- Comparative Analysis (industry)
- Longitudinal Study (time)
- Observational Study
- Survey
- Self-Report

LEADERSHIP

TYPES OF DATA ANALYSIS

- Descriptive – what are the main aspects of the data that is being analyzed?
- Exploratory – Unknown relationship are sought out.
- Inferential Analysis - Taking a small sample to infer information about the larger population.

LEADERSHIP

TYPES OF DATA ANALYSIS

- Predictive Analysis – Predicts future events by looking at current and past events or scenarios.
- Causal Analysis – What happens to one variable when you change another variable?

LEADERSHIP

UNDERSTANDING YOUR DATA

- Line Graphs – What are the trends (trend line)
- Bar Graphs – What is the comparison?
- Fishbone Diagram – Contingent understanding or prediction
- 5 Why Exercise – Root cause analysis

LEADERSHIP

Data Tells A Story

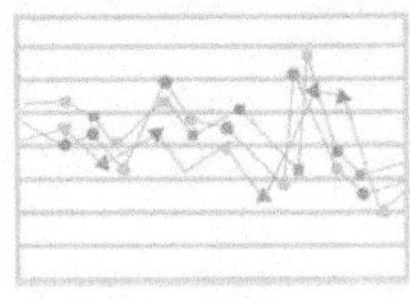

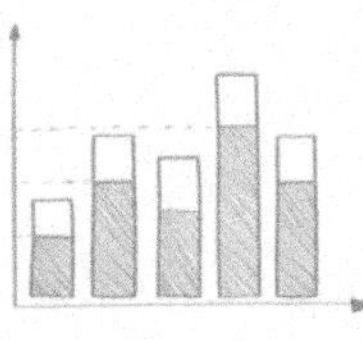

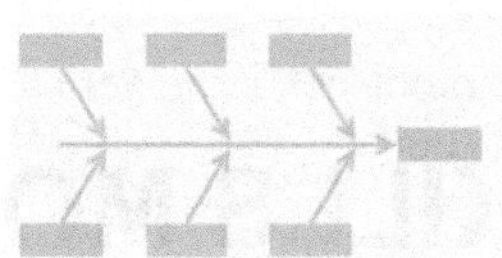

Learn2Lead
Supervise · Influence · Motivate

LEADERSHIP

5 WHY EXERCISE

Why didn't we deliver the product on time?
The equipment failed.

Why did the equipment fail?
Because we did not maintain it properly.

Why did we not maintain it?
We were told not to spend any money no matter what.

Why did you think that meant maintenance too?
Because we were yelled at last time for spending on maintenance?

Why did the manager yell?
That is how they manage.

Learn2Lead
Supervise · Influence · Motivate

The things that stop problem solving from happening

WHAT KILLS MOMENTUM?

LEADERSHIP

ARE YOU ALL IN? WHAT STOPS PROBLEM RESOLUTION?

- A lack of buy-in from key players is the fastest way to lose momentum in solving a problem.
- A lack of buy-in from leadership
- A lack of accountability by the team
- A lack of motivation to solve the problem
- A lack of humility
- Others?

10 GROUP DECISION-MAKING / GROUPTHINK

How to make bad decisions at work…

Supervisors and leaders who make bad decisions will do so for only one reason with two sides to the reason. That reason relates to the leader's clarity in the process. One of the most difficult and critically important aspects of being in charge is being connected. Without true connection, it is impossible to know what is true and what is not true in a relationship. The primary reason that a supervisor or leader will make a bad decision is because of a lack of clarity related to that truth. This lack of clarity is a two-sided coin. On one side, there is a lack of external clarity. This would mean not being clear on what is actually going on around them. Supervisors who "hide out" in their offices and don't spend time with their teams will fall victim to this one. The other side of the coin is a lack of clarity related to what is going on inside of themselves. This relates to not having a clear picture of where they are going, why they are going there, and what values will guide them along the way.

For the purpose of this illustration, let's say that the tails side of the coin is what is going on outside of the person and the heads side of the coin is what is going on in their own head. If you only flip the coin and don't account for all of the research and/or options, you miss the full picture. You learned to measure data in the problem solving chapter, to see both sides of the coin. Very often, leaders make decisions in a vacuum. They take into account their past experiences and their current perceptions related to those experiences, but not the collective experience of the team. By engaging with the team and encouraging their input, a leader opens up the opportunities to expand the knowledge of the situation rapidly. By taking those experiences and then using that to create a data collection process, the information available expands again. By following the information that the data has to offer and listening to what the data says, even more information is available. When those things are not considered, however, it is just a shot in the dark. The leader is just guessing as to what might work, just flipping a coin. The danger with a leader that just guesses is that they are generally the ones that blame others when their own ideas don't work. Doing this further kills the creativity and contribution of others. The data gives you a clear picture of the tails side of the coin.

The other side of the coin is what is going on inside of the supervisor's own mind. A supervisor that doesn't have a clear picture of their "why" will not operate with the right compass intact. The understanding of why the work is important helps to filter the decisions that are made. This lack of clarity in direction very often takes leaders off of the right path. The second aspect of what is going inside the mind of the supervisor that leads to bad decisions is not having a clear picture of the goals for the department as they relate to the goals of the organization. This means that they will not have the right daily habits that lead to the weekly, monthly, quarterly, and annual success that they desire. Finally, supervisors who make bad decisions have not developed enough self-confidence to make a decision and take action. They will second guess themselves, mistrust their research and mess with the heads of the people around them.

One of the greatest causes of failure to make good decisions rests with a phenomenon known as "group-think." This aspect of bad decision making has killed more successes than any other aspect of the decision process. When a person in charge, or an aggressive person in the group, is allowed to create group think or when there is a lack of trust that leads to group think, you can rest assured that bad decisions will follow. Many people have had the experience of an overly strong personality indicating that their idea would be the one that is implemented and the rest of the group simply agreeing in the meeting. Then, when people leave the meeting, they immediately begin talking to each other about how bad the idea is and how "that person" always has horrible ideas. Yet, in the group setting, everyone seemed to agree with it. Well, at least nobody spoke up to disagree with it so it seemed like everyone was agreeing.

There was a parable told that helps to illustrate the point of just what group think is. It is paraphrased and shared below. For a full understanding of it, you can pick up a copy of the book, The Abilene Paradox And Other Meditations On Management by Jerry Harvey. You can find it on Amazon and you can find multiple videos on YouTube with the subject: The Abilene Paradox.

The Abilene Paradox Summary

A father, a mother, a daughter, and a son-in-law sat on a porch in the small West Texas town of Coleman. It was mid-morning on an overly hot summer day. As the they sat and visited that morning, at nearly 11 AM, the father said, "If you guys wanted to, we could go over to Abilene and eat at the Dixie Pig for lunch." The setting was in the 1950's and neither the family's house nor their car was equipped with air-conditioning. After a short pause, the daughter said, "If that's what you want, that's fine with me." Not wanting to displease his new wife, the son-in-law responds with, "If you want to go to the Dixie Pig sweetheart, that sounds good to me." The mother looks at all of them and says, "I was planning on just making sandwiches, but if that is what all of you want, I am okay with that as well." At this point, none of them had actually said that they **wanted** to go to Abilene to the Dixie Pig. The father had suggested it, the daughter agreed, the son-in-law supported, and the mother succumbed to it. Nobody had actually indicated that they wanted to go though. By not disagreeing, they had been seen as being in agreement.

So, the family loads up in the car and heads out of town for the 46 mile drive to the Dixie Pig for lunch. The windows are cracked for good air flow on a day that was already approaching 100 degrees Fahrenheit. Right as they get to the edge of town, a West Texas dust storm picks up, blowing dirt and debris everywhere. As a result, the windows on the car go up and the heat inside of the car rises quickly. At only about 50 miles per hour, this one hour ride had turned into miserable ride in a 'mobile sweat lodge.' The family stayed quiet and miserable as the father, who was upset about his family wanting to take this dumb trip, drove them to Abilene. When they finally arrived at the restaurant, the dirt storm was subsiding. They piled out of the car and headed for the door. As they opened the door, they quickly became aware of the number of other people that had the same idea to eat lunch there that day. The place was packed and there was a 30 minute wait just to get a table. Dripping with sweat and not smelling their best, the family waited with very little conversation. Nerves were becoming raw. The daughter was upset that her dad wanted to go to Abilene. The son-in-law was annoyed that his wife wanted to take the trip and the mother was mad because she could have just made sandwiches and enjoyed her own home.

When the family finally gets seated, it is another long wait for the waitress to take their drink order. Even though they were ready with their full order, she says that she will just get drinks right now and will get their full order when she comes 'right back.' It took almost 15 minutes for the drinks to get to the table. By this time, they are dehydrated, irritated, and each person knows that the problem could have been mitigated by simply not going. The waitress takes their order, they finish their drinks, and they wait. She finally refills their drinks a minute or so before their food is ready. At this point, they are simply ready to eat and go home, but the orders are all wrong. Never in their lives had they seen someone mess up every order at the table! They complain to the waitress, but then just eat it as it is anyway because it would take too long for her to get it right. After eating what they didn't want in a restaurant that smelled of grease and cigarette smoke, they paid their bill and were ready to leave. Their only silver lining was that the dirt wasn't blowing outside.

Windows down and a breeze in the car, they head off to go back to Coleman, TX. But, just as they make it a mile outside of town, they notice the dirt still blowing like before. So, the windows went up. The temperature rose, and the tempers intensified as well. An hour later, when they made it back to the other side of the dirt storm, they piled out of the car stinking of sweat, grease, bad attitudes and smoke. Right about the time that they made it to the porch, the father couldn't hold his tongue any longer. "I can't believe you guys wanted to go to Abilene. I hated that trip and the food was horrible!" The daughter, now livid, responds, "Us!? It was your dumb idea in the first place. I hate that place and I only went because you said you wanted to go." The father quips back, "I never said I wanted to go! I said we could go if that was what you wanted and you said you did." The daughter says, "I never said I wanted to go, it was my husband that wanted to go." The husband is now in the ring for the fight as well, "Whoa! I only went because you and your dad wanted to go. You know I don't like car rides or going to the Dixie Pig." The mother begins to cry and says, "I just wanted to make sandwiches and stay here but all of you wanted to go to Abilene." Although none of them really indicated that they wanted to go, none of them indicated that they didn't want to go either. This was a classic case of mismanaged agreement.

The Lesson In the Abilene Paradox

The lesson is actually pretty simple and yet it perplexes even the largest of companies in the world. Too many times in a group setting or a team meeting, we don't speak up with what is really going on inside of our heads for fear that we will be shot down, rejected, or somehow shunned for being honest. The simple reality is that nobody wanted to go to Abilene. The father made the suggestion and everyone seemed to be afraid to disagree with him. For that era, it was fairly common for the man of the house to drive the decisions. In a workplace setting, when the boss makes a suggestion, group think has the potential to rear its ugly head. This is particularly true when the boss says something like, "I have an awesome idea that I want to share with you guys and get your opinion on." When it is presented like that, does the boss really want an opinion or does she want an affirmation? That's right, she wants support, not criticism. This means that discussion was never really welcomed and this means that group-think is almost guaranteed to occur. The lesson is that trust has to be built as a foundation for good decision making. People have to trust one another at a deep enough level that they know that it is alright to disagree and have a discussion. They need to be comfortable to speak up and say, "I don't want to go to Abilene." When that trust level is there, the first step is solved. The second component that must be present is that the boss has to want the contribution and opinions of others. If it is perceived that they don't want that or if they have shut people down in meetings in the past, then the trust factor won't be there. Be open with your teams and allow and encourage them to be open with you and with each other.

What are the causes of good decisions at work? As you think about the opposite of making a bad decision, you realize that you need a framework that will guide you on the path to the right decision. The objective is to avoid having that overly dominant person controlling people through fear of objection and subsequent rejection. This fear is what leads to people falling victim to group-think. When you have a boss that walks in and says something like, "I had a brilliant idea last night and stayed up all night working on it; I just want to get your opinion on it and that is why I called this meeting," that is when you know that they don't really want your opinion. What they are looking for is your support. Bad decisions are made every day when the wrong model is in place for making decisions. Good decisions at work are the result of proper thought processes. The following T.H.I.N.K. framework is the model that will allow you and your team to truly think instead of group-think. It will help you along your path to success.

Talk It Through

T – Talk it through. The idea behind making good decisions begins with the objective of talking through every aspect of the decision that is to be made. Too often, supervisors will go in with a pre-conceived notion of what they want to say instead of being willing to hear all of the angles. In fact, many supervisors have only one angle that they plan to discuss and that is the one that supports their belief about the matter at hand. In order to ensure that you and your team talk through all of the aspects of the situation, it is ideal to appoint half of the team to focus on the good of the idea and half of the team to focus on the bad of the idea for the first portion of the discussion. Whatever time is allotted for the discussion, say 20 minutes, is split into two halves. At the 10 minute mark, have the two sides switch directions and talk about the other side of the issue. By doing this, you make it okay for each person to explore the opposing views of the issue. Make sure that you specify the timeframe for the discussion. Make sure that you have each person talk in favor of as well as against the idea. And, make sure that you establish the ground rule that the objective is the right decision that supports the mission of the organization.

It isn't just about the idea itself, it is about doing the right thing.

Have A Clear Understanding

H – Have a clear understanding of what each person said, including yourself. In the Abilene Paradox, the father indicated that he would go to Abilene if that is what the others wanted. His unintentional statement was indicating to the others that he actually wanted to go. By suggesting the idea, it was essentially his idea and his desire. The others said that they would go if one or more of the others wanted to go. If the father had said something else, the outcome would have been different. The father could have said the following. "Let's determine what we want to do for lunch. One idea is to go to Abilene to the Dixie Pig. What are some other ideas?" By stating it in a clear manner so that others understand that it is okay to have their own opinion, the others are more likely to share what they are thinking as well. Had the son-in-law been clear that he did not want to go to Abilene, but was willing to do so if that was the wish of the father-in-law, then the father-in-law would have understood him better as well. With each person, the clarity of their message was missing. In addition to using the right words, it is up to you, the supervisor, to watch the physical responses of your people to the ideas presented. When you see a negative response, know that they are disagreeing, even if they don't audibly say anything about it. When you see this, ask them about their disagreement and let them know that you are good with them saying what they need to say. The more you build trust, the easier it is for them to share openly.

Investigate All Of The Possibilities

I – Investigate all of the possibilities through the use of problem solving. If you have used the model of problem solving that you learned in the previous chapter, then you have already brainstormed the possibilities. If you have not done this yet, you will want to step back and follow the problem solving process, particularly the brainstorming component. If you are having trouble getting your people to talk about both sides of the possibilities, appoint a devil's advocate for the duration of the discussion. Their job is to disagree with the ideas and ask for more clarification until the idea is fleshed out. It is a good idea NOT to use the same person each time because they will begin to feel that the group doesn't want to hear from them. Instead, rotate the responsibility from one person to another. Dig into the ideas and discuss what could go wrong as well as what could go right with each of them. One idea should generate another idea and that idea should generate yet another idea. Dig in and look for all of the options. When you land on an idea, discuss why that idea is a good one and then ask what could possibly go wrong. Keep pushing until the team is confident that the idea has merit and should be moved forward.

Never Dodge A Good Discussion or Good Conflict

N – Never dodge a good discussion or good conflict. Patrick Lencioni in his book, The Five Dysfunctions Of A Team, establishes that a team is dysfunctional when they avoid conflict. The avoidance of conflict stems from a lack of actual trust in one another. It isn't always easy, but learn to have fun with your team and learn to encourage disagreement. One way to open up a decision making meeting or process is to say, "I want to remind everyone that it is good and even encouraged to disagree with ideas. Our goal is to look at ideas from every angle and to ensure that we are making the right decision. The goal is never to protect my ego." I would then encourage you to smile and open up the meeting. Think back to what you learned in the conflict resolution chapter. When you make the conflict about behaviors and/or an idea instead of about the other person, then the conflict is positive. When the conflict becomes about another person, then the conflict turns negative. As long as you focus on the good of the organization and NOT the bad of another person, the conflict resolution process will get you what you are looking for.

Know Your Desired Outcomes

K – Know the outcomes that you are looking for. Too often, supervisors think about their ideas as being an extension of themselves instead of being a reflection of the overall goals of the company. When you think about what you are trying to accomplish, it should be filtered through the overall objectives of the organization. In the goal-setting chapter, you learned about setting goals and then creating milestones along the way toward the achievement of that goal. When you keep the overall goal, as well as those milestone goals in the forefront of your mind, you tend to make decisions that support the desired end result instead of decisions that are contrary to it. Hopefully, in the portion of this where you are NOT avoiding conflict, someone would have brought up the fact that the direction was off from the stated objectives, if that was the case. Every discussion should be filtered to fit the overall goals of the company as well as the overall goals of your department. Also, remember the component of problem solving that outlined determining the need instead of focusing on the problem. When the need is the focus, the discussions support that direction.

Additionally, you will want to consider each of the following related to the outcomes that you desire. You will want to know the timeframe in which the decision must be implemented. Knowing the milestones and the end date is critical in order to properly delegate responsibility. Additionally, you will need to understand and clearly communicate what is expected of each person and have those expectations connected to that timeline. Finally, you will need to keep the lines of communication open in order to stay on top of any potential issues as the process progresses.

The Structure And Model of Meetings

According to Atlassian (www.atlassian.com), the average supervisor is attending 62 meetings per month, for a total of 31 hours per month in meetings. Of those meetings, meeting attendees considered ½ of their time wasted. This means that the average supervisor is losing 16 of their 160 work hours every month to meetings that produce nothing worthwhile or measurable. Looking at all meeting goers, including your employees, 91% of meeting attendees said that they daydreamed during meetings. 96% say that they have missed meetings on purpose. 39% of meeting goers report to have fallen asleep in at least one meeting at work. 73% of meeting goers reported that they did other work during meetings, unrelated to the meeting. This puts the cost of meeting time for employees, where nothing is considered to be accomplished, at $37 Billion Dollars annually. That is a lot of time wasted and a lot of money thrown into the wind without result.

There are four different types of meetings that you, as a supervisor, should be conducting. When you ensure that you meet in the right manner with the right restrictions, your meetings are worthwhile and effective. As a supervisor, you probably identify with the stats in the previous paragraph and think, "I am experiencing death by meeting. Jody! Save me!" The truth is that when we meet in the wrong way, we waste a lot of time. As we move into discussing the four types of meetings, keep in mind that the most important thing that you can do is to know who should be invited to which meeting and who should NOT be invited to those meetings. If you are being invited out of courtesy, and you are not expected to contribute, nor do you, then ask to be excluded from the meeting itself. If you are having meetings that require no discussion and you find yourself reading reports to one another, then email the reports instead of reading them to each other. There is a very good chance that your people can read or they know someone who can. Don't meet for the sake of meeting or because it has "always been done that way." Meet because you need to accomplish something. Having said that, the following four types of meetings are actually necessary and should be done where you can see one another. You can use technology, such as Skype® or Goto Meeting ®, or you can be face to face for these meetings. You do need to be able to read non-verbal language as a part of these meetings, so make sure that you can.

M.E.E.T.

M – Make sure we are on the same page. The first meeting is a daily meeting. It has often been called a standup meeting or an info-only meeting, and it has only one purpose. It is designed to ensure that you and your team are on the same page with what is going on today. Each person has 60 seconds or less to explain what they have going on. It is not a meeting designed to discuss agenda items, or solve problems, or even to plan strategy. It is a meeting designed to share what your top priorities are for the day. This is a time saver for everyone involved. Employees and supervisors alike waste an inordinate amount of time tracking each other down and finding out what they have going on in their day. If everyone knows right up front, then you can each plan accordingly. The only other purpose that this meeting serves is for you, the supervisor, to rearrange some of the priorities if they seem out of line from what you know needs to happen.

E – Engage in discussion about short term strategy. The weekly staff meeting should be no more than 30 minutes long. It should have a clear agenda of what is to be discussed. The agenda items need to relate directly to where you and your team are on your short term goals. You will discuss what happened in the previous week and what is coming up in the next week. You will resolve problems related to that 2-week window. You should clearly map out what is to be accomplished in the meeting. It is not the time that you review long-term goals or discuss the 5-year strategic plan. Those come in the next two types of meetings.

E – Engage in discussion about long term strategy. The quarterly meeting should be approximately two hours in length, and not more than about three hours. This meeting is designed to review what happened in the last quarter and to adjust the plan in order to ensure that the right things happen in the next quarter. If everything was good from the last quarter, very little adjustment will be needed, if any. You will want to limit your discussion to that six month window (one quarter completed and one coming up). If you find that the topic begins to wander toward the annual plan or the 5 year plan, pull the discussion back to what is relevant to the timeline component you are discussing right now. The toughest and perhaps the most important part of running a meeting is keeping things on topic. Stay focused and minimize the fluff or filler in the meeting so that people can get in, do what is necessary, and get out.

T – Talk about annual goals and objectives. Once per year, you and your should team should take between half a day and a full day to focus on how you fit into the overall vision of the organization. This annual planning is what maps out what you will do and what you will accomplish for the next year. Think about how your department ties in with the organization as a whole. In this meeting, you will be mapping out the goals, plans, and strategies that will ensure that you and your entire team are successful. You will be mapping the (GPS) to the organization's overall goals and objectives. You will be filtering the discussions through the mission of the organization and ensuring that you stay on track. It is ideal that you have an outside facilitator for this annual meeting. This can be a consultant, or it can even be another supervisor that has been trained on how to facilitate group discussions. This outside person can keep things moving in the right direction and ensure that you accomplish all that is necessary for your success.

When you meet on purpose and with purpose, the decisions that you make are significantly more effective. When you understand that an overly dominant personality can kill the success of your team, you put strategies in place to ensure that things don't get out of control. When you see that you have people not contributing, you work to build more trust in the team and get their participation. Your job as a supervisor is to ensure that work is accomplished in the right manner with the right resources. Learning to make good decisions and lead meetings where good decisions are made increases your ability to succeed. Take the time to learn your processes. Keep your team in the loop and ask for their input, even their disagreement, when things seem to be getting off track. Go out of your way to ensure that you never "blast" the ideas of others. Encourage participation and praise it publicly. When you are focused on building the trust of the team and leading them away from the Abilene Paradox, you will find that they contribute more, enjoy the process more, and work in a more engaged manner. Good decisions are the result of good supervision and a trusting team. Good decisions require that we all be okay with disagreeing when necessary. They require that we make people comfortable with conflict and we keep it focused on behaviors and ideas instead of on people. You are moving your capacity for success forward with each new skill that you master. Scott Adams, famous cartoonist and author, says that you double your odds of success with each new skill that you attain. Running good meetings and making good decisions should count as a double helping of new skills for you!

THE WORLD AROUND US IS CHANGING!

LEADERSHIP

LEARNING OBJECTIVES

Understand the concept of **"mismanaged agreement".**

How to find your "why" for success

Describe how your perception of risk and benefit influence your participation in "group thinking"

Develop effective personal patterns of participation in group decision-making

Develop communication strategies to help you and your team make honest and open agreements.

Learn & Lead
Supervise · Influence · Motivate

GROUPS ARE NATURAL

- Groups are one of the most "human" things about us. We are social animals. The impact of groups is present even when we are alone.
- For good or ill, groups often accomplish goals that individuals cannot. As *group members, we* frequently behave in ways we do not as individuals. And our behavior as group members may fluctuate from group to group.
- Not all collections of individuals are groups.

LEADERSHIP

WHAT IS A GROUP?

The business dictionary defines a group as…
A collection of individuals who have regular contact and frequent interaction, mutual influence, common feeling of camaraderie, and who work together to achieve a common set of goals.

Read more: http://www.businessdictionary.com/definition/group.html

Additionally… Both the individual and the group recognize their membership in the group.

LEADERSHIP

WHAT CONSTITUTES BEING IN A GROUP?

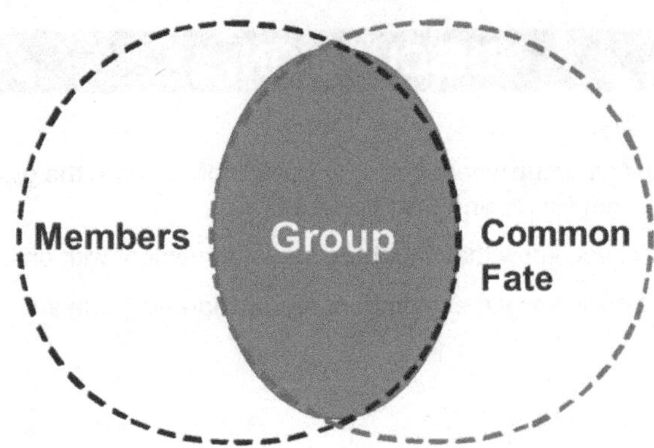

Learn2Lead
Supervise · Influence · Motivate

LEADERSHIP

ELEMENTS OF A GROUP

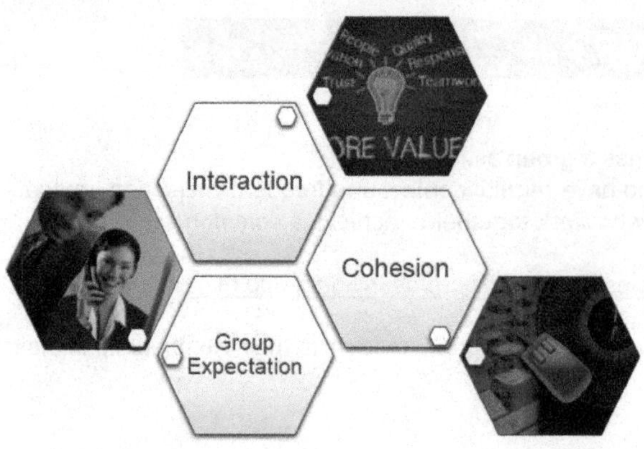

LEADERSHIP

DISCUSSION...

- Have you recently been in a group where it seemed as if individuals in the group wanted to go one direction, but held back from expressing their opinions?
- What non-verbal signs let you know that members are in agreement with an idea?
- What non-verbal signs let you know that members are not agreeing with an idea?

LEADERSHIP

AGREEMENT VERSUS DISAGREEMENT

Signs of Agreement: Attention focused on the leader, nodding heads, and eagerness to comment or contribute are actions that suggest excitement or genuine support for a proposal.

Signs of Disagreement: Silence may suggest confusion or disagreement. People looking down at their notes, fidgeting with paperwork, avoiding eye contact with the leader, etc. may suggest a desire to withdraw from the discussion.

Learn2Lead
Supervise · Influence · Motivate

LEADERSHIP

GROUP DYNAMICS – PATRICK LENCIONI

Inattention To Results

Avoidance of Accountability

Lack of Commitment

Fear of Conflict

Absence of Trust

LEADERSHIP

GROUP DYNAMICS MATTER!

- The quality of a group's decision-making is only as good as the trust, conflict, commitment, accountability, and results of the team.
- Factors that have nothing to do with the subject at hand, or the decision, can influence the direction of the discussion and the decisions ultimately made. Examples of these factors include our comfort level in the group, issues in our personal lives, or reporting relationships with others in the group. This is the nature of group dynamics.

LEADERSHIP

INTER-ROLE CONFLICT...

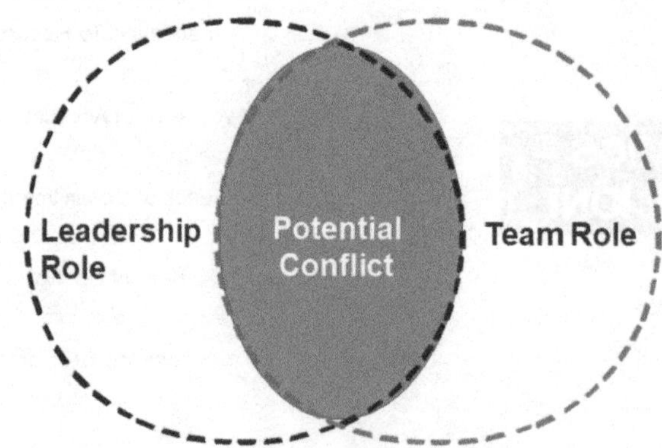

Learn2Lead

LEADERSHIP

HOW WE DEAL...

- Segregate or Compartmentalize
- Use Role Specialization
- Negotiate Role Performance
- Prioritize Roles
- Queue or Sequence Role Obligations

Learn2Lead
Supervise * Influence * Motivate

LEADERSHIP

GROUP CONFORMITY

What are some examples of ways that we conform to group norms and expectations?

- Wear clothes in public
- Obey traffic laws
- Obey social conventions
- Show up to work when we are supposed to (hopefully)

Learn2Lead
Supervise * Influence * Motivate

LEADERSHIP

GROUP "SOCIAL ROLES"

Groups establish well-defined social roles.

Social roles are shared expectations in a group about how particular people are supposed to behave (eg, boss, employees).

Whereas norms specify how all group members should behave, roles specify how people who occupy certain positions in the group should behave.

LEADERSHIP

TYPES OF POWER WITHIN A GROUP

Expert Power

Referent Power (Similarities)

Reward and Punishment

Legitimacy

Meaning and Information

Identification

Status or Prestige Power

Learn2Lead
Supervise · Influence · Motivate

LEADERSHIP

WHY PEOPLE JOIN GROUPS

Because forming relationships with other people fulfills a number of basic human needs. Indeed, so basic that there may be an innate need to belong to social groups.

Baumeister and Leary argue that people join groups because in our evolutionary past there was a substantial *survival advantage* to establishing bonds with other people.

LEADERSHIP

WE JOIN BECAUSE...

When we join a group, it helps us to identify who we are as well as who we intend to be in the future.

Being a part of a group motivates us to be a part of something bigger than ourselves. Social change results from group membership. (O'Neill, 2000)

LEADERSHIP

WHAT DO GROUPS OFFER…

- Resources
- Acceptance
- Proximity
- Recruitment
- Similarity

LEADERSHIP

MISMANAGED AGREEMENT

When we fail to create the right environment and the right culture for our team, we end up with dysfunctions that lead to "Group Think."

LEADERSHIP

PARADOX

Paradox: A seemingly contradictory statement that may be true. i.e. When a person thinks one thing and says another

The Abilene Paradox is a paradox in which the limits of a particular situation force a group of people to act in a way that is directly the opposite of their actual preferences.

Learn 2 Lead
Supervise · Influence · Motivate

LEADERSHIP

THE ABILENE PARADOX

Learn 2 Lead
Supervise · Influence · Motivate

LEADERSHIP

DISCUSSION

- Why is it so difficult to disagree with what the group seems to be thinking?
- How many of you encounter situations in your team or group meetings where its difficult to disagree? Rarely? Occasionally? Often?
- Would you say that in the story, the characters were in conflict with one another?

LEADERSHIP

THE ROAD TO ABILENE

- Group Think is when you are on the wrong road.
- It is when you are intimidated by honest and direct conversation.
- It is when there is a lack of trust in the group because of a fear of rejection, oppression, or lashing out.
- It is when we have a fear of no longer belonging to the group if we disagree with a strong group member. We don't want to get kicked out of the club.

LEADERSHIP

WHERE DID THE TERM COME FROM?

Groupthink is a term coined in 1952 by William H. Whyte in Fortune Magazine and later redefined by psychologist Irving Janis (1972) to describe a process by which a group makes bad or irrational decisions.

In a groupthink situation, each member of the group attempts to conform his or her opinions to what they believe to be the consensus of the group.

In a general sense this seems to be a rational way to approach the situation. However this results in a situation in which the group ultimately agrees upon an action which each member might individually consider to be unwise.

LEADERSHIP

COMMON CHARACTERISTICS WHEN IN GROUP THINK

- They agree individually *in private* about the nature of the situation or the problem facing the organization
- They agree individually *in private* about the steps that need to be taken to cope with the problem
- They fail to accurately communicate their desires and beliefs to one another
- Failing to communicate, as a group they make decisions that make them take actions counterproductive for their intent
- As a result, they become frustrated
- The cycle of disability to manage agreement will repeat itself if not dealt with accurately through communication

Learn 2 Lead
Supervise · Influence · Motivate

LEADERSHIP

GROUP THINK – HARVEY

Harvey (1988) points to six characteristics symbolic of a group failing to manage agreement effectively:

1. Members individually agree about the situation in the organization but keep their opinions private.

2. Members individually agree how to deal with the situation but again keep their opinions private.

3. Members fail to communicate their desires and/or beliefs to one another. Frequently they do just the opposite - leading the members of the group to draw the wrong conclusions about the collective opinion.

4. Based on these misperceptions of the collective opinion the group takes action that is contrary to what they want to do. Thereby arriving at results that are counterproductive.

5. Based on these counterproductive actions the members experience frustration, anger, and dissatisfaction with the organization. Often this leads to the forming of sub-groups that take combative or blaming positions toward each other.

6. Finally, members are destined to repeat this unsatisfying and dysfunctional behavior if they do not begin to understand the genesis of mismanaged agreement.

Harvey, Jerry B. (1988). *The Abilene Paradox and Other Meditations on Management.* Lexington, Mass: Lexington Books.

LEADERSHIP

GROUPS INFLUENCE BEHAVIOR PATTERNS

We tend to modify our beliefs to fit the collective, or interpreted beliefs of the group that we are a part of at the time.

LEADERSHIP

SOCIAL FACILITATION

Why does the presence of others produce behavior shifts?

There are three theories:

- The presence of others makes us *more alert*
- It makes us *concerned* for what others think of us (apprehension evaluation)
- The presence of others *distracts* us (distraction/ conflict).

LEADERSHIP

SOCIAL LOAFING

Social loafing is the tendency for people to *do worse* on *simple tasks*, but better on complex tasks, when they are in the presence of others and their individual performance cannot be evaluated.

Rationale: being observed by others where performance cannot be evaluated is *relaxing*.

Relaxation impairs performance on *simple tasks,* but enhances performance on *complex ones* (see Jackson & Williams, 1985).

LEADERSHIP

GENDER, CULTURE, AND LOAFING

There are *gender and cultural* differences in the tendency to loaf.

Karau and Williams found that the tendency to loaf is stronger in *men* than in women.

Similarly, the tendency to loaf is stronger in *Western* than in Asian cultures.

LEADERSHIP

DEINDIVIDUALIZATION

Being in a group not only affects how hard we work, but it can also lead to *an increase* in impulsive and deviant acts. This seems to be related to *deindividuation.*

Deindividuation is the loosening of normal constraints on behaviour when people are in a crowd, leading to an increase in impulsive and deviant acts.

LEADERSHIP

GROUP SIZE MATTERS – MOB MENTALITY

Throughout history, there have been many examples of groups of people committing *horrendous acts* that no individual would do on his/her own.

The *savagery* of the act is related to the *size* of the group (Mullen, 1986). Mullen content analyzed news reports of lynchings in the U.S. from 1899-1946 and found that the *larger* the mob, the greater the *savagery* with which they killed their victims.

Learn2Lead
Supervise · Influence · Motivate

LEADERSHIP

WHAT IS CONSENSUS?

- A General Agreement
- A cooperative, caring, nonviolent process in which people share their best ideas and come up with agreed upon decisions
- Everyone has a voice even if not everyone gets their way.
- Consensus: agreement; accord; compromise; consent

LEADERSHIP

WHAT IT IS AND WHAT IT ISN'T...

- Consensus is not unanimous agreement
- It is the process of deciding what is best for the group
- It is a cooperative process
- It is not used by people who cannot or will not cooperate
- It is a step in the right direction toward democracy

LEADERSHIP

3 STAGES OF CONSENSUS

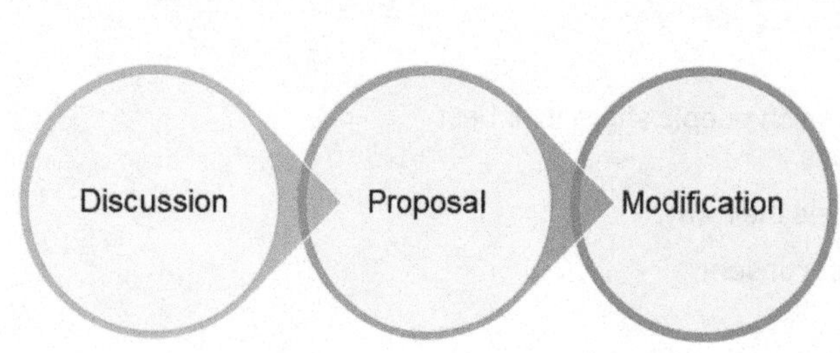

LEADERSHIP

IT ISN'T ALWAYS PAIN FREE!

Good consensus process relies heavily on problem-solving, questioning, empathy, self-sacrifice, and nonviolent direct action. In a good process, conflict is not ignored or covered up, but encouraged. Issues and proposed solutions are thoroughly thrashed out until a good solution is found.

Consensus requires the skill of and the desire to cooperate!

LEADERSHIP

GROUP THINK DETERIORATES DECISION MAKING

If we are not working toward a common goal, or if we operate with a lack of trust, we WILL suffer from Group Think!

Learn2Lead

LEADERSHIP

WHAT HAPPENS WHEN GROUP THINK OCCURS?

There are a number of symptoms that occur when Group Think is happening.

LEADERSHIP

WHEN DOES GT HAPPEN?

Groupthink is *most likely to occur* when certain preconditions are met, such as when the group is
--Highly cohesive
--Isolated from contrary opinions
--Ruled by a directive leader who makes his or her wishes known.

When these conditions are met several symptoms appear

LEADERSHIP

THE SYMPTOMS OF GT INCLUDE...

- Illusion of invulnerability
- Collective rationalization
- Belief in inherent morality
- Stereotyped views of out-groups
- Direct pressure on dissenters
- Self-censorship
- Illusion of agreement
- Self-appointed 'mind-guards'

LEADERSHIP

INVULNERABILITY

- Ignore obvious danger
- Take extreme risk
- Become overly optimistic
- Frame decisions incorrectly

Learn 2 Lead

LEADERSHIP

COLLECTIVE RATIONALIZATION

- Discredit Warnings
- Explain away warning signs
- Group takes on a life of its own
- Momentum takes over
- Contrary information is deleted, distorted and generalized

BELIEF IN INHERENT MORALITY

Members believe in the rightness of their cause (or position) and therefore ignore the ethical or moral consequences of their decisions

 www.jodyholland.com

Learn 2 Lead
Supervise · Influence · Motivate

LEADERSHIP

STEREOTYPED GROUPS OF OUT-GROUPS

Negative views of perceived "enemy" (those who disagree with us) make effective responses to conflict seem unnecessary

"I see we are split between those who like my tie and those who prefer unemployment."

www.jodyholland.com

LEADERSHIP

SELF CENSORSHIP

Doubts and deviations from the perceived group consensus are not expressed

www.jodyholland.com

LEADERSHIP

ILLUSIONS OF UNANIMITY

The majority view and judgments are assumed to be unanimous.

"Emphasize our unique differences, pass it down."

© 2016 Jody Holland www.jodyholland.com

SELF APPOINTED "MINDGUARDS"

Members protect the group and the leader from information that is problematic or contradictory to the group's cohesiveness, view, and/or decisions

"Today's theme is 'Getting Beyond Group Think'."

© 2016 Jody Holland www.jodyholland.com

LEADERSHIP

REMEDIES FOR GROUPTHINK

- The leader should assign the role of critical evaluator to each member
- The leader should avoid stating preferences and expectations at the outset
- Each member of the group should routinely discuss the groups' deliberations with a trusted associate and report back to the group on the associate's reactions

www.jodyholland.com

MORE REMEDIES FOR GROUPTHINK

- One or more experts should be invited to each meeting on a staggered basis and encouraged to challenge views of the members.
- At least one member should be given the role of devil's advocate (to question assumptions and plans)
- The leader should make sure that a sizeable block of time is set aside to survey warning signals.

© 2016 Jody Holland

www.jodyholland.com

LEADERSHIP

WHAT CAN WE DO ABOUT IT?

"What if we don't change at all ... and something magical just happens?"

www.jodyholland.com

LEADERSHIP

CHALLENGE OTHERS TO THINK

THINK ABOUT UNDERLYING ASSUMPTIONS AND IMPLICATIONS

www.jodyholland.com

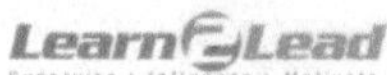

LEADERSHIP

KNOWLEDGE IS POWER

- Access a variety of information sources from industry training, journals, websites, and books
- Think carefully and deeply about actions, policy, and their underlying assumptions

 www.jodyholland.com

LEADERSHIP

REVIEW

Eight Main Symptoms of Group Think

1. **Illusion of Invulnerability**: Members ignore obvious danger, take extreme risk, and/or are overly optimistic.
2. **Collective Rationalization:** Members discredit and explain away warning contrary to group thinking.
3. **Illusion of Morality**: Members believe their decisions are morally correct, ignoring the ethical consequences of their decisions.
4. **Excessive Stereotyping:** The group constructs negative stereotypes of rivals outside the group.

 www.jodyholland.com

LEADERSHIP

REVIEW

Eight Main Symptoms of Group Think

1. **Pressure for Conformity:** Members pressure any in the group who express arguments against the group's stereotypes, illusions, or commitments, viewing such opposition as disloyalty.
2. **Self-Censorship:** Members withhold their dissenting views and counter-arguments.
3. **Illusion of Unanimity:** Members perceive falsely that everyone agrees with the group's decision; silence is seen as consent.
4. **Mindguards:** Some members appoint themselves to the role of protecting the group from adverse information that might threaten group complacency.

 www.jodyholland.com

LEADERSHIP

AVOIDING GROUPTHINK

- The group should be made aware of the causes and consequences of group think.
- The leader should be neutral when assigning a decision-making task to a group, initially witholding all preferences and expectations. This practice will be especially effective if the leaders consistently encourages an atmosphere of open inquiry.
- The leader should give high priority to airing objections and doubts and be accepting of criticism.

 www.jodyholland.com

LEADERSHIP

AVOIDING GROUPTHINK

- Groups should always consider unpopular alternatives, assigning the role of devil's advocate to several strong members of the group.
- Sometimes it is useful to divide the group into two separate deliberative bodies as feasibilities are evaluated.
- Spend a sizable amount of time surveying all warning signals from rival groups and organizations.

 www.jodyholland.com

LEADERSHIP

AVOIDING GROUPTHINK

- After reaching a preliminary consensus on a decision, all residual doubts should be expressed, and the matter reconsidered.
- Outside experts should be included in vital decision-making.
- Tentative decisions should be discussed with trusted colleagues not in the decision-making group.
- The organization should routinely follow the administrative practice of establishing several independent decision-making groups to work on the same critical issue or policy.

 www.jodyholland.com

11 HIGH PERFORMANCE TEAMS

Teams versus Groups

Groups are united by a common set of obligations. They are gathered together for learning, for working, or for volunteering. In one way or another, they have committed to accomplish a task or a set of tasks. They may or may not have similar backgrounds. They may or may not even want to work together. A group pushes its members to do something.

Teams, on the other hand, are united by a common set of values and behaviors. Typically, they started out as a group and through some type of unification morphed into a team. They are focused on the same results. They are supportive of one another. They want to work together. They are pulled by a sense of purpose. Their values bond them in such a way that they can push past any obstacles that might get in the way. They are together to do something great, not just to accomplish a task. A team is pulled by its values to succeed at something worthwhile.

The distinction between a group and a team lies fundamentally in what drives them towards accomplishing their stated purpose. With a team, the pull is the "why" of the team. They understand very clearly why they are there and why they are doing what they are doing. They have learned to translate the passion of their "why" into how they carry out their job and ultimately into what they do. They start with WHY though and then work their way into the other components.

With a group, their fundamental drive is what they are supposed to do and how they are going to carry out that mission. They are driven not by a sense of purpose, but more out of a sense of obligation. They know the stated goal and will often work toward that goal as long as there is enough personal benefit to them. They often work for their own individual success, whereas the team works for the collective success of the team. With a group, it comes down to individuals in the group doing what they are supposed to do that creates a result. With a team, it is the individuals in the group working in harmony with one another and for the good of each other that creates both satisfaction and a result.

There are countless numbers of groups working inside of companies across the nation. Most are not functioning as teams because they have never learned what it means to be a team, nor have they united themselves with a true common purpose, shared values, and group accountability. It isn't easy to build a high performance team, but it is very much worthwhile. Think back to what life was like for you in elementary school. If you are old enough, you remember the games of dodge ball played either in P.E. or on the playground. Think back to the strategy that was used when choosing your team, if you were team captain. The captain always wanted to get the kids that were fast, strong, and would bring an advantage to the team. They understood that in building the team, they built their success or their failure. For some reason, as we have gotten older, we have forgotten that the success or failure of the team is still largely dependent on which members get added, which ones get deleted, and which ones get passed over. Jim Collins in the book, Good To Great, discussed the idea of getting the right people on the bus in the right seats, and the wrong people off of the bus. That 3-pronged concept is critical to building a high performance team. We often forget about the part where the wrong people need to get off of our bus and onto the right bus for them.

Teams that perform at a top level have lower turnover. They have higher productivity and performance output. They have more emotionally satisfying lives at work. They are more confident in the direction of the organization. They are less likely to suffer a layoff or a termination. High performance teams make a higher net profit for their organizations. They are better in virtually every way than a low performing team or a group. They are what thousands of employees have told me that they want to be a part of. When you have the opportunity to be a member of a high performing team, you never want to let it go. The feeling of victory that you got from winning in dodge ball was nothing compared to what it feels like to be on a winning team at work and in life. So, let's dive in and discover what it takes to C.R.E.A.T.E. as a great team!

C.R.E.A.T.E.

Come Together

Come together in order to get the team moved from a group to a team. The first step in the process of creating a great team is to unite yourselves through the creation of a common set of values and the establishment of a shared mission and vision. So often, organizations create a "mission statement" but it doesn't really mean much. They say things like, "It is our mission to provide a place of healing and hope, where employees are family, our customers know that they are first, and where unicorns play nice with one another." Ok, maybe the unicorn thing isn't usually in there, but the rest is fluffy and pretty and mostly meaningless. When there is no depth of meaning to the statement; when it is long and drawn out; when it cannot be remembered by the team, then it is ineffective. The most effective mission and vision for a team is a simple sentence that will discuss the "why" of the organization or team. Blue Buffalo pet foods started with just dog food. The father and son team were the stars of their own commercials, along with some happy dogs. The dogs represented their reason for being. They state, "We just love dogs. That's why we make great dog food." It is a simple driver for performing their very best and doing what they do. And you know what… they are doing a great job of it. They are very busy, very profitable, and very tough to compete with. All of this began with a clear statement of why their employees were there. They were there because the company just loves dogs. That is their "why" for making incredible dog food. What is the fundamental reason, the why, behind your team existing? What is the driving force behind the existence of the company? When you know that for sure, you will begin to act in the right manner. You will begin to filter your interactions with your team, your decisions, and everything else that you do through your "why." Know your **why** and your **how** and your **what** will take care of itself.

Respond To Conflict; Don't React

Respond to conflict, don't react to it. Far too many teams begin to crumble because the team leader doesn't have a clear idea of what they will do when conflict arises. Think back to the conflict resolution chapter and remember that you spend more than a month, full-time, resolving conflict each year. When you react, you expand the conflict. Reacting is doing something without a plan and is based on emotion rather than on logic. It isn't that you won't have emotion when you are dealing with conflict. It is that you won't let the emotion be the reason for the conflict. Conflict is actually very good for the team when it is done right. It is devastating, however, when it is done wrong. The pattern that you use in handling yourself is the pattern that your people are likely to follow. If you explode, they explode. If you remain calm, they remain calm. They are looking to you as their example of what to do in a tough situation.

When you look at the origin of the word react, it has meant from the beginning to exert force in direct response to an outside force. It is the ball bouncing back after being thrown against a wall. It mentions nothing about a conscious choice. It mentions nothing about choosing a path, or moving in a specific direction. To react is to be controlled by an outside force. When you look at the origin of the word respond, it comes from the Latin *respondere*, and it means to answer to or to promise in return, to pledge a direction. Every aspect of the original word indicates that the person who responds is making a choice about what happens next. They are in control of themselves. They are evaluating the situation and pledging to go in a specific direction as a result.

When you make your conflict intentional and purposeful, you flex the decision making muscles of the team. You create opportunity to expand the possibilities related to the problem or challenge that you are facing. Conflict is at the heart of every great story and it is at the heart of the great story your team is writing right now. Learning to do conflict in the right way, with a positive purpose, and pledging to work together in conflict will propel you forward.

Ensure That People Get To shine

Ensure that people get to do what they do best, and as often as possible. One of the components of a fully engaged workforce is that of creating opportunities for people to live into their gifts. In school, we learn that we are to do what we are bad at until we get good at it. In life, we learn that we are to do what we are good at until we are great at it. One of my favorite parables related to this is that of the young forest animals that decide that they want to be better at being forest animals. They seek out the wisdom of the owl and ask the owl if he will be the headmaster of the school that they are forming. The owl agrees and the story begins.

On the first day of school, the owl, being wise and knowing that there is a large river in the middle of the forest, decides that the animals need to know how to swim. After all, there is a high likelihood that they will encounter the river that divides the two sides of the forest. So, the young animals, including a rabbit, a fish, a squirrel, and a bird, each await instructions on how to swim from the owl. He lectures them on buoyancy, currents, and all of the things necessary for them to be good swimmers. Then, he has the fish go first. The fish was phenomenal! It was like he was made to swim. He went up the stream, down the stream, and back and forth across the river. He had no trouble at all. He could even jump out of the water and land perfectly back in the water and keep going. He got an A+ for the day. The bird had been hunting for insects in the water so he was able dive in and come out, as well as flitter across the top of the water. He wasn't really swimming and the owl knew this, but he still gave him a B for his efforts. The squirrel jumped in the water and kicked like crazy. He floated fairly well and could keep his back legs behind him to make it across the water. It was hard work, but he did really well. The owl gave him an A- for the day. Finally, it was the rabbit's turn to jump in. When he did, he went straight to the bottom and pushed off as hard as he could. His front legs didn't do much for him in trying to paddle and he couldn't get his back legs out behind him. So, he bobbed up and down in the water, pushing off of the bottom of the river and struggling for air when he came up. He was horrible at it and the fish even had to help him make it back to the side without drowning. Disappointed, the owl told him that he had failed for the day and would need to focus only on swimming until he had mastered it. So, the next day, and the next, and the next, he struggled to survive while swimming. By the time that the end of the week rolled around, he approached the owl and said that he was quitting school because he simply wasn't any good at it. The owl, having witnessed him fail daily at swimming, agreed and the rabbit was out. He had given up on being a part of that team because he couldn't do what the fish could do.

What if he was never supposed to do what the fish could do, though? In fact, what if they had started with hopping as their first subject? Don't you think that the rabbit would have been successful and the fish would have 'flopped?' (Pun intended) The simple truth about each of us is that we are no different than the animals in this story. If we are given the opportunity to do what we do best every day, then we love our jobs and value our team. But, if we are required to only do the things that we struggle with, then we will soon become discouraged, then disengaged, and then finally… we quit altogether. Go out of your way to discover the talents of your team members. Find ways to get them plugged in doing what they do best and you will see them flourish as members of a great team and a great organization.

Acquire A Winning Spirit

Acquire a winning spirit – Make it fun and worthwhile to be a part of your team. In order for the relationships on the team to grow and become stronger, you will need to have the right mindset as a team. According to Dr. Carol Dwek, the mindset of individuals, as well as the mindset of the team, often result from the mindset of the leader. One study on how the mindset of a teacher impacts the mindset of a student showed that when a teacher was told that their class was full of only the most gifted and talented, the smartest and most dedicated students, the students flourished. When a teacher was told that their class was full of kids who struggled, who were incapable of learning, who caused trouble and made things difficult, the students did very poorly. The amount of work accomplished by the class expected to be full of top performers was more than 5 times that of the class that was expected to perform poorly. The reality of the situation was that there was nothing special about either class. What was special was the expectation of the supervisor of the students… the teacher.

A winning mindset begins with the leader of the team. It begins with the idea that the team can, should, and will succeed. When that is the belief of the leader, then the leader will look for those things in their team. This is not some mystical transformation that happens but rather a simple adjustment in the conscious filter. The Reticular Activating System is the portion of the brain that lets the conscious mind know what to look for. As we discussed earlier in this book, the subconscious mind has the capacity to process 400 Billion bits of information per second. The conscious mind can only process 2000 bits of information per second. This means that the human mind has to have filters so that the conscious mind doesn't get overloaded. Habits operate out of the subconscious. Our cardiovascular and respiratory requirements happen at a subconscious level as well. But the conscious mind spends it's time deleting information, distorting it to fit within its beliefs, and generalizing what comes its way. So, if a leader has a belief that their people are lazy and inept, then the conscious mind is triggered to find those things in the team. The theory of quantum reality says that by putting attention on a thing, we create its existence. This means that we are creating self-perpetuating prophecies in our people. We are literally turning them into superstars or disappointments by focusing on one end of the performance spectrum or the other. Not magic, but science explains why some people perform and others do not. It is such simple science that many people will have trouble accepting it. The simple science is that where your attention goes, your results will show.

Having a winning attitude means beginning with the image of your team being built of top performers. It means beginning with the image of the very best coming from each member of the team. The more you hold this vision in your mind, the easier it becomes to expect that level of performance from your team. When you expect it, are willing to coach toward it, and believe with all of your heart that you have a winning team with the potential to do anything that they set their minds to, then your team will live into your image of them. Start with the image. Hold that image in your mind every day for at least five minutes. Set that level of performance expectation. Believe with all of your being that your team can and will succeed. Then, go out of your way to prove yourself right for believing in them. That is the formula for creating a winning attitude about your team, and ultimately in your team.

Trust Your Team To Be A Team

Trust your team to be their own team and they will become the team you had always desired them to be. It is only in trusting them that they will know that we believe in them. Trust is the belief in the reliability, truth, ability, and strength of the team. It is founded in faith instead of fear. Too often, the supervisor of a team operates out of the fear of "but what if." The question plagues the minds of supervisors and makes them wonder if the team will ever be good enough. It makes them question the actions of each team member and creates a divide between members. It makes them want to micro-manage the team and causes them to distrust the actions of the individual members of the team. This fear mentality creates distrust in every direction.

Think about what it is like to wonder if others want the best for you. Think about what it is like to be unsure of the motives of others and then to have your mind wander into the darkness and imagine only the bad things. Now, think about what it is like to know that others want only the best for you and for their team. Think about what it is like to be sure of the motives of others and to know without any doubt that those motives are good. Imagine your mind wandering into the light and seeing that the team is there to win and only to win. Imagine that they wake up every day excited about the opportunity to work with you, their supervisor. Imagine how different your life is when you see the good in others versus the bad in others.

One of the key components of doing this is to spend time every single day looking at the good of the team in your own mind. Hold a vision of what they have to offer and focus on your belief in their ability. It is in holding a positive vision of their success that you create that very vision in their minds. Even more importantly, it is only in holding that vision of them in your mind that you will begin to act according to the positive vision. You will act according to what you believe about your team. All human action begins with a belief about something. That belief becomes your thought. That thought becomes your action. And that action creates your result. Believe good about your team. Trust them enough to let your guard down. Look for the good that they bring to the table, and they will bring more and more of it every day.

Every Person Matters

Every person matters. When one leaves, the team starts over. When a new one arrives, the team starts over. There isn't a single person on the team that does not have value. If that were the case, the causation would be that they were hired without a purpose and were not selected with any measure of scrutiny. Your team matters first because each member of the team matters. Your team experiences true motivation and true connection when they fully understand the purpose that they serve and are given the opportunity to operate within their area of brilliance.

Take the time to know each member of the team fully. This is accomplished by spending time with each of them. When you spend even five minutes on a weekly basis in one-on-one conversation with your direct team, then you create a deeper bond with each person. Some supervisors worry that they will care too much about their people if they do this and will not be able to "make the tough decisions" when they are necessary. Keep in mind that respect is always a two-way street. When you develop that bond with your team members, they also develop that bond with you. The more they trust you, the more driven they are to perform for you. Your objective was always to accomplish work through other people because they wanted work accomplished through them. You are there to get them to want to do what you need them to do. This requires a relationship. It is not accomplished simply for the sake of a paycheck.

In developing this depth in the relationship, you find out for sure what their personal area of brilliance is. Once you have discovered what it is that they are truly great at, you can begin to create opportunities for them to live into that brilliance on a daily basis. Go out of your way to give them the chance to do what they do best. Give them the chance to shine in front of their peers and in front of you, their supervisor. When you give them this opportunity, they are filled with intrinsic motivation, which endears them further to the team, which drives them to want to perform at even greater levels. Think about the way in which you operate the best with your manager. When they find ways for you to shine, you automatically believe that they want the best for you. When you do this for your people, they believe in you, their leader!

P.E.R.F.O.R.M.

In order for the team to function at its best, you must do the following. Each of the letters in this acronym represents an action that should be integrated as a part of your daily routine with your team. The more you practice the components of the book the easier it is to turn them from an idea into a habit. Once they are a part of the way that you supervise and lead, there are new neuro-pathways that are formed. Charles Duhigg indicates that these habit loops operate out of a different portion of the brain than conscious thought. They can run in the background with virtually no effort on your part, once they are habit. Spend time each and every day focusing on building the habits of a successful person and it will pay off for you in the end.

Pay Attention

Pay attention to what is not being said. 93% of all communication is non-verbal. This is true of the individual and it is true of a group. In the communication chapter, you learned to watch for signs from others that would indicate how they really feel. The same is necessary within a team setting as is necessary within one on one communication. When you see one employee roll their eyes, or wince slightly, or give off a negative sign, you need to connect with them and ask what is going on. Depending on the trust level of the group, you may be able to have that discussion at the exact time that the negative sign happens. It is actually ideal to be able to talk about it right then. Chances are good that others on the team saw the same thing that you did and would like to know what it meant as well.

Engage Your People

Engage your people every single day. This can be done very simply with the old MBWA strategy. This is Management By Walking Around. You cannot engage people that you are not connected with. As a supervisor, your people need to see you. They need to know that you are thinking about them and want them to perform at their very best. Engage them in conversation. Discuss the work that they are doing. Find ways to affirm their good behaviors. Coach their negative ones. Be in continuous contact with them in order to help them see their own potential. You being engaged as a leader will result in them being engaged as followers. You go first. You invest time in them through random acts of kindness and senseless acts of beauty. Appreciate them. Talk to them. Engage with them.

Reward Top Performance

Reward top performance. Peter Drucker, considered one of the greatest management gurus to have lived, taught, and inspired, admonished that rewarding performance was required, not recommended. He said that the greatest sin of leadership is to not reward performance. A top performer should be rewarded in both the soul and the wallet. It is unfortunate when an organization sets up pay for tenure programs instead of pay for performance programs. As you learned in the motivation chapter, money is not the driver for performance. However, what money represents is the driver for performance when it comes to the top performers. When they are appreciated with bonuses, raises, and the like, they are more apt to continue performing at their very best. When a non-performer is given the same raise or the same bonus as a top performer, it demoralizes the top performer and does nothing to help the non-performer. Typically, your top 20% in your department should get the best raises. Your average 60% should get a cost of living raise. And, your non-performers, if you have them, should not get a raise at all. This keeps your top performers feeling appreciated and puts the attention on their performance. By doing this, you encourage the average folks to behave more like the superstars.

Focus On Results

Focus on what you want more of. When you focus all of your attention on the couple of folks that are not bringing you results for the teams, then you tend to have average performers declining in their productive work output. When you put your focus on the top performers, then you tend to drive your average folks up toward top performance. This, in turn, drives the top performers even higher in their productive output. Where your focus goes, your results show. Knowing this, focus your attention on the things that you want from the people that are already demonstrating their drive toward success. You are setting the entire team up for success when you put your attention and your appreciation on the top performers on your team.

Observe Behaviors

Observe behaviors every single day. You should be a student of your employees when it comes to the things that they are doing. When they are on their game, you should appreciate them by recognizing the specific positive behavior that they exhibited. When things aren't going well, you have to notice that also. The sooner that you notice the good and the bad behaviors, the sooner you get more of the good and less of the bad. It is in the behaviors that your employees exhibit that you can recognize when things are going right in their lives and when things are going wrong. It is in seeing the subtle changes in the way that they do their job that you can stay ahead of the coaching curve. Think about the concepts that you learned in the coaching chapter and apply those to your people by knowing what is going on in their lives every day.

Require Results

Results matter, so drive your team toward them and allow them to drive themselves. It is ideal that they look for ways to hold themselves accountable for results. This begins with you establishing the truth that every choice creates a result. It isn't really about positive or negative accountability. It is about teaching your team that their choices simply lead to results, or outcomes. When you have established the end-goal of the team, then you can observe the behaviors that they are exhibiting, and map out the behaviors to results at the end and back to choices in the beginning. Your focus is on getting them to make all of the right choices because they lead to all the right actions, and ultimately to all the right results. You were hired or promoted to achieve results. This is done by establishing that the results do matter. Then you must help the team understand what choices lead to the results that you are looking for. It is in our moments of decision that we create our outcomes.

Make The Team MORE First

Make the team more first than the customer and they will make the customer first. Too often, companies will tell their employees and their supervisors that the customer is first and that they matter more than any employee. Too often, companies will teach their supervisors to operate out of fear and to scare, cajole, and at times fire employees to satisfy an angry customer. This simply does NOT produce the long-term positive effects that companies indicate that they want. I have heard from hundreds of companies and witnessed this phenomenon over and over again. When you go out of your way to take care of the customer but not the employee, then the employee will not take care of the customer. When you go out of your way to take care of the employee and to ensure that they are well-trained, motivated, engaged, and safe, then they go way out of their way to take care of the customer. If you are going to make your customer first, then you simply have to make your employees MORE first. Take care of the people that take care of the customer and the profits will take care of themselves.

THE MOST SUCCESSFUL TEAM IS ONE WHERE EACH INDIVIDUAL IS FOCUSED ON THE SUCCESS OF EVERY OTHER MEMBER OF THE TEAM!

LEADERSHIP

LEARNING OBJECTIVES

- Understand a team versus a group and learn how to come together as a team
- Learn the stages of team development and how they impact our interactions
- Understand and identify the roles that we play within a team
- Learn to move through the developmental stages to team success
- Identify the characteristics of a team and learn to manage expectations
- Learn to identify and deal with the potential problems within a team

LEADERSHIP

DO TEAMS WORK?

"Most teams aren't teams at all but merely collections of individual relationships with the boss. Each individual vying with the others for power, prestige and position."

--Douglas McGregor

LEADERSHIP

TEAMS VERSUS GROUPS

Groups are united by a common set of obligations. A group pushes its members to fulfill an objective.

Teams are united by a common set of values and beliefs. A team pulls its members by a sense of purpose.

LEADERSHIP

WHAT TEAMS HAVE YOU BEEN A PART OF?

SPORTS	**VOLUNTEER**
ACADEMIC	**FAMILY**
WORK	**OTHER?**

C.R.E.A.T.E

Come together
Respond to conflict, don't react
Ensure that people get to operate in brilliance
Acquire a winning spirit
Trust your team to be their own team and yours
Every person matters

COME TOGETHER

When we form as a team, we tend to give people the benefit of the doubt, but often skip getting to really know one another.

Learn the people on your team. Study their personalities. Understand their goals and drives.

LEADERSHIP

RESPOND TO CONFLICT

Positive conflict is the basis for good decision making. It is natural to have disagreement. When the process of disagreement is mastered, the team continues to move forward and grow. If it is not mastered, the team stagnates and does not move forward.

LEADERSHIP

ENSURE THAT PEOPLE GET TO OPERATE IN BRILLIANCE

Finding the "Points of Mastery" is one of the 3 critical components that Dan Pink discusses in his book, Drive.
When people get to do what they are each good at, they are more engaged and the team finds its niche'.

LEADERSHIP

ACQUIRE A WINNING SPIRIT

When the team knows one another, is good at conflict, individually and collectively get to operate in brilliance, then results / outcomes must be the next target.
It is a lot of fun to win as a team! When you keep the winning concept in front of them and inspire them to greatness, then everyone wins together!

LEADERSHIP

TRUST YOUR TEAM TO BE THEIR OWN TEAM… AND YOURS

Empowerment is the process of providing clear direction, co-establishing goals, equipping your team members to win, and helping them learn from failures and setbacks.

It is not the absence of a leader or the abdication of responsibility!

LEADERSHIP

EVERY PERSON MATTERS – APPRECIATE THEM

When the team knows one another, is good at conflict, individually and collectively get to operate in brilliance, then results / outcomes must be the next target.
It is a lot of fun to win as a team! When you keep the winning concept in front of them and inspire them to greatness, then everyone wins together!

Bruce Tuckman (1965 and 1972)

THE STAGES OF TEAM DEVELOPMENT

LEADERSHIP

STAGES OF TEAM DEVELOPMENT

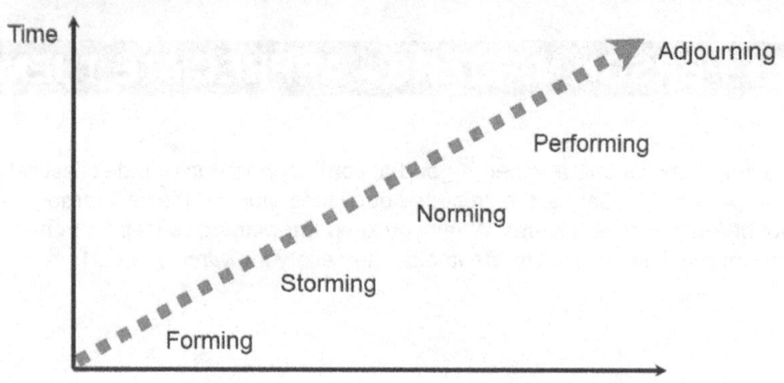

Learn2Lead
Supervise · Influence · Motivate

LEADERSHIP

FORMING

- Anxiety
- Dependence on Leader
- Uncertainty over what behaviors are acceptable
- Lack of clarity regarding the purpose and future of the group

LEADERSHIP

WHAT DOES THE TEAM DO DURING FORMING?

- Defines the problem
- Agrees on goals and formulates strategies for tackling the tasks
- Determines the challenges and identifies information needed
- Individuals take on certain roles
- Develops trust and communication

LEADERSHIP

STORMING

- Conflict between sub-groups
- Opposition towards group leader
- Resistance and Conflict
- Lack of Control
- Polarization

LEADERSHIP

WHAT DO TEAM MEMBERS DO DURING STORMING?

- Realize that the task is more difficult than they imagined
- Have fluctuations in attitude about chances of success
- May be resistant to the task
- May have poor collaboration
- Must learn to disagree without destroying relationships

LEADERSHIP

NORMING

- Cohesion emerges
- Norms are developed through practice
- Group identity promoted
- Resistance and conflict reduced

LEADERSHIP

DURING NORMING, THE TEAM WILL ACCEPT...

- Each other as a team
- The team's rules and procedures
- Their specific roles in the team
- The individuality of fellow members, and embrace their diversity

Learn 2 Lead
Supervise · Influence · Motivate

LEADERSHIP

PERFORMING

- Interpersonal problems no longer occur
- Roles are clear while also flexible
- Structure is geared to achievement of the goals of the group

Learn 2 Lead
Supervise · Influence · Motivate

LEADERSHIP

DURING PERFORMING, THE TEAM MEMBERS HAVE...

- Gained insight into personal and team processes
- Developed a better understanding of each other's strengths and weaknesses
- Become skilled in the ability to prevent or work through group conflict and resolve differences
- Developed an identity as a member of the team and become attached to the team emotionally and psychologically

ADJOURNING

- The group come to a natural end
- This can occur when...
  - The task or purpose of the group has been achieved
  - The task or purpose of the group cannot be achieved
  - There is a significant change in the group (leader / key member / etc)

Learn2Lead
Supervise · Influence · Motivate

LEADERSHIP

WHAT HAPPENS WHEN WE ADJOURN?

The team can and often does experience sadness over the loss of the team identity

The team may experience upset or anger over the lack of success, if the team failed to meet its objectives

The team may seek out ways to "re-form" in order to come back together (getting the band back together)

LEADERSHIP

SUMMARY

Understand the advantages, disadvantages and application of various types of group communication

Understand the difference between groups and teams

There are five stages of group development

1. Forming
2. Storming
3. Norming
4. Performing
5. Adjourning

LEADERSHIP

According To Research By Belbin, There Are Specific Roles That We Fill On Our Teams.

WHAT ROLES DO WE PLAY ON TEAMS?

LEADERSHIP

BELBIN'S MANAGEMENT TEAM ROLES

THE IDEAL PERSON/THE PLANT

Shares novel suggestions

RESOURCE INVESTIGATOR

Evaluates which contributions are practical and discovers where resources can be allocated

MONITOR/EVALUATOR

Determines how valid the contributions are and to whether the group is meeting their objectives

LEADERSHIP

BELBIN'S MANAGEMENT TEAM ROLES

TEAM WORKER

Maintains the group through humor and agreeing

COMPLETER/FINISHER

Tries to get things done and suggests conclusions

LEADERSHIP

BELBIN'S MANAGEMENT TEAM ROLES

THE COMPANY WORKER

Ensures that the organization's priorities are followed

THE CHAIR

Ensures that all perspectives are heard and keeps things moving

THE SHAPER

Influences by use of argument and by following certain topics

Learn2Lead

HOW DO WE MOVE THROUGH TEAM DEVELOPMENT TOWARD SUCCESS?

P.E.R.F.O.R.M

Pay attention
Engage your people
Reward top performance
Focus on behavioral results
Observe behaviors
Require outcome results
Make the team MORE first

LEADERSHIP

P: PAY ATTENTION

Focus on your team! Don't get bogged down in administrative tasks and forget that you are there to lead people, and… to get the paperwork done.

Watch the performance of your team. Know when it is time to connect and motivate.

Learn2Lead
Supervise · Influence · Motivate

LEADERSHIP

E: ENGAGE YOUR PEOPLE

Provide the chance to work independently, to control their own destinies, without ignoring them.

Build their skills in areas that they love and help them master their world. Always keep the "why" in front of them. Help them live with purpose.

LEADERSHIP

R: REWARD TOP PERFORMANCE

Drucker… "It is a leadership sin to not reward your top performers in both the soul and the wallet."

Appreciate Performers
Build Them Up
Reward Them and Inspire Them

LEADERSHIP

F: FOCUS ON BEHAVIORAL RESULTS

Reinforce Good Behaviors
Confront and Coach Bad Behaviors
Clearly define the expected outcomes
Stay tuned in to your team to guide them along the path

LEADERSHIP

O: OBSERVE BEHAVIORS… AND RESPOND

- You set the tone for what the employees do or don't do.
- Your level of engagement as the team leader has a tremendous impact on the actions of the team.
- Pay attention to the results that you are getting and adjust "YOU" if necessary.

LEADERSHIP

R: REQUIRE OUTCOME RESULTS

Every team that you were on when you were young required that you "DO" in order to be on the team.

The leader sets the tone for the outcomes that are expected and will be achieved. You are here to accomplish great things!

LEADERSHIP

M: MAKE THE TEAM MORE FIRST!

Richard Branson – "It is perfectly okay for the customer to be first as long as the team is more first."

People work for a leader that inspires, protects, drives, and engages them.

Learn2Lead
Supervise · Influence · Motivate

LEADERSHIP

ACTIVITIES TO BUILD THE TEAM

25 Activities In A Bag

Socialization

Development

Planning

Learn2Lead
Supervise · Influence · Motivate

LEADERSHIP

What are the characteristics that will make your team either win or lose?

CHARACTERISTICS OF EFFECTIVE TEAMS

LEADERSHIP

CHARACTERISTICS OF EFFECTIVE TEAMS

- Membership Standards
- Performance Goals
- Collaboration
- Interaction
- Shared Values
- Shared Vision
- Identification
- Interdependency

LEADERSHIP

5 PHASES OF GROUP SOCIALIZATION

An appreciation of the role of groups within the organization offers considerable benefits to the employee, manager and organization

THERE ARE FIVE PHASES OF GROUP SOCIALIZATION

Investigation
Socialization
Maintenance
Resocialization
Remembrance

Learn2Lead
Supervise · Influence · Motivate

LEADERSHIP

SUMMARY

Group cohesiveness is the extent to which a group is committed to remaining together

The forces that create cohesiveness are attraction to the group, resistance to leaving the group, and the motivation to remain a member of the group

LEADERSHIP

4 STAGES OF GROUP PROGRESSION

There are four main stages of group progression

1. Mutual Acceptance
2. Communication & Decision Making
3. Motivation & Productivity
4. Control & Organization

LEADERSHIP

There are a number of things that can prevent a team from winning together. One of the most impactful is not realizing and embracing the idea that you are a team and you are supposed to win TOGETHER!

POTENTIAL PROBLEMS WITHIN A TEAM

LEADERSHIP

TEAM CHALLENGES

Mismanaged Conflict
Power & Politics
Overbearing Experts
Unclear Focus
Mismanaged Agreement
Lack of Participation
Dominated Participation (1 Person)
Lack of Follow-Through

LEADERSHIP

DEALING WITH CONFLICTS

- Symptoms
    - Feuding
    - Disagreements
- Tips
    - Be alert; nip resolve conflict while small
    - Look for areas of agreement (win / win)
    - Keep comments focused on topic
    - Avoid judgmental language
    - Help each understand the other's point of view
    - Ask for help
    - "No one can whistle a symphony. It takes an orchestra to play it."

-- H.E. Luccock

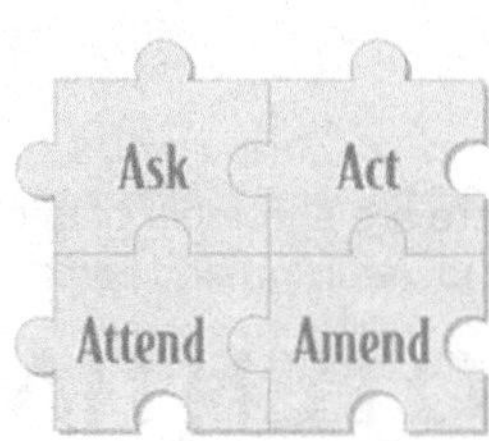

LEADERSHIP

PROBLEMS WITH POWER

- Symptoms
  - Dominant individual decides and everyone falls in line
  - Dominant individual discourages discussion
  - Team does not say what they think when dominant individual is around
- Tips
  - Well-defined ground rules
  - Ask "followers" for input first
  - Avoid situations when discussion is discouraged
  - Speak up when someone's power is hurting team

"It's what you learn after you know it all that counts."

-- John Wooden

LEADERSHIP

OVERBEARING EXPERT

- Symptoms
  - Expert discourages discussion
  - Expert uses excessive technical jargon
  - Team members follow without challenges
- Tips
  - Do not let team substitute "expertise" for "discussion"
  - Ask experts to discuss in plain language or explain meaning; ask experts to draw picture
  - Ask experts to teach team

"If we don't discipline ourselves, the world will do it for us."

--William Feather

LEADERSHIP

LACK OF FOCUS

- Symptoms
  - Flounderingor wandering off the path
  - Too much to do
  - Too many distractions
- Tips
  - Clarify team's purpose, deadlines, limits, etc.
  - Use agendas - set time limits for topics
  - Discuss one issue at a time
  - If off track step back and summarize

"There are no short cuts to any place worth going."

-- Beverly Sills

LEADERSHIP

TOO MUCH AGREEMENT

- Symptoms
  - No one disagrees or raises objections
  - No alternatives are offered
  - All focus on why it is right – "bandwagon" effect
- Tips
  - Avoid groupthink
  - Brainstorm before discussing any specific alternative
  - Speak up if you have different point of view
  - All ideas should be examined for merit
  - Solicit "devil's advocate" to challenge solution

"Team player: One who unites others toward a shared destiny through sharing information and ideas, empowering others and developing trust."

-- Dennis Kinlaw

LEADERSHIP

UNEVEN PARTICIPATION

- Symptoms
  - Some members talk too much
  - Others talk too little
- Tips
  - Establish ground rules that everyone is expected to share
  - Speak up when you have something to say
  - Proactively use methods for hearing from all members take turns; ask quiet members for their viewpoints
  - Break into smaller groups to encourage participation

"None of us is as smart as all of us."

-- Ken Blanchard

LEADERSHIP

LACK OF FOLLOW-THROUGH

- Symptoms
  - Tasks do not get done on time
  - People do not do assignments between meetings
  - People will not volunteer to do tasks
- Tips
  - Coach team members
  - Schedule time on calendar for volunteer tasks
  - Ask for help if having trouble completing task
  - Ask for help prioritizing or re-scheduling overload
  - Short interval scheduling
  - Ask "How'z it goin'" from time to time

"Up is never where you are now."

-- Belasco & Stayer

LEADERSHIP

TEAM ROLES AND THE LEADER

- Task Master
- Innovator
- Organizer
- Evaluator
- Finisher

"I am easily satisfied with the very best."

-- Winston Churchill

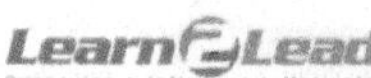

LEADERSHIP

TEAM BUILDING

- Everyone wants to feel like they "belong"
- So each team member needs to:
    - Be treated with respect
    - Be valued and allowed to contribute
- Leaders lead best by serving/example
- Leaders lead best by using their influence to improve lives

"We must all hang together, or assuredly, we shall all hang separately."

-- Benjamin Franklin

12 ETHICS, VALUES, CULTURE

The ethics in which we frame our world will determine the world in which we live. In business, as in life, if you have ethics, nothing else matters. If you don't have ethics, nothing else matters. The world that you will ultimately create will be based on the ethics, values, and culture that you create. Some companies are creating their world on accident. The smart ones are creating it on purpose.

When you trace the origin of the word, ethics, it refers to the "science of morals." It can also be traced to Aristotle's work, Ta Ethika. Morals, in the origin of the word, comes from the 14th Century and means pertaining to character or temperament. Good morals represent proper behavior of a person in society. Bad morals represent improper behavior of a person in society. The ethical standards by which we operate have changed over the years. However, the understanding that the ethics by which one operates is a reflection of who that person is has remained a constant.

We have transitioned from an absolute set of ethical standards to an optional set of ethical standards. Over the past four generations, a trend line can be seen that would depict the change in what it means to operate with ethics. Every country will have a set of standards, often unspoken, that demonstrate what it means to be a person of ethics. Some religions have different standards of ethical interaction that will vary based on whether the other person is a member of your religion or not. It is important to point out that the ethics of a society belong to that society. Therefore, to operate in an ethical manner in one society may not be accepted or may be too stringent or too loose in another society. Your ethics are your behaviors related to the beliefs of both you and the people around you.

In order to illustrate this, we will go through four different levels of ethical thought patterns. Each of these thought patterns is simply that, a thought pattern. Most people will find that they do NOT operate with a set of absolutes in their life. As an example, ask yourself whether or not stealing is wrong. Then, ask yourself whether or not stealing in order to feed your starving family is wrong. Quite often the context of the question is what determines the person's thoughts about the ethics of the situation. A more extreme example, but one that makes a person think is answering the question of whether or not it is wrong to kill. You then ask, is it wrong to kill for fun? Finally, if someone is trying to kill you and your family, is it wrong to kill them in order to save the lives of your family? The point is that things often seem black and white, easy to understand, until you add in situational subjectivity. Taking yourself out of a situation and looking at it from a different perspective often gives you the vantage point that you need in order to make a good decision. We have to take a look at life from every angle in order to know for sure which angle is the one that we will choose. The following poem helps to illustrate that outside perspective on ethics.

A Poem About Ethics

When you step away from your first person view of your life and look from a distance, what do you see?
Are you the person that your mother, your father, your family, or society wanted you to be?
Do you have a set of standards that guide your every thought?
Do you carefully look at life and consistently do what you ought?
Life is full of choices about who you are and what the world will mean.
Establish your standards now; eliminate the uncertainty, or you will surely be caught in between.
Your life is what you make it in the choices that you choose.
Having high moral standards will set you on the path to win, but low standards will make you lose.
You are a product of your beliefs, and your thoughts flow out of these.
When your thoughts are aligned with good ethics, knowing what to do is a breeze.

Ethics are not always at the forefront of the minds of business people. It is unfortunate that people don't always think about their behaviors and the impact that those behaviors will have on other people, as well as on their business. When you move up into supervision or even higher into management/leadership roles, your conduct is scrutinized more intensely. The higher up you move in an organization, the more closely others will observe you to see what you are doing. Knowing this to have been consistent over the years, you will want to have a clear understanding of the four levels of ethics and will want to determine how you will be known by others.

A.L.S.O.

Absolute – There is an absolute right and an absolute wrong. In the past, this type of ethical viewpoint has been referred to as "religious ethics" or "unwavering ethics." The idea behind this viewpoint is that there are absolutes in life. Often times, people will think that they operate with this model until a situation arises that makes them choose. Historically, older generations were more likely to operate within the absolutes. The traditionalists, for example, often viewed life as a set of clear cut options regardless of the situation that existed or the crowd that a person was with. John Maxwell even wrote a book titled, There's No Such Thing As Business Ethics. Maxwell wasn't saying that ethics don't exist in business. His point was that ethics were set and did not waver from business to personal.

Legal – Right and wrong are measured by legal means without regard to absolutes. The American Justice System operates with this set of standards for ethics. Laws are often enacted in order to clarify what is right and what is wrong. For example, it is wrong to kill, unless you are imposing the death penalty in a state where that is legal, or in cases where it can be proven that you were defending your life or the life of your family. It is wrong to steal. It is wrong to give false testimony. It is wrong to do a whole list of things. Thousands of new laws and regulations have been put into place in the last decade to clarify the ethics of any given situation. As the thoughts drift more toward situational and optional ethical standards, the necessity for legal standards to clarify the situation become more critical.

Situational – Right and wrong are measured by the situation that the person is in at that moment. This means that a person will have to evaluate every situation that they are in and determine what the acceptable behavior is related to the situation. It is not necessarily wrong to do anything unless it is done in the wrong context. It is the context that gives the ethics life or makes them illegitimate. This is much more difficult to manage because the interpretation of the situation comes into play. Every person has their own version of reality and therefore their own version of what ethical behavior actually is.

Optional – Right and wrong are relative to whether or not the person gets caught and whether or not they feel bad about what they are doing. A disturbing trend of politicians, CEOs, and other leaders since 2009 is the idea that they know better than the rest of the world. You see politicians rewriting laws as well as the Constitution in order to fit their plans/agendas. You see CEOs stealing money in the name of… but I was helping. Ethics have taken a sharp nosedive and become much more customized to what each person wants. The challenge with this type of thinking is that there is no end to the dilemma. If there is no set standard in how a society is to treat one another, then there is no order in that society. Think about people that you know or have observed that operate from a viewpoint of doing whatever they feel is right regardless of laws, norms, regulations, etc. Think about what that type of interaction means to society as a whole and how it impacts you specifically. What if there were no rules governing the way that people do business with you? What if each person simply chose their version of ethical and moral behavior? What would society look like then?

Values

Values are the abstract ideals that shape an individual's thoughts, decisions, and behaviors. Think of values like the moral compass that is always guiding the thoughts of a person. These ideals can be derived from the religious upbringing of a person, the philosophical exposure that a person has had, and/or from the teachings of their family or other key influencers. Ultimately, we are the sum total of the labels that we have given to the varying experiences in our lives. Think back to what your life was like between the ages of 7 and 14. What was going on in the world? What was the world like? Who were your role models? The things that they did, said, and ingrained in your mind are the things that shaped a large chunk of your values.

Your instrumental values are the ones that pop up in your every day life. They are what comprise your habit loops, the rituals that you follow, and your daily routine. They guide the simple decisions on how you interpret the world. Most people don't think about these values because they are running like a background program in their minds. They were developed in your mind before the age of 14 and they seem like simple truth because you have had them as a part of your being for so long.

Your terminal values are what guide your "end game." The idea of getting to heaven or what you believe for the "afterlife" is perhaps the biggest terminal value model that you have. Other terminal values also guide people. Things like financial success, self-sufficiency, power, influence, or virtually anything that you seek out to accomplish by or before the end of your life are considered terminal values. One of the ways to know what your terminal values are is to conduct the "tombstone test." This is the process of determining what you would want people to say about you in a eulogy about your life or what you would want printed on your tombstone when you are gone. One of the eye-opening exercises that you can do is to compare what you think people would say no if you died versus what you want them to say. Based on that comparison, it allows you to determine what changes in your value structure you would need to make in order to receive the eulogy that you actually want.

Organizational Values

Organizational values are the collective set of filters that an organization uses to determine the direction, behaviors, and ultimately the culture of the company. Organizational values reflect the essence of who the company is. They are what drive the decision-making of the organization and ultimately the outcomes. These organizational values are the skeletal structure of the culture that exists within a company. Consider the values that you believe are the heart and soul of your organization. Do you believe in integrity, or performance, or profit, or employee care, or something else? What are the values that you see in the behaviors of your organizational leaders? Even more importantly, what are the values that your employees see you demonstrating as their supervisor? When you think about the way that you behave and what values those behaviors reflect, you get a picture of what is actually going on. If you don't like the picture that you see, then think about what behaviors would reflect the values that you want to be known for. Then, demonstrate those new values through your behaviors every day. Ultimately, you are responsible for your behavioral choices. Those choices reflect a larger truth about the values that drive you in business and in life.

Culture

The culture of a company is essentially the personality that the company portrays. It is a collective representation of how the company sees the world and what the company is doing to establish its identity. When you think of culture, think of it as the heartbeat of the company. It is what makes the company click. When the company culture is dead or is toxic, then the employees get sick, or at least sick of coming to work. The culture that exists for any given company is what will ultimately determine whether or not the company is profitable. A company can have the very best product or service in the world and they will still fail if the culture is bad. Culture itself is what keeps life pumping in the veins of the company. The employees in this scenario are the cardiovascular system. They respond and react to what is going on in the heart and brain of the business. When the culture is bad, then the cardiovascular system is weak and it underperforms.

The objective of any organization should be to create the best culture possible so that the body of the company functions at its peak potential. In order to understand this more fully, the following acronym will help outline what it takes to create a great culture in your organization.

C.U.L.T.U.R.E.

C – Creative expression

Each person has something at which they are truly brilliant. They have an ability or a talent that needs to be expressed in order for them to feel fully alive. It is in the expression of their gift that they feel they are living into what they were made for. As a supervisor and coach, a big part of your job is to be tuned in to your employees. You will need to understand who they are, how they think, what motivates them, and what they are really good at. Think back to the story of the forest animals in this book. In that story, when the rabbit was required to do what he was bad at over and over again, he eventually quit. That parable describes much of what modern education is like. It requires kids to do what they are not good at instead of creating an environment where they get to do what they are really good at. Since most of us grew up with that as the model for us to follow, most of us have followed that flawed model even in business. Your focus has to shift away from overcoming weaknesses and towards a strength-based model. This requires that you be in touch with and know your people.

By taking the time to speak with each of your direct reports on a weekly basis, even if it is just for five minutes, you learn about them as a person. When you learn who they are as a person, you begin to get an image in your mind of who they are and what they bring to the table. That image continues to grow in clarity as you create opportunities for your people to shine. From a sports perspective, you would never put a really great lineman (football) at running back. Those are two different skillsets. In business, when you hire people, you do so because you needed a person to fulfill a need and they need a job to fulfill their own needs. Once you have them, invest time in that person in order to understand where they will be the happiest and most productive. Find ways to shape the job to fit the person if possible. After all, happy employees consistently produce more results and better results. Every single day, give each employee the chance to do something that they can win at. This keeps their mind focused on winning and their hearts in the game. People find ways to express their creativity and their strengths in a culture that embraces that expression. Creativity is self-expression and self-expression is the embracing of membership within that team.

U – Understanding

Understanding runs in several directions. Employees need to understand the organization's purpose and its process for accomplishing that purpose. More importantly, however, employees need to know that their supervisors, managers, and leaders understand them as a person. As the old saying goes, "People don't care how much you know until they know how much you care." When you evaluate the way that you are supervising others, would you say that it is easy to see that you care about them? Do your employees know without any doubt that you want the very best for them? If you can't answer that with definiteness of purpose, then you may not be on the right track. You will want to step back and evaluate your interactions to ensure that others will interpret what you are doing as caring.

If you don't know your people, they won't know you. If you don't know at least three things about them personally, they will not feel that you are connected to them. It doesn't take a lifetime to create a connection. A connection, once created, will often last a lifetime though. When you are sitting down with each of your team members, learn the following five things.

1. Their birthday – Put their birthday on your calendar and have it repeat yearly. By doing this, they will be amazed at the fact that you think about them on this special day.
2. A hobby – Learn about something that they do for fun outside of work. Discover what it is that jazzes them up, gets them excited, and makes them feel alive when they are spending time elsewhere.
3. An event that helped shape them – When you discover something that happened in their life that helped turn them into who they are, you can increase your connection. Those major events that

shape people are what create thought patterns and reshape their values.

4. A dream – You need to discover something that they hope to do or accomplish in their life. For example, you may have an employee that dreams of getting a college degree. You may have another that dreams of going to a Major League Baseball game. Whatever the dream is, know it and talk to them about it. Encourage them to pursue it and believe in their ability to achieve it.

A talent or skill – As discussed earlier, it is critically important to know what a person is good at, related specifically to work. When you talk with your employee and simply ask them what skills they bring to the table, you will begin learning how to inspire and engage them.

L – Leadership

As you learned earlier in this book, and in the program if you have gone through the full training, leadership is not about the title that you have. It is, however, about the influence that you have with others. Leadership isn't just about those in charge. Leadership is about providing opportunities at all levels for your people to lead through influence. Anyone with influence is leading in their own way. When you trust them to do their job and you listen to what they have to say, then you learn from them. When you learn from them, they are expressing influence with you. At some point in history, people began to think that being a leader was about being able to tell other people what to do instead of what the truth really is. The truth is that leadership is about changing a department from a bunch of individuals into a collective master-mind that is propelling that department on the right trajectory.

Napoleon Hill was introduced to the master-mind concept by Andrew Carnegie. The concept is that when more than one mind is in harmony and focused on the same outcome, then the outcome is almost inevitable. Great leadership is just that. It is the ability to create harmony in the minds of others in order to accomplish a specific goal. One of the keys to the master-mind group is that it must operate in harmony. This doesn't mean that conflict is avoided. Instead, it means that conflict is managed in the right way in order to enhance both the decisions of the team and the commitment of the team.

T – Teamwork

Teamwork is creating a common vision with shared values and a united purpose in order to accomplish something of significance. Cultures that are great are driven by 1 Team mentalities. Your company is the 1 Team. Your department is a member of the 1 Team. Your employees are a team within a team within a team. The more you focus on the organization being the team and your department being a part of that team, the easier it is to have positive interdepartmental teamwork. Building the team isn't just about building your team. It is about building your team in such a way that they see themselves as a part of the bigger picture, the 1 Team.

The primary way that a team will begin seeing themselves as a part of the bigger picture is to be very deliberate about the wording that you use when discussing other departments. As a supervisor, when you go out of your way to make sure that the other departments are protected from negative comment, you position them as teammates. When a supervisor says negative things about other members of the 1 Team in front of their employees, they create animosity. You are always welcome to positively confront the other supervisors in a one-on-one setting, away from your employees. You should never go around saying negative things about other supervisors, management, or leadership. When you have an issue with someone, you have an ethical responsibility to handle it in a positive manner.

You have three options of how to handle a difficulty with another supervisor or with leadership. These are presented in order of lower tension to higher tension levels.

1. Change your own perspective. This requires no confrontation and allows for quick and easy cooperation.
2. Confront the other person and ask them to change. This is not bad or even negative, it is just a little stronger tension. When done with the right conflict-resolution model, this can be very effective.
3. Change your environment so that you don't have to deal with the issue. This could mean positioning

yourself so that you don't witness what upsets you, or changing the organization that you work for. I don't like this option because it isn't really dealing with the problem, but it is an option.

Learning to be a team player isn't about giving up on what you believe. It is all about looking for the good in others. It is about keeping your focus on the team being effective, fun, and connected at all levels. This team that you are a part of is the one that you chose to be a part of. It only makes sense to make it great!

U – Understanding why

Understanding why the team exists and what the underlying "why" of the organization is determines whether or not there is really any understanding at all. Simon Sinek in his book, Start With Why (http://bit.ly/ssinekstart), helps readers to understand that there are three levels to the way that a business thinks. On the outer circle, there is **what** the business does. On the middle circle, there is **how** the business does what it does. And in the middle of the circle, the bull's-eye on the target, there is **why** the business does what it does. Many organizations create a mission statement for themselves, but very few of those mission statements actually have meaning behind them. Scott Adams, in The Dilbert Principle, says that most mission statements are pointless. He says that his mission statement for his company has been to scratch his bald spot once per day. He indicates that he has been much more successful than most businesses in accomplishing his mission, which also has never helped him make money. As a cartoonist, Adams gets to see the world from a different angle, but he has a point. Most mission statements do very little if anything to create actual understanding, motivation, or culture for a business.

If anything, many mission statements have had a net negative effect on organizations. This is because so many businesses come up with great, powerful, and fluffy mission statements, and then never live by what they said. They talk about creating amazing environments for their employees, and then treat them poorly. They talk about always taking care of the customer, and then let money become more important than respect. When a mission statement is written, it should be simple, easy to understand, and followed! Don't indicate that you are going to do anything that you have no intention of doing.

R – Responsibility

Ethics refers a set of behaviors. In a survey conducted by The Brennan Group in Canada, they found that the top characteristic employers wanted in an employee was showing up. The second characteristic was working hard. The third was getting along. It is interesting to think about the responsibility that is expected from employees, but sometimes not received from supervisors and up. A responsible employee is one that does what is necessary in the timeframe that is required. Think about a person that you know that you would consider to be responsible. How is it that you know they are responsible? How is that you know that you can count on them?

The reality is that we know a person's responsibility from their behaviors. What we miss, however, is that we also know they are responsible based on our expectation of responsibility from them. Our own conditioning can play into what we see in the other person. It plays into what we are looking for, and what we look for is generally what we see. Also remember that your definition of responsible is very likely different from another person's definition. When you ask someone to be responsible, they will demonstrate their version of that. So, circling back to the behaviors of responsibility… you will need to define the behaviors that you expect from your people. This is more true today than it has been in the past because of the shifts in generational thought. With each new generation, there is a new set of definitions of what it means to work hard, be responsible, be ethical, and the like. Your definition is based on the labels that you gave to events in your life. Their definition is based on their labels. The two may or may not line up, so be very clear about what you are asking for and be sure to demonstrate any behaviors that you would ask for from others.

E – Engagement

Engagement is one of those words that is used quite a bit in training supervisors. You are continuously asked, or directed, to increase employee engagement. What I think is meant is that the organization is looking for an increase in employee performance without having to force them to be engaged. The Gallup organization indicates that 2 out of 10 employees are fully engaged; 2 out of 10 employees are disengaged; and 6 out of 10 fall somewhere in the middle of that continuum. This would be the equivalent of a 10 person bicycle, with 2 people hitting the brakes as hard as they can, 2 pedaling as hard as they can, and 6 people coasting. This makes for a very frustrating experience for the 2 that are pedaling as hard as they can. With this happening, the tendency of most supervisors is to put all of their energy and focus on the 2 that are hitting the brakes to get them to play nice. That has proven over and over again to NOT get the results that are desired.

The truth is that you need to find a way to get the other 6 folks pedaling and for the 2 hitting the brakes to jump off of the bike. The 6 in the middle are watching you to see where you put your focus. Are you giving attention to the top performers or to the non-performers? Whichever way you put your focus, that is the direction that the 6 in the middle will move. Knowing this, it makes the most sense to put your attention on the top performers. When you praise them in front of others, focus on the work that they are accomplishing, and invest in their development, then you move the average people up and the non-performers either up or out. Most non-performers are who they are because they have chosen to be that way. Most average folks just need to be inspired. Like the other end of the spectrum, most top performers are who they are because that is simply who they are. If we know that the top and the bottom are living into their definition of self, then we also know that we will do very little to influence them to change. However, knowing that the 60% are looking to be inspired and to get attention, then we have a tremendous opportunity to inspire them to do more, be more, and have more in their work. In one of my other programs, *Engagement Leads To Accountability*, I discuss the two components of engagement. There is both rational and emotional engagement. Understanding both sides of the engagement coin leads to deeper and deeper levels of commitment from your team.

The values that you live by will determine the behaviors that you exhibit. The attitude that you hold toward your people will lead to the engagement or disengagement that you get from those in the middle. Non-performers are generally who they are because that is their self-definition. Top performers are generally who they are because that is their self-definition. So, your greatest opportunity is to build the skills of the top performers and invest in them in order to inspire the average folks to move toward the direction of top performance. This pattern allows you to live for the greater good of the organization and your people.

Spend your time looking for the good in others. Even more importantly, spend your time demonstrating good. You will operate out of absolute ethics, legal ethics, situational ethics, or optional ethics. The higher your standard of ethical thought and ethical behavior, the more likely your team is to demonstrate strong ethics. You will not get what you are unwilling to demonstrate. Therefore, your behaviors in all of your dealings with the team are critical to the development of the right behaviors in the team.

"Ethics is knowing the difference between what you have the right to do and what is right to do."
--Potter Stewart

Learn2Lead
Supervise • Influence • Motivate

LEADERSHIP

LEARNING OBJECTIVES

What are ethics?
How do I apply them?
Where do they come from?

How do ethics in business impact us and how do we apply standards at work?

What is ethical leadership?

What are values and how do they impact our businesses?

What is culture and how do we intentionally create it?

Ethics, values, and culture are all interconnected. We will discuss how they influence one another.

LEADERSHIP

IS THERE ANY REAL RIGHT OR WRONG?

Ethics involves the use of critical thinking to make the best possible choice in the face of a challenging circumstance.

Ethical Absolutism – An unchanging moral code exists
Ethical Legalism – Compliance with a code of conduct
Ethical Relativism – Dependent upon the situation and thus subject to change

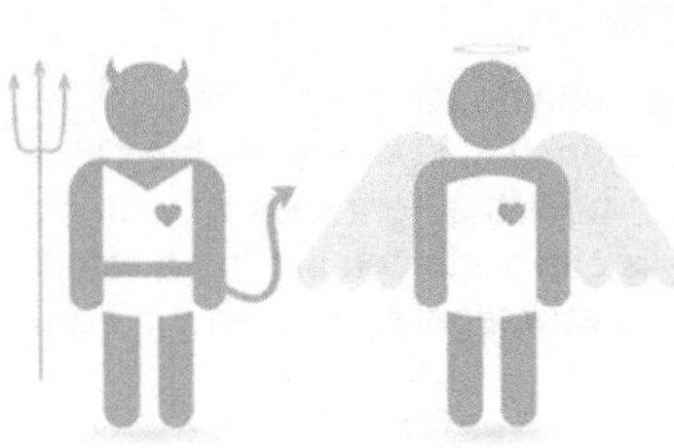

LEADERSHIP

ETHICAL ABSOLUTISM

- A higher authority provides the rules and they are absolute.
- Behaviors are intrinsically either right or wrong (no grey)
- Situations and context are irrelevant
- The "Golden Rule" applies
- Right is right and wrong is wrong

LEADERSHIP

ETHICAL LEGALISM

- Laws enacted to bring order
- Adherence to laws makes the behavior ethical
- Must have the right laws/rules in place to maintain order
- Laws can and often are interpreted
- If it is your legal right, then it is right

Learn2Lead

LEADERSHIP

ETHICAL RELATIVISM

- Everything is dependent upon the situation that you are in.
- Rules can be applied to one group and not applied outside of that group.
- Judging others has no meaning.
- Right is right, unless there is a solid reason why it is not

LEADERSHIP

WHAT ARE ETHICAL CHOICES THAT WE FACE?

Related to…

- Family
- Relationships
- Work
- Politics
- Business Choices
- Other?

What are the models for making the right choices?

ETHICAL DECISION MAKING

LEADERSHIP

UTILITARIAN DECISION MAKING

- Epicurus of Samos (341-270 BCE)
- Some good and some bad will necessarily be the result of our action and that the best action will be that which provides the most good or does the least harm, or, to put it another way, produces the greatest balance of good over harm

Learn2Lead
Supervise · Influence · Motivate

LEADERSHIP

EGOIST DECISION MAKING

- This is the ethics of self-interest
- Applicable within economic theory
- Thrasymacus (459-400 BCE) – Might makes right!
- Ayan Rand (1905-1982) - Self-Interest is a requirement of self-respect and respect for others
- Stay out of other people's business and take care of yourself.

LEADERSHIP

COMMON GOOD DECISION MAKING

- Plato (427-347 BCE) – Our actions should contribute to the good of others
- Jean-Jacques Rousseau (1712-1778) – The best society should be guided by the "general will" of the people.
- It should be about respect and compassion for others.

LEADERSHIP

DUTY-BASED DECISION MAKING

- Immanuel Kant (1724-1804) – Doing what is right is not based on the consequences, but rather on the right intentions.
- "Act only according to that maxim by which you can at the same time will that it should become a universal law."
- Example: Lying is unethical because you could not make "One should always lie" a universal maxim.

LEADERSHIP

RIGHTS-BASED DECISION MAKING

- John Locke (1632-1704) – The best decision is one that protects those that the decision impacts.
- Immanuel Kant – "Act in such a way that you treat humanity, whether in your own person or in the person of another, always at the same time as an end and never simply as a means to an end."

LEADERSHIP

JUSTICE-BASED DECISION MAKING

- The Law Code of Hammurabi in Ancient Mesopotamia (1750 BCE) – All free men should be treated alike, and all slaves should be treated alike.
- John Rawls (1921-2002) – Ethical principles are those that free and rational people would choose in a situation of equality.

LEADERSHIP

DIVINITY-BASED DECISION MAKING

- William Ockham (1285-1349) – That which is right is that which is ordained by God.
- Soren Kierkegaard (1813-1855) – Truly right action must go beyond everyday morality… Think Abraham being willing to sacrifice his son.

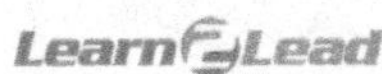

LEADERSHIP

VIRTUE-BASED DECISION MAKING

- Aristotle stated that ethics should be concerned with the whole of a person's life.
- Confucius (551-479 BCE) – Act according to the right virtues even when in a variety of situations.
- The objective must be to live life in order to attain higher levels of virtue.

Building the right framework for your decisions take some of the decision angst away.

FRAMEWORKS FOR ETHICAL CHOICES

LEADERSHIP

CONTINGENT CONSEQUENCES

- If I make this decision, what will be the ripple effects of the decision?
- The objective must be to produce the most good as a result of these actions.
- One must think pragmatically in order to use this framework.

LEADERSHIP

RESPONSIBILITY FRAMEWORK

- One must consider what they are obligated to do or supposed to do.
- It is our responsibility to treat everyone with dignity and respect.
- It is less about desire and more about obligation.

Learn 2 Lead
Supervise · Influence · Motivate

LEADERSHIP

SELF-CONCEPT FRAMEWORK

- One must consider what they are obligated to do or supposed to do.
- It is our responsibility to treat everyone with dignity and respect.
- It is less about desire and more about obligation.

Is it really impacting people if a business makes poor ethical choices?
Are our choices any different from business to our personal lives?

WHO IS IMPACTED BY OUR CHOICES?

LEADERSHIP

WHO IS IMPACTED?

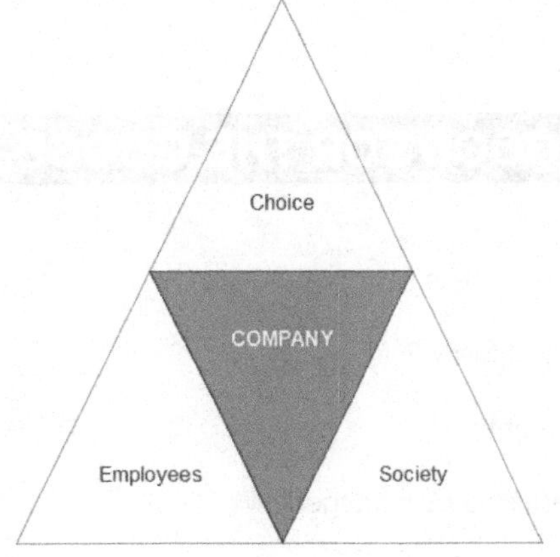

What is the real value of operating with, or without values?

THE VALUE OF VALUES

LEADERSHIP

WHAT'S GOOD FOR THE GOOSE...

Multi-National Companies…

Whose laws do you follow?

Which culture is right?

How should operations be managed?

LEADERSHIP

MAKING SENSE OF VALUES

"If men were angels, there would be no need for government."

James Madison,
4th President of the
United States

- Personal Values
- Morals
- Ethics
- Norms

LEADERSHIP

VALUES ARE NOT SEEN, BUT FELT

It isn't what is above the water in a business that will impact you the most. Like an iceberg, it is always what looms beneath the surface that eventually sinks the ship.

Learn2Lead
Supervise * Influence * Motivate

LEADERSHIP

VALUES

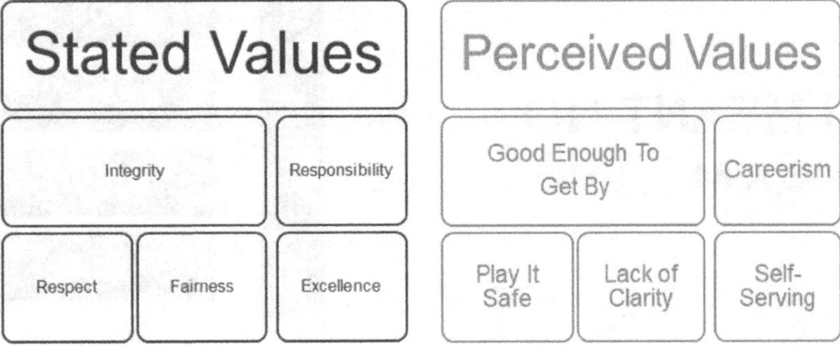

Learn2Lead
Supervise * Influence * Motivate

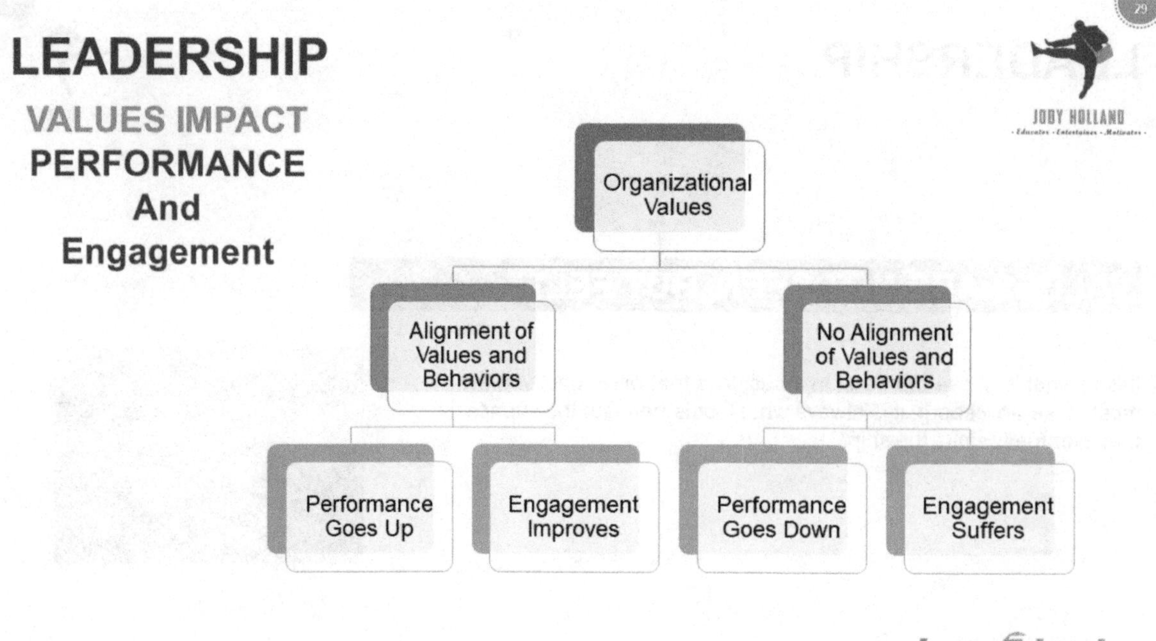

LEADERSHIP

BUT I MEANT NO HARM…

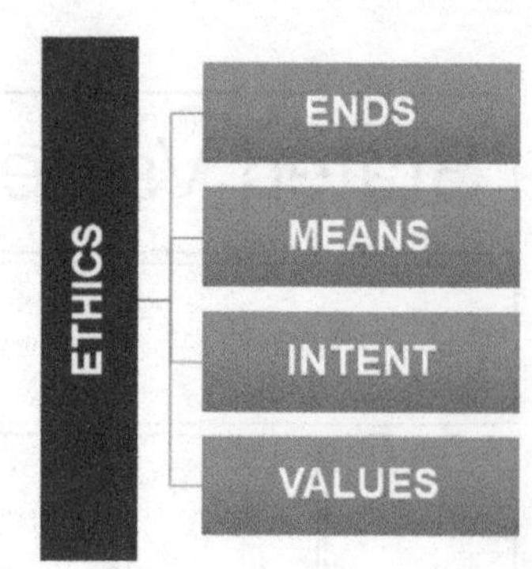

Learn2Lead

LEADERSHIP

WHAT PRICE WILL WE PAY?

The real test of values is whether or not we do what is right, even when it will cost us more than doing what is wrong.

Learn2Lead
Supervise · Influence · Motivate

LEADERSHIP

BERNARD GERT'S COMMON CORE VALUES

- Not killing others
- Not causing pain
- Not disabling
- Not depriving freedom
- Not depriving pleasure

- Being truthful
- Keeping promises
- Being honest/ethical
- Obeying the law
- Doing your duty

LEADERSHIP

DISCUSSION

Is it more or less profitable to operate your business under strict ethical principles?

Do you have to be ethical as a person to do business ethically?

What is the upside of ethical thought and practice?

LEADERSHIP

ETHICAL DECISIONS MODEL

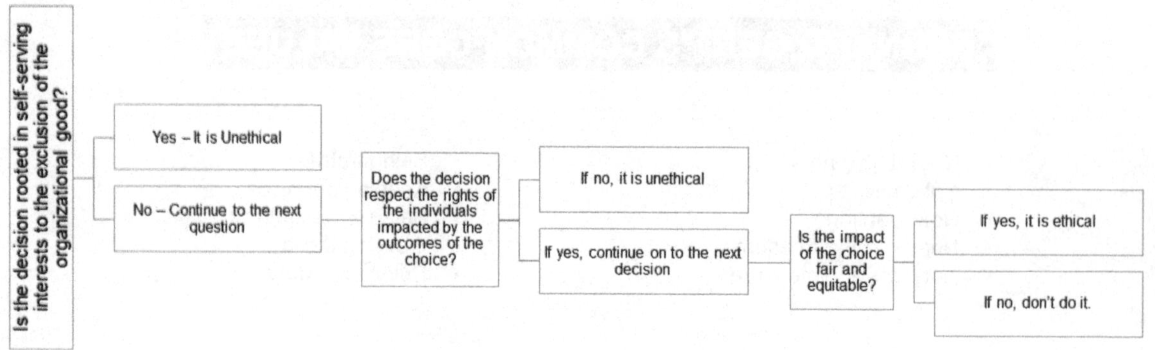

LEADERSHIP

COMPONENTS OF ETHICAL LEADERSHIP

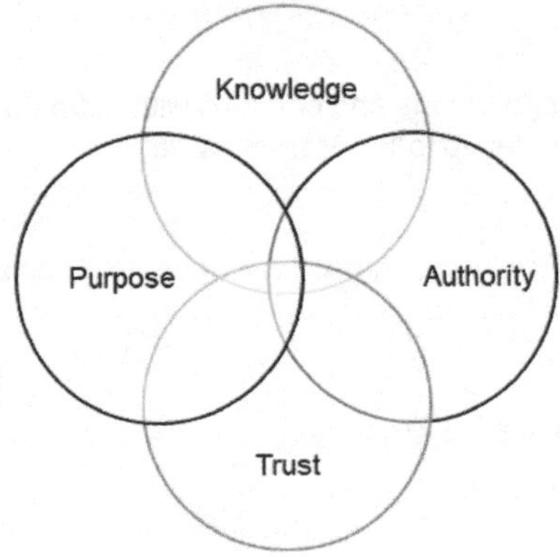

LEADERSHIP

WHICH LEADER DO WE CHOOSE?

It is time to elect a world leader, and yours is the deciding vote. Here are the facts about the three leading candidates:

Candidate A: He associates with crooked politicians and consults with astrologers. He's had two mistresses. He also chain smokes and drinks up to ten Martinis a day.

Candidate B: He was ejected from the office twice, sleeps until noon, used opium in college, and drinks a large amount of whiskey every evening.

Candidate C: He is a decorated war hero. He's a vegetarian, doesn't smoke, drinks an occasional beer and hasn't had any extra-marital affairs.

LEADERSHIP

WHICH LEADER DO WE CHOOSE?

It is time to elect a world leader, and yours is the deciding vote. Here are the facts about the three leading candidates:

Candidate A: He associates with crooked politicians and consults with astrologers. He's had two mistresses. He also chain smokes and drinks up to ten Martinis a day.
Franklin D. Roosevelt

Candidate B: He was ejected from the office twice, sleeps until noon, used opium in college, and drinks a large amount of whiskey every evening.
Winston Churchill

Candidate C: He is a decorated war hero. He's a vegetarian, doesn't smoke, drinks an occasional beer and hasn't had any extra-marital affairs.
Adolf Hitler

LEADERSHIP

WHEN ETHICS ARE BAD, WHAT ARE YOUR CHOICES?

- Get over it and be loyal – Change yourself or the environment
- Voice your opinion and push for what is right – Make sure that you are always respectful. Make sure it is not just emotional. Be able to back it up with truth.
- Leave – This is the most direct response, but it doesn't create lasting change.

LEADERSHIP

6 PILLARS OF CHARACTER

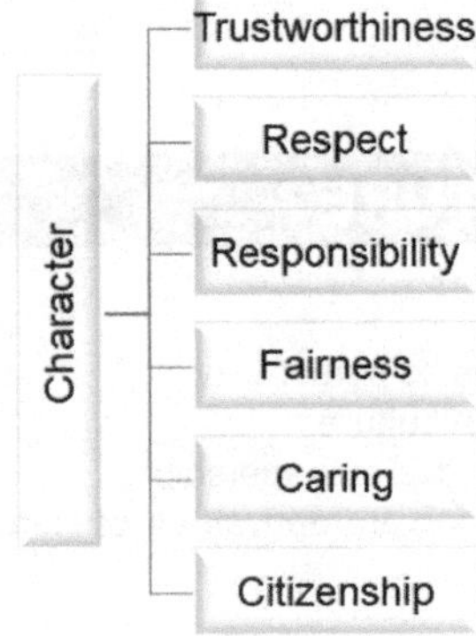

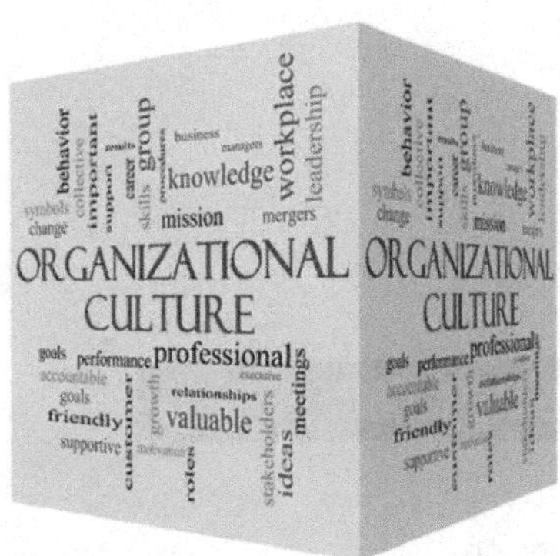

CULTURE EATS STRATEGY FOR BREAKFAST –Peter Drucker

LEADERSHIP

WHAT IS CULTURE?

- A company's culture is its personality.
- Behaviors come out of culture.
- The culture is a derivative of leadership.
- Creativity and innovation are derivatives of culture.

LEADERSHIP

CULTURE CREATES RESULTS

Culture makes it safe or not safe for a person.
It sets the tone for creativity, innovation, and intrapreneurship.

A bad culture creates low morale, low innovation, absenteeism, turnover, injuries, and a host of other challenges

LEADERSHIP

CULTURE PROVIDES MEANING

Culture gives contextual meaning to the work that people do.
Culture sets the tone for what people believe about their work, their purpose in life, and their fulfillment.
When you observe the results of a company, you find the behaviors. The behaviors reveal the thoughts. The thoughts reveal the beliefs. The beliefs ARE the culture.

LEADERSHIP

THE BIG IDEA

- Culture is created by Leadership!
- Culture ALWAYS starts at the top and trickles down.
- Not being intentional about culture is to intentionally create the wrong culture.

Learn2Lead
Supervise · Influence · Motivate

LEADERSHIP

HOW IS CULTURE REVEALED?

- Employees watch their supervisor, who watches their boss, who watches THE boss.
- Everything from service to sales to attitude to mindfulness to action come as a result of the cues that are given through leadership.

LEADERSHIP

EFFECTIVE CULTURE...

- Opens minds
- Opens doors to success
- Inspires collaboration
- Makes everyone feel valued and appreciated
- Develops the potential of the teams and individuals
- Creates positive action

LEADERSHIP

CULTURE IS...

- The personality of the organization
- The sum total of the values of the top leaders being passed down
- The linchpin that creates or kills success
- The driving force behind motivated action…
- In any direction that action goes

LEADERSHIP

SELF-SERVING CAN BE COMPANY SERVING…

- When the focus is on creating profits through people
- When the focus is on continuously developing the potential of your teams
- When the focus is on building the success of the company by inspiring greatness in your people.

LEADERSHIP

SELF-SERVING KILLS COMPANIES WHEN...

- It is about oppressing your people
- It is about taking more money for yourself and limiting the success of your people
- It is about avoiding the development of your team's potential

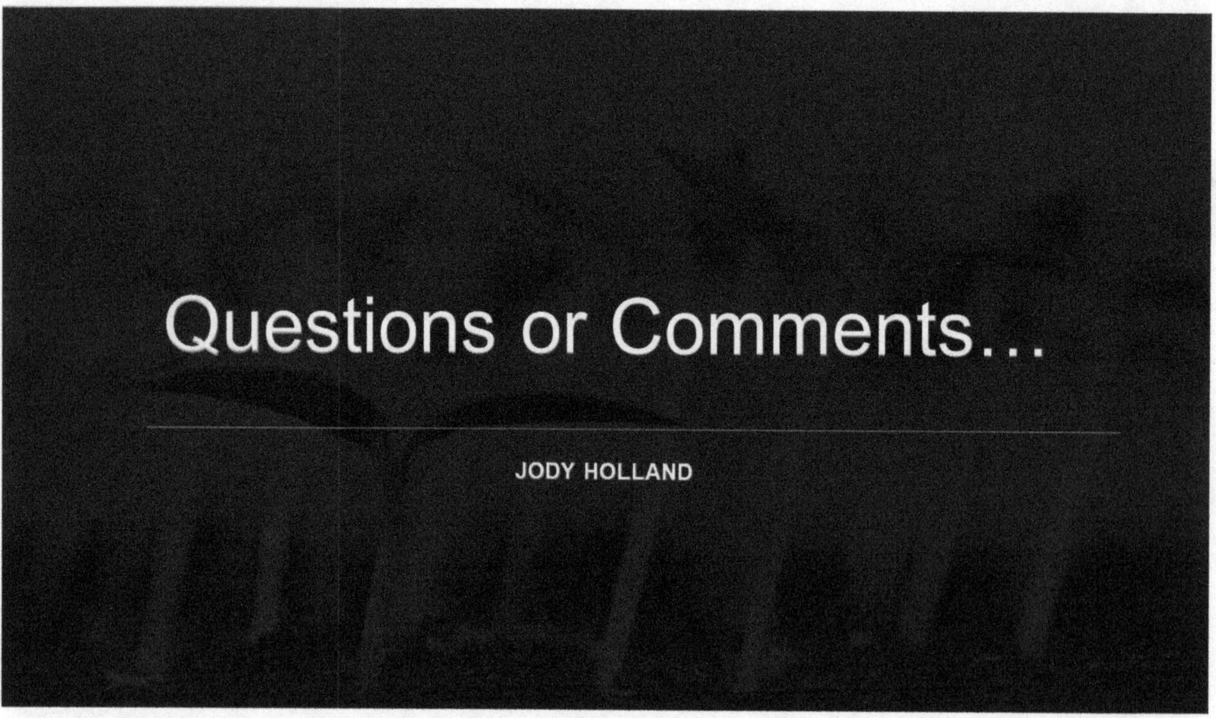

13 PRIORITY MANAGEMENT

The World is Changing Fast

The world we live in today is not the same as the world that we used to live in. When I think back to my own childhood, I remember what it was like to sit and watch the news with my father. When Walter Cronkite was on the news, it was just Walter. There was nothing else on the screen. He would come on and let us know what was going on and then he would go off. Nothing scrolled across the screen. There were no pictures inside the pictures. There was no upcoming story. There was just Walter. I believe that we're trying to cram more into our time than we have ever tried to cram before. I don't think that this is making us a happier society. I think the simple reality is we are trying to make time fit into our schedules instead of making our schedules fit into time. We haven't learned how to say no or how to limit ourselves.

In a study conducted by Pitney Bowes Inc. and San Jose State University, in late 1996, they looked at 1000 executives from top companies and what interrupted them, or kept them from accomplishing what they needed to on a daily basis. They received responses from 972 employees from those Fortune 1000 companies. It revealed that, in 1996, the average executive received 178 messages each day. These were in a combination of telephone calls, emails, voicemails, and other mediums. 84% of respondents indicated that at least three times per hour they were interrupted by messages. And don't forget, this was in 1996! In my informal surveys with a few hundred companies that I work with, the average executive is interrupted significantly more than 178 times a day. We get a lot more emails than we used to get. We get Facebook notifications now as well. There are so many ways to get in touch with us electronically that there isn't a "shut off" button for our socially intertwined lives. The simple reality for executives today is that they have to take control of their time. They have to just make time for the things that actually matter. They also have to protect their time from the things that don't matter. According to a Financial Express article in January 2006, interruptions consume 2.1 hours a day or 28% of the average workday. Most executives were not fully focused again until 25 minutes after the interruption. This means that most executives never gain a long enough time without interruptions to ever be fully focused.

One of the fundamental points that I intend for you to get through this chapter is that you have to make time for what matters. You can't allow the world to control your time. You have a very limited supply. The following are five hints that will help you in this changing world to control your time.

1. Give yourself a timeout. Take a specified amount of time, say 30 minutes, at either the end or the very beginning of each day. This is your planning time. You should not have your email open. You should not be taking phone calls. You should not allow people to walk into your office during this time. This is your time to reflect on the previous day's work and to plan for tomorrow's work. Many people go through their day trying to scramble and figure out what is important. By taking time out to plan, you've already started down the right path and moved toward your priorities. Giving yourself this time to plan prevents you from having to work as much overtime. It prevents you from allowing things into your life that really don't matter. It keeps you on track and keeps you moving forward.
2. Be the boss of your technology. Technology can be an absolutely wonderful thing… if it's used in the right way. Set up auto responders on your email to let people know when you're not available. Schedule your emails to go out at a very specific time in order to control when people see information. Hit the "do not disturb" button on your cell phone at a certain time in the evening. When you start working in blocks of 15 to 30 minutes at a time, you will get more and more comfortable with keeping technology out of your way while you work. One example would be that it is ideal to go through and mark specific emails as spam that are irrelevant to you. By limiting the number of emails that come to your actual inbox, you prepare yourself for being truly successful. Most executives will receive over 200 emails in an average day.

More than 80% of all emails that are sent in the United States on a daily basis are actually spam. This means, there might be 40 realistic emails to look at for the average executive. Learning how to work your technology and setting up your technology to work for you makes your life much easier. Utilize technology in your hiring processes to make things work smoother and more quickly. Utilize technology, such as GoTo Meeting ® in meetings so that you don't have to travel as much. Sometimes it is a good idea to stand face-to-face with a client or prospect. However, many times, they are just as busy as you are and would appreciate a shorter meeting that gets to the point.

3. Strategically design your meetings to meet your needs. In any meeting that you attend, make sure that there is a point. Do not attend meetings for the sake of attending meetings. It is an excellent idea to have a standup or quick information meeting first thing in the morning with your staff. By doing this, each person receives between 45 and 60 seconds to indicate what they have on tap for the day. This lets everyone know the direction of each of the key players. Your weekly meetings are designed to give you an overview of what was accomplished in the past week and what is coming up for the next week. This meeting is not intended to be a strategy session. Your monthly meetings focus on short-term strategy and adjusting priorities in order to stay on track with your quarterly and annual goals. These meetings should not be more than two hours in length. Quarterly planning meetings can be up to three hours long. These dig into the short-term and long-term strategies that you are using to meet your goals. It is important to map out specific tactics to go with your strategies during these meetings. Once per year, it is ideal to go away with your staff for one to two days as an executive retreat. You should do your annual planning and celebrate your successes for the year. By keeping your meetings organized and relevant, you will actually limit the number of meetings that you conduct. The ones that you do conduct will provide value to you and to the members of your team.
4. Create some boundaries. When I first went into business (gained professional status), I wanted to be on every nonprofit board that asked me to be. I love to help people, and really enjoyed being needed as well. I found myself on seven boards. That produced between seven and 21 meetings per month to participate in. While it can be difficult to know which nonprofit gets the axe, I highly recommend that you pick only two. Choose the nonprofits that mean the most to you. These should be the ones that you would be passionate about no matter what. Everyone has a cause, but you need to identify which cause most closely resembles your belief system. You have to train yourself to say no to great opportunities to volunteer. Only say yes to two at a time. If a third board comes along and you think that it is the best board that you have ever seen in your entire existence, then decide which of the other two has to go. Keep in mind, your objective should be to stay balanced with the wheel of life. When you volunteer too much, it takes away from your family and from your paying job. When you volunteer too little, you don't receive the fulfillment that you need in that area of your life. Two is my number. Your number may be different. Whatever your number is, make a decision about it and stick to it.

When Would NOW Be A Good Time?

Why put off till tomorrow what you can do today? That is a good question indeed. It seems that there aren't really a lot of good answers to this question, though. Most people can't verbalize why they have not done what they know is necessary for success. They understand, at a logical level, what the required behaviors or activities are, but they can't seem to make themselves move forward. This has its significant costs to the person and their success in life.

Procrastination has shifted the tide of wealth, and not in a good way. It seems that the richest place on earth isn't a country or even a region, though. The richest place on earth is the graveyard. This is the place where all of the unwritten books, the unlived dreams, the un-started entrepreneurial ventures, and the unfulfilled promises reside. There are more unfulfilled riches in the graveyard than anywhere else on earth. The big question, though, is why?

William James, the Father of American psychology, said that there are only two motivators in the human psyche. Those two motivators are the avoidance of pain and the pursuit of pleasure. When you think about it, everything that we do in life could be explained in one of those two directions. Are we avoiding or pursuing? We were avoiding actual, or more often, imagined pain when we did not take the actions that could have moved us forward. It is only when the real or perceived pleasure of an activity is great enough that we take action, or pursue. Most people want to complicate things more than this, but it really is that simple. We avoid pain, real or perceived. We pursue pleasure, real or perceived.

Procrastination could be defined as choosing to avoid a task or decision with the understanding that doing so will make things worse for you, but not right now. This "pain delay" principle is used regularly by people all around this globe. The part of this definition that is the most fascinating, though, is that people know that they will be worse off. They know that taking action now would actually make it better. If you have ever told someone that you work better under pressure, then you have intentionally made things worse for yourself. Taking specific "non-action" in order to find a way to actually motivate yourself towards action later generally leads to a worse product or service. This means that procrastination could really be traced back to a matter of motivation. If you can identify the best ways to motivate yourself toward action now, then you will be able to avoid the pain of procrastination and attain the pleasure of less stress while you achieve success.

Building up your positive energy and tearing down the negative takes a specific focus. Think about something in your life that you have really wanted to achieve. When you thought about that end result, you likely experienced a sense of joy and accomplishment, or a sense of relief. It is the emotion that drives the motion. Your job is to fulfill the laws of physics in your daily activity.

A body in motion tends to stay in motion. A body at rest tends to stay at rest.

This isn't just relative to understanding the velocity of an object. It is relative to understanding the velocity of your success. You have to be that "body in motion." In order to achieve that, you begin to build up positive energy about the things that you need to do and begin to build up negative energy toward the results of not doing the things that you need to do. For this reason, it is critical to build up the positive energy and thought about what the end result will be if you take action and accomplish your objects. By the same token, it is critically important to build up negative energy and thought about staying the same and choosing to NOT take action.

This is what I refer to as an "action-stack." It is a way of stacking your emotions in your favor in order to induce action now. You need to have enough positive emotion for the desired activity and enough negative emotion against not taking action. NOW is the time to act!

When would now be a good time? Too many people in this world walk around wondering when a good time would be to take action. They wonder when "the right time" would be for them to become an entrepreneur, start painting, write a book, choose to succeed at work, or any number of other things. The truth of the matter is that "NOW" is the right time to take action and make your life what you want it to be. Now is the time that exists. There really is no future or past. There is only now. The present is the one true reality. So, the question that you have to answer for yourself is…

When would NOW be a good time to take action?

The Pareto Principle

Vilfredo Pareto was an economist, engineer, and philosopher who came up with the 80/20 rule. We have seen this rule applied over and over again in business and with respect to a variety of focus areas. Often times, it has been used in human resources to describe the concept that 20% of a company's employees produce 80% of the results. The original theory, however, had to do with land ownership in Italy. As Pareto looked at the normal distribution of land ownership, he found that 20% of people owned 80% of the land. He dug further into this premise and began discovering some very interesting correlations with his 80/20 Rule.

He found that this rule could be applied to almost anything that we do in life. It could be applied to workers. It could be applied to relationships. And, perhaps most importantly in this case, it could be applied to where we get our results. From an economic success perspective, Pareto discovered that the vast majority of success in the endeavors that we undertake could be traced back to a small amount of actions taken. It is consistently 20% of our activities that produce 80% of our results. His economic and success theory held that we needed to identify the 20% of things that would get us the greatest results and then make those things primary in our day. After all, if you don't get those things done, it would have a tremendous economic impact on you and your business. Conversely, if you didn't get something done from the 80% category, which only produced 20% of the results, it wouldn't really matter that much.

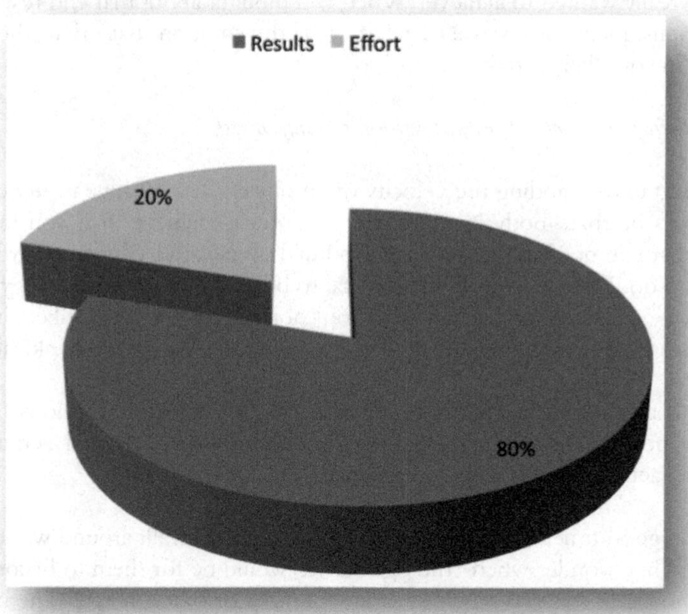

This is great news for us! This means that we simply have to figure out what matters the most and do that first. In a program that I have conducted for entrepreneurs for the last couple of decades, I have helped them discover what that 20% really is. I have seen that most people spin their wheels, so to speak, throughout the day. They do the things that are easy before the things that are hard. They do the things that they like before the ones that they dislike. They do what they know before what is unfamiliar. By taking the easy road, they miss out on the road that leads to success. The objective of this book is to help you find the road to success and prosperity, however you define that in your own life. This means that you have to first answer these two questions…

Am I willing to do what works instead of just what is easy or familiar?

☐ Yes ☐ No

If I were choosing, I would rather be:

☐ Right ☐ Successful

How you answered those two questions is very important to your success in life. If you checked "yes" on the first question and you really meant it, then you have demonstrated that you are ready to do what is necessary, even if it means that you have to stretch yourself a bit. If you answered "successful" on the second question, then you have stepped into a realm that is occupied by most of the successful people of this world. The truth is that we spend an inordinate amount of time trying to be right instead of trying to be successful.

One of the keys to learning, growing, and winning is the willingness to "unlearn" what you already know. We must be willing to unlearn, or empty our preconceived notions in order to fill our minds with new information and set up new habits for success. Napoleon Hill referred to our habits as the things that would either bring us success or bring us misery. Our habits become automatic when they are practiced for at least 21 days in a row. This means that doing what you must do, every single day, without allowing things to get in your way, will set in motion the laws of success. Drifting into the habits of failure will set in motion the laws of failure. The choice is really up to you as to which direction you establish your habits.

Classifying What Goes Into Your Time

You have the glorious opportunity to identify what is important and what is not important in your world, and then to take right action. One of the best ways to do this is to begin classifying the items that come into your work-life in one of the following categories.

1. Daily Habits of Success
2. Critical now
3. Critical, but not right now
4. Important to others
5. Not important to success

You can pick whatever labels you would like for the things that you face. It isn't the label itself that is important. Rather, it is the fact that you are learning to categorize things that is important. The first item in the above list is the one that needs your greatest focus. It is the one that will set you on the path of success if it is mastered or set you on the path of failure if it is not.

Each of us has 5 or fewer things that can be considered the habits of success in our jobs. These are the things that you need to do every singly day in order to be successful. Use the following form to write out your critical habit list and to record the other stuff that you do as well.

Habits of Success	Other Stuff I Do
1.	
2.	
3.	
4.	
5.	

You really only have four choices on how to handle the things that are thrown at you throughout the day. If you will make it a habit to choose which path you are going to take any time an item is thrown your way, then you will find that your day becomes more productive and less stressful.

You can **do it, delegate it, delay it, or delete it**. If you find that you are doing all of one or none of one, you will want to step back and evaluate your decision model for tasks that come your way. You should find that there is a fairly consistent balance between the four. When you have labeled something as critical right now, you do it. When you have labeled something as important to others, you either do it, but not right now, or delegate it, or if you need to be the one to do it, but you can't right now, you delay it. Your decision-making muscle is just like any other muscle. The more you exercise it, the easier it becomes to perform the required tasks. You must develop the habit of controlling your time instead of allowing the circumstances of life to control you and your time. Time is a limited resource. When you put the important things into your time first, then everything gets taken care of. For that reason, you should make sure that you perform your habits of success as soon as you can each day, and before the other areas of your life, the busy-ness and noise, take over.

Never forget to ask yourself… When would now be a good time to do what matters most?

Priority Management

JODY HOLLAND

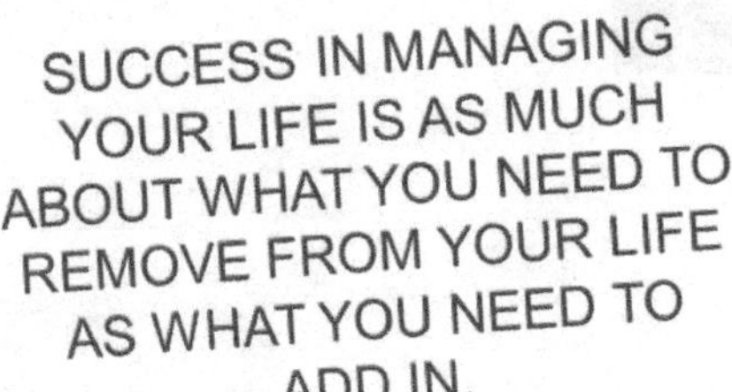
SUCCESS IN MANAGING YOUR LIFE IS AS MUCH ABOUT WHAT YOU NEED TO REMOVE FROM YOUR LIFE AS WHAT YOU NEED TO ADD IN.

Learn2Lead

LEADERSHIP

LEARNING OBJECTIVES

Identify the key concepts associated with time management

Identify the main obstacles to effectiveness in time management

Understand the nature of time management

Discover ways to reclaim your time

AKA – Essentialist Thinking

Explore Time and Life Management Tools and Techniques

Understand the basics of project management as it relates to time and priorities

LEADERSHIP

WHY MANAGE TIME?

"He, who every morning plans the transactions of the day, and follows that plan, carries a thread that will guide him through a labyrinth of the most busy life."

--Victor Hugo

LEADERSHIP

WHY MANAGE TIME?

- Increased Productivity
- Decreased Stress
- Additional Time For Fun
- Greater Impact As A Leader
- Enhanced Self-Image

LEADERSHIP

HOW DO WE DEFINE PRIORITY MANAGEMENT?

Priority management is the act or process of planning and exercising conscious control over the amount of time spent on specific activities, especially to increase effectiveness, efficiency or productivity.

A priority management system is a designed combination of processes, tools, techniques, and methods.

LEADERSHIP

PRIORITY MANAGEMENT HAS 5 MAIN ASPECTS

- Planning and Strategy
- Managing Self
- Managing Others
- Allocating Your Time
- Getting Results

The first four work together to produce the fifth!

LEADERSHIP

WHAT IS TIME?

Time is a finite resource. We cannot produce more of it. We cannot get it back. When it is gone, it is gone.

- Time is a commodity
- Our Habits Are the Framework
- Our Estimations Determine Our Outcomes

LEADERSHIP

HOW MUCH TIME DO WE HAVE?

The average American lives to the age of 78.4.

That represents…

Weekends:	4,076
Days :	28,616
Hours :	686,784
Minutes :	41,207,040
Seconds:	2,472,422,400

LEADERSHIP

I'M NOT AVERAGE

LEADERSHIP

11

WHAT IS AVERAGE?

If you are average…

- Each week you will watch TV for 25 hours
- Read for just under 3 hours
- Receive the most phone calls between 10 and 11 AM.

Most people have a very poor concept of how they spend their time.

The average child…

- Spends more than 50 hours per week with technology
- Spends more than 40 hours per week on school
- Spends more than 8 hours per week on activities outside of school (like sports)
- Spends more than 10 hours per week around friends
- Has to multi-task!!!

12

IS MULTI-TASKING A HELP OR A HINDERANCE?

Being busy may seem like more is getting done. It often leads to leaving lots of projects incomplete.

It is focusing on one thing at a time, not doing more things at once that will bring you greater success.

Stay focused, be consistent, get it done.

LEADERSHIP

I JUST DON'T HAVE ENOUGH TIME!!!

The most productive people…

- Know what they want – outcome
- Know why they want it – purpose
- Know the actions to take – plan

LEADERSHIP

TAMING TIME ACTIVITY

Write a list of all of the things that you did yesterday at work.

Once you have your list, you have $100 to spend on the activities. Each activity must have a value from $0 to $100.

Which ones have zero value?

Will you keep doing those things that have no value?

Will you shift your focus toward the things that have the greatest value?

LEADERSHIP

BULLDOZER

Behavioral Cues:
- They make decisions very quickly
- They love to be in charge
- Their focus is on the task(s)
- They have a low tolerance for whining or slow work
- Accomplishing goals is their domain

LEADERSHIP

BULLDOZER

MOTIVATION:
They are motivated by the feeling of succeeding at their objectives.
Typically is a hard-working, go-go type of person, who likes to push themselves to accomplish as many things as possible.
They take great satisfaction in checking things off of their daily list.
They attempt to cram as many things into their time as possible, not wanting to miss a single moment to get things done.
They are seen as "the achiever" but they often bulldoze over people as they push to accomplish.

LEADERSHIP

ENERGIZER

Behavioral Cues:
- Expressive and outgoing
- Motivating and inspiring
- Adventurous and fun-loving
- Energetic and fast-paced

LEADERSHIP

ENERGIZER

MOTIVATION:
They are the most engaged when there are plenty of options in front of them.
They love to have fun at work. When they look at time, it seems like there will always be more than enough.
They are generally excited about new projects because they love to put new ideas into motion.
Problem-solving and creativity are exciting.
They have a lot of fun, usually right up until they have to go do the work.

LEADERSHIP

HARMONIZERS

Behavioral Cues:

- They don't like conflict
- They work well with others
- They manage the process to achieve outcomes
- They need time to decide
- They don't like change

Learn2Lead
Supervise · Influence · Motivate

HARMONIZERS

MOTIVATION:
They are most engaged when there is consensus.
They are characterized by being harmonious at work. People like them because they work slow and steady and generally don't rock the boat.
They are process oriented and are the only type that is balanced between task and relationship.
They search for consensus with the group and want everyone's goals to be met.

LEADERSHIP

CEREBRALS

Behavioral Cues:
- Analytical
- Rational
- Organized
- Cautious and Conscientious

Learn2Lead
Supervise · Influence · Motivate

LEADERSHIP

CEREBRALS

MOTIVATION:
They are the most engaged when they are able to do the right things in the right process and do them well.
They will feel that they always need just a little more time. Time seems to dominate them.
They operate as perfectionists, or with those tendencies, and never feel that they were given enough time to get it just right.
They are generally dissatisfied with the work that is done because it needed a little more time.
They often prefer to work alone because they can better manage the work.

LEADERSHIP

THE PLAY ETHIC

THE OBJECTIVE OF THIS MODEL…

Pat Kane, author of The Play Ethic, A Manifesto For A Different Way of Living, hopes to build a bridge between work that is driven by production and work that is driven by meaning.

QUESTION…

Do people who enjoy their job work harder?

Do people who are happy get greater results?

LEADERSHIP

WHICH IS MORE PRODUCTIVE?

ORGANIZED

DISORGANIZED

CHAOTIC

LEADERSHIP

THE NEWS IS GETTING BUSIER!

Learn 2 Lead
Supervise · Influence · Motivate

LEADERSHIP

YOUR SCARCEST RESOURCE – UNINTERRUPTED TIME

U.S. Executives receive an average of 200 emails per day, or more than 30,000 per year!

I.M. and cloud collaboration tools are compounding the problem.

Executives attend more than 16 hours of meetings per week

Learn 2 Lead
Supervise · Influence · Motivate

LEADERSHIP

8 PRACTICES THAT HELP

1. Make the agenda crystal clear
2. Create a time budget for meetings and stick to it
3. Require a business case for all new projects
4. Simplify the organization

LEADERSHIP

8 PRACTICES THAT HELP

5. Delegate authority for time investments.
6. Standardize your decision-making process
7. Implement standardized time discipline processes
8. Provide feedback to manage organizational load

LEADERSHIP

THE FIVE BIGGEST TIME WASTERS

- A colleague stopping by
- Being called away from your desk, or leaving on your own
- The arrival of a new e-mail
- Distractions by multiple tasks being open on the computer
- Phone calls

LEADERSHIP

INTERRUPTIONS COST

- Interruptions cost us an average of 2.1 hours per day of productive work time
- The average employee loses 28% of every day due to interruptions that take them away from the task they were working on
- It takes an average of 25 minutes to regain full focus
- Most never have their full focus

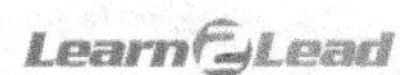

LEADERSHIP

QUICK KEYS TO TAME TIME

- Take Time To Plan Daily
- Control Your Technology (There is an off button)
- Only Meet When There Is A Point & An Agenda
- Learn To Say No To Things Outside Of Your Filtered Mission
- Delete Things That Don't Matter

LEADERSHIP

REALIZE THE VALUE OF TIME

Time is valued according to you and the task that is at hand
It's slow and dull when bored to tears and fast when life is grand

For the husband or wife who holds the hand of a mate who's at death's door
Each minute is precious, each breath is cherished, as they beg for an hour more

For the teen who's free and has no cares, time will never end
Each day is faced with reckless abandon with more time around the bend

In 3rd grade, on the final day, with just ten minutes left in class
Time slows down, each second stretched, hoping it will pass

But on vacation, relaxed and cool, having fun at every turn
Time flies by as fast as light as the week just seems to burn

Chasing purpose and living life is meant to be full of fun
So live your life and love your work to be fulfilled when life is done

Jody Holland

LEADERSHIP

HOW MUCH IS YOUR TIME?

Base Salary: $40,000 / Year
That is $19.23 per hour counting vacation time.
Plus Benefits at an average of $13,200 per year or $6.35 per hour
It would cost approximately $60,000 to replace a supervisor at 40k per year (turnover cost)
If you are turning supervisors over, that is $54.42 per hour, or $25.58 per hour without turnover.

LEADERSHIP

WHAT IS YOUR SLOGAN?

- Do more with less!
- Do less with more!
- Just do it!
- Give me multi-tasking or give me death!
- Busy is really the new "fine"

Most people follow a predictable schedule for what they do… or don't do.

OUR TENDENCIES

LEADERSHIP

WE TEND TO…

- Do what we like before what we dislike
- Do what can be done quickly before what takes time
- Do what is easy before what is difficult
- Do what we know before what is new for us
- Do what is urgent before what is important
- Do what is imposed before what we have chosen

LEADERSHIP

SPIN THE WHEEL OF LIFE CAREFULLY

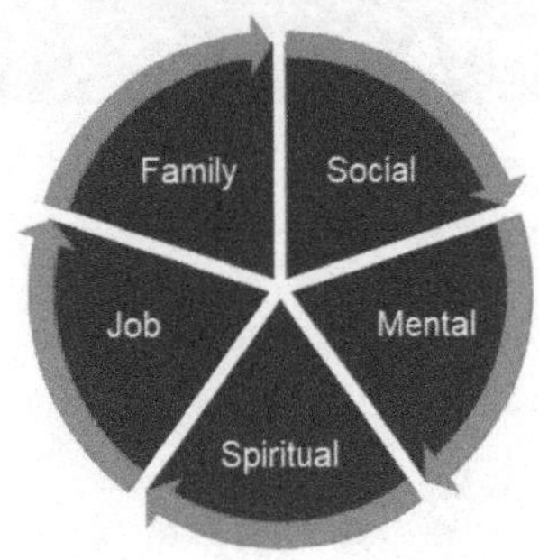

LEADERSHIP

QUICK TIP: MANAGING TIME WISELY

Do what you have to do and do it now.

What's Important Now (W.I.N.)

It isn't just about what you like or want to do. It is about doing what you should do and in the right order.

Learn2Lead

Supervise · Influence · Motivate

LEADERSHIP

A LEADER'S GOTTA DO WHAT A LEADER'S GOTTA DO!

- Bring Balance To Your Life
- Reduce Your Stress
- Plan, Organize, and Execute
- Take Better Care Of Yourself
- Seize New Opportunities
- Take Time To Communicate
- Develop Yourself Personally

LEADERSHIP

CIRCADIAN WORK SCHEDULE

Learn2Lead

LEADERSHIP

ARE YOU TRYING TO TICK WHEN YOU REALLY OUGHT TO TOCK?

Circadian rhythms are internal biological clocks that regulate many functions and activities, including sleep, temperature, metabolism, alertness, blood pressure, heart rate, hormone levels and immunities.
24 Hour Cycles
Reset By Sunlight

Learn2Lead

LEADERSHIP

WORK WITH YOUR RHYTHM

- When you learn to listen to what your body is saying, you can work with your rhythm instead of against it.
- Your effectiveness depends in part on doing the right things at the right time.

SHORT TERM MEMORY FROM 6 AM TO 10 AM

If you need to do some last-minute reviewing for a presentation, or cramming for a test, early morning is your best time.

LEADERSHIP

COGNITIVE TASKS FROM 8 AM TO NOON

Tasks such as reading, problem-solving, calculating, and planning are done best before noon.

LEADERSHIP

LONG TERM MEMORY FROM 1PM TO 4PM

If you need to memorize a speech or study the mission of your organization, or commit business strategy and goals to memory, the afternoon is your best bet!

LEADERSHIP

MOTOR SKILLS WORK BEST BETWEEN 2PM AND 6PM

Whether it is typing up a report, or building a cabinet, or any other task requiring that you have good hand-eye coordination, the afternoon is your best bet.

Learn2Lead
Supervise · Influence · Motivate

LEADERSHIP

TIME TO WORK OUT FROM 4PM TO MIDNIGHT

Large muscle coordination is at its peak from 4PM to Midnight when our body temperature is naturally higher.
You will perceive the workout to be easier in the evening.
Give yourself approximately 5 hours before bedtime to finish your workout.

LEADERSHIP

JET LAG OR LIFE LAG

- Are you creating the equivalent of jet lag by keeping an inconsistent sleep schedule?
- Answer the following to find out…

LEADERSHIP

DO YOU HAVE JET LAG?

Do you get up about the same time each morning?
Yes No
Do you wake up without an alarm most days?
Yes No
Do you always get between 7 and 9 hours of sleep?
Yes No

LEADERSHIP

POSSIBLE JET LAG SYMPTOMS

- Constipation
- Clammy Sweat
- Diarrhea
- Ear Ache
- Fatigue
- Headache
- Hemorrhoids
- Impaired Coordination
- Impaired Vision
- Anxiety
- Impatience
- Insecurity
- Insomnia
- Irregular heartbeat
- Lightheadedness
- Loss of Libido
- Low Blood Sugar
- Memory Loss
- Nausea
- Susceptibility To Illness

LEADERSHIP

Are You Working Your Off?

One of the primary reasons that we experience overwork is because we are working on the things that do not produce the right results.

The Pareto Principle helps us to understand what should be cut instead of what should be added.

LEADERSHIP

You Are In Control Of You!

You are the only you that there is so plan your life wisely.

LEADERSHIP

THE BIG ROCKS PRINCIPLE

LEADERSHIP

DON'T PROCRASTINATE!

Tim Urban, in his TED Talk, discusses the frustration of having an instant gratification monkey in his head which can be thwarted only by the panic monster.

Who is driving your ship? Is it you or the monkey?

LEADERSHIP

Organize Your Day To Win

- Start With Thankfulness
- Plan Your Goals
- Map Your Schedule
- Check In Mid-Day
- Evaluate And Regroup
- List Your Wins
- Lessons Learned

LEADERSHIP

THE ONE WORD FILTER MODEL

What is the one word that you could filter the next month through that would change your focus?

Choose a word that is important to you and your organization, that helps to reduce the distractions.

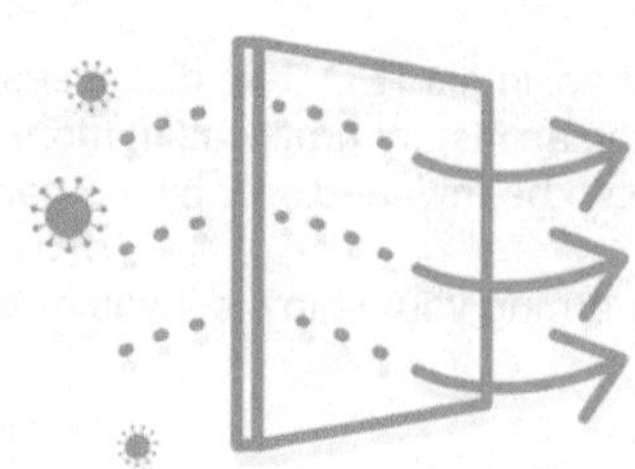

14 NEXT STEPS

One of the mantras that I hope you will live by after completing this book, and hopefully going through the training program as well, is "There is always something new to learn." When I was young and first achieved my black belt in TaeKwon Do, my instructor sat me down and said, "This is not the end of the journey, but rather the beginning." His point was that when you get to a level of competence through learning and practice, you move into a new level in life. That new level requires new learning and new skills and new practice. When you are ready to move to yet another level, that is well within your control because you are taking responsibility for yourself. You have the choice to be anyone that you want to be. You can be the greatest supervisor that the world has ever seen. Or, you can be a horrible supervisor. The proof will be in what you do and the results that you achieve. You learned in this book that your results are simply a reflection of your actions. Your actions are simply a reflection of your thoughts. And, your thoughts are simply a reflection of your beliefs. Do you believe that you can learn and grow? Do you believe that you are in control of you?

In order to continue moving yourself forward, you can follow the following acronym. I organize the lessons into acronyms because it is easier for people to remember the components of the message. This is a trick that I learned in Jr. High. I would organize the things that I needed to memorize into acronyms and then I could use the letters of the word to prompt my memory. So, here are my final thoughts in this book to help you become the best next version of yourself as a supervisor. What happens after this is truly up to you.

F.O.R.W.A.R.D.

Find Your Next Top Performer

Every top performer that works in your organization was discovered at some point. Either they were discovered through the placement of an ad that they responded to or they were discovered through a network of contacts. They may have even been discovered in-house already. Regardless, they were discovered. There are several ways that you can find your next superstar. There are also ways that you can engage your team in finding the next superstar and gain their commitment to the new person's success.

The first thing that you should do in order to find your next top performer is to have a clear definition of the way that a top performing person thinks, what they believe about work, and the way that they demonstrate those behaviors through their actions. Having a clear definition of who the person is as a top performer allows you to be on the lookout for people that fit those beliefs and behaviors. You will often find your next superstar in an unrelated field or at a time when you are simply tuned in to what is going on around you. Always be on the lookout for a great person.

Organize Your Thoughts For Success

The way that you think begins with the models of thought that you adopt. It starts with positioning yourself to be success minded. You learn to expose yourself to positive things and to avoid negative ones. This doesn't mean that you don't deal with problems. What it means is that you don't fill your mind with negativity. Instead, you go out of your way to fill your mind with positive thought. You can frame your thoughts in any direction that you choose, but you do have to choose a frame. By not choosing it deliberately, you put yourself on the path towards negativity and failure. Don't let circumstances dictate the way that you view the world.

A great model for framing reality is to believe that there is always something that you can do to improve yourself. When you live with a growth mindset, one that states that you are in control of you and you are in control of how you respond to any outside stimulus, then you don't blame others or create excuses. The opposite of this mindset is one that is stale, stagnant, or fixed. This type of mindset looks for others to blame, thinks that someone else is always at fault for their situation and doesn't believe that there is anything that they can do about it. Organize your mind in such a way that you focus on what you can do instead of on what you can't do. Focus on what brings you success and moves you forward. Focus on the truth that there is always something that you can choose to do to make your life and your organization better.

Read

One of the quotes that I love is "leaders are readers." There is always more to learn. There is always wisdom to be gained from those who have already faced the problem or challenge that you are facing. You should strive to be both intelligent and wise. Intelligence comes from experiences that you learned from and challenges that you have overcome. Wisdom comes through learning how others have created the right path and then being able to put things in place so that a problem never gets a chance to exist. To be successful, you need to develop skills in both of these areas.

One of the easiest places to find the wisdom that will help you is in books. Thousands of people have faced challenges, learned their way through them, and then written out a plan to move you along the path to success. There is no reason for you to make all of the mistakes yourself. After all, you would likely run out of time to make all of those mistakes on your own. It makes more sense to consistently develop your own potential. It has been said that the most intelligent people in the United States read 1 book per month for personal development. This is not an impossible task. In fact, this is easily doable. You should challenge yourself to invest every month in your own potential. Scott Adams says that an easy formula to apply is that for every new skill you acquire, you double your chances of success. Go out and double your chances this month!

Work With Your Team, Not Above Them

Always remember that being in charge of a team does not mean that you lord over the team. It means that you are there to inspire them to succeed and support them along the way. Your job isn't to know all of the answers. It isn't to direct them or push them. It is to believe in them and build relationships with them. Andrew Carnegie made it a habit, when building his steel empire in the late 1800's, to never direct anyone to do anything. He could have easily told his people what to do, but he didn't. Instead, he always practiced the habit of asking them if they wouldn't mind doing something, or if they had time to do something. He approached them as if they were always doing something important instead acting as if only his ideas were the important ones.

To work with a team is to be the inspirer of success instead of the creator of fear. Motivation is about internal drive. Internal drive comes from a connection to the person that is leading you and a belief in that person. Motivation, then, is a choice that employees make based on a desire to succeed for the leader/supervisor that they work for. When you are working with the team, you help out. You jump in when a member of the team looks overwhelmed. You encourage the team when they need it. You inspire thought in your people. You work to get the team to choose the right direction and to choose top performance. You are not working against the team. You are not pushing or controlling them. Instead, you are lifting them up and bringing out the best in them.

Ask For Input From Your Team

Most employees want to know that they have a voice in their place of business. Marcus Buckingham in First Break All The Rules indicates that employees having the opportunity to contribute to the direction of the organization helps to engage them. In the thousands of conversations that I have had with leaders, supervisors, and employees over the last couple of decades, people at all levels indicate that they want a chance to shape their own future. This only happens when you have the conversation with them and give them a voice.

A couple of things to keep in mind as you talk with your employees about their ideas on the business are as follows…

1. Don't promise to do every idea that is suggested. Instead, be willing to listen to all ideas and be willing to have conversations about those ideas. Most employees are not looking for you to automatically accept their ideas. They are, however, looking for you to have an open conversation about them.
2. Never "shut down" an idea. When an employee has an idea related to the way that business is carried out, it is ideal to ask them to do some research and make a business case for their idea. This puts them in the driver's seat for propelling the idea forward, but it also tests to see how much they believe in the idea. If they are not passionate about it, they will not present a business case for it. If they are passionate, they will make their case.

Relate To Your Team

Relating to your team requires that you know who they are both personally and professionally. You have to have those consistent conversations with them so that you know them and they know you. You have to be a likeable person. In the past generations of leadership, it was often thought that being the "tough" leader was what was needed. This was the model of ruling with an iron fist and using fear as the primary motivator. This model destroys relationships and simply doesn't work with younger generations. You have to be liked to the level that others will want to perform for you. You do NOT have to be their buddy and go hang out on Friday nights with them. You just have to be respectful of them and work to deepen the connection with them.

If you know who they are and you are a likeable person, then they will naturally develop a trust in you as their leader. It is this trust that continues to move the team toward higher levels of performance. For an employee to trust you, they have to feel that you have their best interests at heart. They have to feel that you want them to move forward in life and that you believe that they are capable of moving forward. As you put your focus on ensuring that they trust you and that they can depend on you, they become more and more engaged. It is in full engagement that they have the greatest performance output. The model is to move them from knowing you and you them, to them liking you as a person, to them trusting you as a supervisor, to them being fully engaged as a performer.

Develop Your Team's Potential

You cannot manage what you have not measured. The potential that exists within your team will remain inside of them until you begin to create the right feedback process and the right coaching. Performance evaluations are not just for the annual review. Instead, they are incredibly helpful for use on a quarterly basis to keep a strong conversation going on how the person is doing particularly related to their objectives at work. The ideal way to evaluate performance is in the dual review process. When a person evaluates themselves and their supervisor evaluates them on the same questions, the foundation for a dialogue is created. This dialogue is what helps the employee begin to realize the potential that they have. It is important to note that the dialogue must remain positive and you must keep them focused on how to grow and become better. If your focus is just on what they do wrong, you will create a fixed mindset in them. If your focus is on where they are at and how they can move up, as well as on what they have done right, then you will create a growth mindset in them. This measurement and mapping to demonstrate forward movement sets up success in their minds and is critical to growing their confidence.

When your focus is on moving them forward and bringing out their full potential, you are developing a great culture and confident people. Your job is so much more than just being in charge of people. Your job is about being a champion for the success of people. You are there to invest in your team, inspire your team, stretch the potential of your team, and build a community. Your actions as a supervisor have a strong impact on the success of your organization. A great supervisor produces significantly more work through their people because their people are engaged and want to produce more work. A great supervisor generates more profit, reduces turnover to the bare minimum, creates a better world, and brings a slice of happiness to others. What you do matters.

What you do impacts your employees, their family and friends, the organization that you work for, and the world around you. Invest in yourself and continue to grow. This is not the end of the journey. Instead, this is the first step at the next level in your journey.

I wish you nothing but success!

Jody N Holland

Check out more great content, courses, books, and more at: www.jodyholland.com

Subscribe to Jody's YouTube Channel at: bit.ly/jodytubesub

Follow Jody on Twitter at: https://www.twitter.com/thejodyholland

Books on Amazon: bit.ly/jodyholland

Online Courses: https://www.jodyholland.com/coursesoffered

Facebook: https://www.facebook.com/thejodyholland

ABOUT THE AUTHOR

Jody Holland is a speaker, author, trainer, and executive coach. He has published 20+ books, been the keynote speaker over 300 times at conferences, and trained more than 250,000 leaders. He has a fun and witty style that engages his audience and inspires them to see their own potential. Jody is a certified master trainer, has received specialized training in leadership, management, personality assessment and physiognomy (face reading). He earned his B.A. in Communications and his M.S. in Psychology, both from Angelo State University. Jody specializes in helping people become the leader they would follow through the development of strategic skills. The skills taught through the Leadership Academy – Learn-2-Lead program have consistently reduced turnover, increased employee engagement and performance, and delivered an incredible ROI for those participating. Jody has a passion for building programs that educate, inspire, and motivate leaders for success!

Jody Has been in business since 1999. You can find more information on him and his company at www.JodyHolland.com.

Made in the USA
Monee, IL
05 November 2023